D0482448

HERITAGE LOST

Heritage Lost

The crisis in Canada's forests

DONALD MACKAY

Author of
The Lumberjacks

Macmillan of Canada
A Division of Canada Publishing Corporation
Toronto   Ontario   Canada

Copyright © **1985 Donald MacKay**

All rights reserved. The use of any part of this publication reproduced, transmitted in any form or by any means, electronic, mechanical, photocopying, recording, or otherwise, or stored in a retrieval system, without the prior consent of the publisher is an infringement of the copyright law.

Picture Credits

Colour Gordon Baskerville, 9; Canadian Forestry Service, map; J.H. Cayford, 6; J. Flowers, 8; Michael Folkema, 10; Great Lakes Forest Research Centre, 5; Koehring Canada, 3; National Film Board of Canada, 1, 11; Pacific Forest Products Ltd., 4, 12, 13.
Black and white British Columbia Forest Service, 13; Consolidated Bathurst Inc., 12; Kenneth Hearnden, 1, 23; Laval University, Quebec, 6; National Film Board of Canada, 2, 21, 27, 30, 31; Newfoundland Forest Research Centre, Canadian Forestry Service, 25; Ontario Ministry of Natural Resources, 4, 7, 8, 15, 16, 28; Provincial Archives of British Columbia, 10; Public Archives Canada, National Photography Collection, 3, 5, 14, 29; *Pulp and Paper Canada*, 9; Pulp and Paper Research Institute of Canada, 11; St. Regis (Alberta) Ltd., 19.

The maps were drawn by Robin Brass.

Canadian Cataloguing in Publication Data

MacKay, Donald, 1925-
    Heritage lost: the crisis in Canada's forests

Bibliography: p.
Includes index.
ISBN 0-7715-9828-9

1. Forests and forestry—Canada. 2. Forest management—Canada. 3. Forest conservation—Canada. I. Title.

SD145.M33 1985   333.75'13   C84-099736-1

Editing / Robin Brass
Design / NewtonFrank

Macmillan of Canada
A Division of Canada Publishing Corporation
Toronto   Ontario   Canada

Contents

Introduction

TEN YEARS AGO, WHILE INTERVIEWING MORE
than 100 old woodsmen across Canada for *The Lumberjacks*, a
book about how men lived and worked before the modern era
of logging mechanization, I began to realize just how vast was
the difference between the forests they knew as young men and
the depleted woodlands we know today.

Some of them had gone out as teenagers in the long, cold
winters before World War I to cut giant trees that had grown
undisturbed for hundreds of years. But even then, in fact, most
of the white pine on which our pioneer industry was based was
already gone. Now the biggest trees of other species we have
come to rely on, spruce and Douglas fir, are gone as well. A
New Brunswick woodsman I know was speaking only half in
jest when he said the day is coming when a two-by-four will be a
museum piece.

As I was completing this book, a royal commission on
forestry in Nova Scotia declared that the condition of that
province's forests gives cause for "extreme concern." It found
that only one in every three acres of woodland is regenerating
to satisfactory species after logging; that only a small percentage of the logged areas is being replanted; and that eleven
million cords of valuable softwood has been lost in Cape
Breton Island alone due to failure of the government to protect

it from spruce budworm. Striking an unusual note of urgency, the commission called on the provincial government to adopt an "uncompromising policy" to restore, conserve, and improve the province's forests by law. If Nova Scotia is to save its forest industry, the time for half measures is past.

The truth is finally sinking home. Canada, of all places, is running short of timber, or at least of the sort of wood needed to run our industry and keep our forests from looking like silvicultural slums; since Canada is known around the world as a nation of trees, people naturally find this hard to believe. But something is obviously wrong when mills in southern Quebec and southeastern Ontario must import logs from the United States, at a time when the U.S. dollar is so expensive. Or when a mill in New Brunswick imports South American pine into a province once famous for its 150-foot pine trees. Right across Canada there are shortages of the sort of timber needed to supply the mills. Local timber deficits are beginning to aggregate into a national supply crisis.

This book is a layman's effort to present the problem, its causes, its size and ubiquity, and how it affects people's lives, pocketbooks, and well-being, whether they work in the wood products industry or not. It also describes what is being done and not being done. The problem boils down to what sort of wood is in short supply and how much the public is prepared to pay to replace it.

Since the beginning of history, man has destroyed thousands of millions of acres of trees, reducing some of that vast area to permanent wasteland. Many nations have found themselves facing timber famine. Some, like China and Greece, lost their commercial forests centuries ago and with them much of their productive soil, through erosion. In those countries deforestation and poverty followed as night follows day. The United Kingdom, because of a milder, wetter climate, was not so ecologically unfortunate when it lost its forests, but all the same was forced to go to the expense and trouble of becoming the world's greatest importer of wood. France and Germany, and later Sweden, staved off timber famine by introducing the practice of modern forestry while there was still time.

Since World War II forests have been disappearing at an accelerating rate, particularly in the tropics, and the United Nations Food and Agricultural Organization (FAO) estimates the world is losing trees at the rate of fifty acres a minute.

The lessons learned by older nations were frequently ignored by Canada in the past. For one thing, there appeared to be so much timber that the costly business of forest management seemed irrelevant. For another, our political systems did little to maintain the forests, using them for pork barrels in the game of party politics. In any event, political power has been largely centred in urban centres; practical forestry is a rural concern.

So for 150 years of complacency, political patronage, short-sighted economics, and even just plain greed, Canada's forests were exploited rather than managed. Though it would be wrong to say that nothing was done at all, it was usually too little, if not too late. By the time the Ontario government woke up to the depredations of the wasteful tanbark industry a century ago, the eastern hemlock was virtually gone. The white pine, on which Canada was more or less built once pine had replaced fur as the major export, melted away while people were still wondering how to save it. Now, with a similar scenario unfolding, we are facing a dearth of sawlogs and accessible pulpwood to run our most important national industry and our prime source of employment.

The situation in Canada today compares poorly with that in Scandinavia or the United States, where government and industry are more actively committed to forest renewal. Largely because of tree planting and proper husbandry (silviculture) the southern United States from Texas to North Carolina has emerged in the last thirty years as a major forest region that threatens Canada's position in world pulp and paper markets. In the Soviet Union, despite problems of over-cutting and poor silviculture, prompt reforestation is an article of faith, whereas Canada still relies on nature to reforest denuded land.

Waiting for nature to renew our timber is clearly not enough. Too much is lost to fire, to predators like spruce budworm or mountain pine beetle, and to wasteful methods of harvesting that neglect the regeneration work that should go hand-in-glove with logging. The most common harvesting system, large clear-cuts, has left forest regeneration problems in its wake. But despite a growing backlog of poorly reforested land, estimated at 240,000 square kilometres, almost the size of the United Kingdom, only a meagre two per cent of our forest lands are as yet man-made.

Forest inventories have been either out of date or seriously inaccurate, claiming as much as a third more timber than is actually available. Both formulation and application of forest policy have been painfully slow, despite dozens of royal commissions, task forces, conferences, and congresses, all labouring industriously to little effect during the past 100 years. Neither good intentions nor legislation has shown up in the woods where it was needed; responsibilities have been left unfulfilled or have been passed, like the famous buck, from government to industry and back again while the forests wasted away and the search for accessible timber became more urgent and more costly.

World demand for forest products will probably increase by fifty per cent during the next quarter-century, which for Canada could mean increased exports, thousands of new jobs, and an expansion of the nation's major industry. But this can only be achieved if there are ample supplies of suitable timber to feed the mills.

One reason that politicians, the press, and even industry have been slow to grasp the significance of the problem lies in its regional and technical complexity. The growing crisis had lain across the nation like the scattered pieces of a puzzle, and only in the 1970s, after decades of patchwork remedies, did the pieces begin to come together with the clarity that calls for action. Foresters in government, universities, and industry all contributed to the new awareness. A key factor was the report compiled in 1978 by Les Reed, a forest economist, who pointed out in simple, non-technical language that we had for too long been over-drawing on our forest capital. His report became a rallying point for those demanding better forest management and a powerful argument to convert those who felt there was still no need for it. Since its publication there has been a movement in favour of better forestry, though with the recent recession it has exhausted some of its energy and it is not uncommon to hear people in industry renewing an old argument: that the trouble lies in marketing problems rather than in supply problems. By this time it must be clear to all that there certainly are serious supply deficiencies, no matter what the markets may be doing.

One of the problems has always been lack of public engagement, for when all is said and done the real owners of Canada's forests are the people of Canada, each man, woman, and child of us possessing, at least in theory, almost ten productive hectares. As the Council of Resource and Environment Ministers has observed, most people have little appreciation of the importance of the forest to Canada's well-being. "This is serious," said the Council, "and needs correction."

Among organizations anxious that Canadians realize just how much their woodland heritage is in jeopardy is the Canadian Institute of Forestry/Institut Forestier du Canada, the national organization of professional foresters founded in 1908 and now numbering well over 2,600 members in all provinces. It has been with the support and encouragement of the members of the CIF that I have researched and written this book. I would like to mention the scores of people who have given time, information, and support, but since this is difficult because of space, I would like to single out at least a few who shall be representative. These include R.J. Bourchier, executive director of the CIF; I.C.M. Place, editor of the *Forestry Chronicle*; and the veteran foresters Ross Silversides of Preston, Ontario, and Bill Wilton of St. John's, Newfoundland, Gilbert Paillé and André Duchesne of Quebec City, J.H. Cayford of Sault Ste. Marie and Ernest Heidersdorf of Montreal, Bruce Devitt and W. Young of Victoria. Others who provided support over the two-year span of the project, which required travelling from coast to coast, are listed at the back of the book. Above all I would like to thank Michael Folkema, president of the Forestry Awareness in Canada Trust (FACT), associated with the CIF. Without his commitment, time, energy, and knowledge this book, quite literally, could not have been completed.

Owing to the work of such men and their colleagues in government, industry, and the university forestry schools, there has been a great increase during the past few years in the awareness of our forest problems. There has been some progress toward solutions, but since there is still a long way to go this book, written for people with a general interest in Canada's forest heritage, dwells less on the steps we have made toward forest management than on the opportunities we have let slip by. Responsibility for its contents, including its point of view, rests solely with the author.

Donald MacKay,
Montreal, October 1984.

The forest and the trees

FROM AN AIRPLANE 7,000 FEET OVER NORTHERN Ontario the forest is shaggy, two or three shades of green flecked with lakes and the black scars of fire and brown blotches of recent logging. At the high altitudes of a transcontinental jet, the forest looks homogeneous, as unchanging as the ocean, but from this lower elevation half a century of woodland history can be seen in miniature.

This is the heart of the Boreal forest, thousands of square miles of lonely hills, flatlands, and swamps topped by a sea of coniferous, or cone-bearing, "Christmas trees" that stretch in a ribbon 600 miles wide from Newfoundland to Alaska. There was a time, not many years ago, when it was thought to hold unending supplies of commercial timber, particularly the black spruce, whose long, strong fibres made Canadian newsprint the best in the world. Now foresters are fearful that we are running out of our heritage of accessible timber. Certainly from the air, the Boreal can sometimes look like a moth-eaten rug, wall-to-wall but in urgent need of patching.

As the plane flies twenty minutes north of Timmins there is reassuring evidence that spruce and jack pine harvested in the horse-logging days are growing back up, though not as thick as the original timber logged forty years ago. Half-way to Smooth

1

1. A typical large clear-cut in the Boreal forest surrounding what was once a logging road. Although the terrain has been fairly well cleaned up, piles of slash can be seen as well as a few hardwoods of no commercial value.

Rock Falls and Kapuskasing, where the slim white plumes from the pulp mills tower like two smoke signals, regeneration of logged-off land appears much less reassuring. It was harvested more recently, not with horses but with heavy machines that are much more destructive to soil and ecosystem. Horse logging had several advantages in terms of forest renewal. It was usually done in strips, which left standing trees near by to regenerate the denuded cut with suitable seeds. Horses could not work on swampy ground, so logging was done only in winter when the unstable soil of the wet Clay Belt was protected by frost and ice. Machines, on the other hand, can work in summer conditions, and although this may be useful to the people at the mill, the heavy skidders and tree harvesters exact a heavy price in chewing up the soil and creating stagnant pools of water that retard fresh growth for decades. In the machine age, strip logging has long given way to large clear-cuts that look, from 7,000 feet up, like giant playing fields.

Clear-cuts come in all shapes and sizes, some as neat and tidy as a wheat field after summer mowing, some littered like battlefields with forest debris and jagged stumps. Not far north of Kapuskasing lies a clear-cut as exposed and dry in the hot August sun as if a tide had gone out. Six-inch seedlings, planted a year or two ago, struggle for growth amid the biggest raspberry patch in the world—acres of fat, red, useless fruit miles from anywhere. The seedlings are hard to find amid the shrubs and rough ground, but with luck, and good silviculture, they

will eventually provide a new forest to feed the pulp mills of the twenty-first century.

It is vital that such forest land regenerate into useful species, for in northern Ontario wood accounts for three-quarters of all manufacturing. At least twenty communities are totally dependent on logging and the milling of forest products. Without proper treatment, however, there is danger the land will sprout back into "junk forests" that have been logged and left to grow up into brush or useless species on land that can be rehabilitated for commercial use only at great expense. Most of the old logging towns of Canada are surrounded by junk forests.

At Beardmore, George Marek is pessimistic as he shows visitors the ravages left by poor land management and overcutting. Beardmore, some 200 miles west of Kapuskasing, was once a busy mining and lumber town, but the mines closed down and the disappearance of quality timber drove the lumberjacks away. Now it is half its former size. Driving his half-ton truck down a highway where the trees look puny, he remarks that there is little commercial timber within a ten-mile radius of the town and only enough within 100 miles to last industry another decade.

"There is a tremendous problem," says Marek, a wiry, dedicated man who learned forestry in his native Czechoslovakia and who recently retired after almost thirty years as a provincial district forester. "Instead of the original spruce we now have balsam fir or poplar, marginally stocked stands, and a very unstable ecosystem that may be eaten up by the spruce budworm.

"Everywhere I look I see degradation of the original forest. We thought we could do better than nature. Like hell! We are not even tackling the basic deficiencies. The records say one thing; the bush says another. The present forestry practices are so uncertain that wherever I look there is a large degree of failure.

"Some of these black spruce sites: when you cut them, they turn into swamps for five or ten years, after which they dry out because of new patterns of drainage and transpiration. They turn into dry mud pans on which you could drive your car. Between hard pan and the organic soil there are spaces of ten inches where seeds won't grow. There is no nutrition there, and some sites are so vulnerable you'll get no black spruce back."

At Thunder Bay, west of Beardmore, Kenneth Hearnden agrees. To Hearnden, who worked in the Boreal since the 1940s as an industrial forester before heading up the forestry school in Lakehead University, the Boreal is beginning to look like a run-down neighbourhood that has seen better days.

"From every aspect, the Boreal forest scene shows all the hallmarks of a long-standing policy and practice of unmodified forest exploitation and the liquidation of our best natural growing stock," said Hearnden. "Physically, this scene reveals itself in abandoned road systems and cut-over areas in varying conditions of productivity, most of these occupied by lower-quality stands promising lower yields for a second rotation. Our most accessible and productive forest lands have been degraded by repeated pillaging that commenced with the most valuable conifers and is ending with the least valuable species.

"Where deliberate efforts have been made to establish the second forest, too frequently one encounters poor success, or failure, neglect, or *de facto* abandonment. From a technical aspect the scene reveals a woefully inadequate, obsolescent, and misleading forest resources inventory, and a deplorable lack of knowledge of the growth and yield potential of our forests." Strong words, perhaps, but the history of forest husbandry in Canada has been dismal. A litany of neglect, broken promises, and false hopes recurs throughout the annals of Canadian forestry.

Ignoring the painful lessons learned by older forest nations, industry was content to pursue the economic theory of discounted cash flow, which says it is more profitable to let money acquire interest in the bank than to plough it into the long-term future of the forest. So long as timber was plentiful it seemed easier just to push on over the next hill, picking up another batch as a bear picks berries. As a consequence, mills find themselves reaching out for wood in expensively widening circles, like the ripples of a stone dropped in a pond. By the early 1900s, we had run out of the white pine that had fed our early lumber industry. By the 1920s pulp mills began to utilize the species—spruce and jack pine and balsam fir—the old lumberman had found no use for, but unlike the portable sawmills of our grandfathers, a $500-million pulp mill cannot be shuttled around the country in pursuit of a receding timber supply.

Transportation became an ever larger slice—often more than half—of the market price of pulp and lumber; a wood haul of more than 100 miles is already treading on the hem of profitability, and trucks are hauling much longer distances than that. At the same time, a tenth of the nation's productive forest land, an area as big as the Great Lakes, lies neglected, much of it within easy distance of mills but too poor in quality to harvest. You can get an idea of what these junk forests look like by driving beyond the outskirts of almost any old lumber town, where negligence has left a waste of brush and skimpy hardwoods, called "weed trees" because they have no current commercial value, and softwood stands that are too dense to grow properly or have been ravaged by insects and disease. Every year this wasteland is increasing at a tremendous rate, one million hectares annually. Of the forest land harvested every year, about a third is being planted with seedlings, another third is coming back up naturally, and the remainder is more or less left to grow, if it can and however it can. Most of it lies on Crown land owned by the people of Canada.

That Canadians have been unaware that their valuable property is seriously deteriorating is hardly surprising, since most of us have trouble telling one tree from another, and the sheer number of trees of various kinds gives an illusion of plenty. The green façade we usually see is reassuring, but behind it shortages of accessible and merchantable timber have been developing in almost every region. The problem lies, quite literally, in a failure to distinguish the forest from the trees. Few of Canada's 140 species are of commercial value. Apart from the hardwoods used for fuel, a handful such as maple and birch are valued for veneers and furniture. Poplar is being used in small if increasing quantities in brewing pulp.

The important species are softwoods—Douglas fir, spruces, pines, balsam fir, western hemlock, and cedar—the trees that Canada will be running short of during the next generation.

Such shortages show up first in a dearth of sawlogs of required size and quality because too much accessible old-growth timber has been cut or lost to fire or insects. Since pulpwood need not be of such high quality, the shortage is not yet as tight, but nevertheless reserves are much too far from the mills.

Problems have been emerging all over the country. In McAdam, New Brunswick, a veneer mill found itself having to import pine logs all the way from Chile. The balsam fir forest of Cape Breton Island, which was counted on to supply a large pulp mill at Port Hawkesbury, is ruined by the spruce budworm.

In Quebec there are timber shortages and poor forest renewal in the vast Abitibi region of the northwest and in the hills and valleys amid the many tributaries of the St. Maurice River, one of the richest sources of pulpwood in Canada for three-quarters of a century. Like so many Canadian forests it has been hit hard by fires. Around Rivière Trenche lie 400 square miles burned in the early 1940s and still a wasteland. Spruce budworm has degraded fifteen per cent of the Quebec forest, particularly in the Gaspé and on the north shore of the St. Lawrence.

In Newfoundland a quarter of the merchantable wood reaching maturity is lost to insects, disease, and fire. Productive forest covers only about twenty per cent of the land area of Labrador, and only half of this is of commercial value. In Saskatchewan, where half the province, beginning just north of Prince Albert, is forest and where wood is the second-largest manufacturing industry, accounting for one job in fifty, photos taken early in this century show the Little Red River chock-a-block with big spruce logs on their way to the mills. Now northern Saskatchewan is facing timber shortages, particularly around one-industry towns like Carrot River and Hudson Bay near the Manitoba border. To make matters worse, a lot of valuable timber has been bottled up in a huge military-weapons testing range in northwestern Saskatchewan.

In British Columbia, areas in the relatively dry climate of the southeast are facing shortages, but even the fast-growing woods of the coastal areas are not immune. Like other Canadian lumber towns, Terrace in the northwest has had more than its share of boom and bust since the early days when loggers cut cordwood for the Skeena River steamboats and railway ties for the Grand Trunk Pacific Railway. Terrace today is a centre for surrounding sawmills and pulp plants that get their "furnish" in the form of chips that are a by-product of the sawmills. Most of the good, accessible timber in the river bottoms has been cut, and loggers have to push much farther afield, up into the Nass Valley. But even there the harvest exceeds the annual allowable cut, which is the amount of wood it is advisable to harvest without depleting future supplies. Depending on whom you talk to, there is enough accessible timber either for twenty years or for ten, and the fact there are some sizeable forest lands of over-mature hemlock and low-quality balsam farther north is not much help—since they are not accessible and would only be good for pulping anyway, rather than the lumber-cum-chips process on which the B.C. industry is based. Until the river-bottom timber grows back again, supplies will be tight.

In the 1920s, this area was known as "the pole capital of North America," shipping cedar poles as far as New York City. It is a sign of the times that B.C. Hydro, which used to buy tall cedar masts for its high-voltage lines, has taken to ordering standards made of concrete. At Fort Nelson, a town of 4,000 that has been the centre of a $25-million wood industry providing 600 jobs, the Forest Service warns there could be a spruce famine within twenty years. In Canada the free-and-easy days of cheap and plentiful wood are gone.

We have been predators in the forest, competing for our wood with fire and insects such as the spruce budworm, but now we must learn to become an efficient and responsible part of the forest ecology, understanding its biological potential and respecting its ecological limitations.

"Much of traditional economics is concerned with expansion, with growth, and with maximizing short-term returns on investment," says K.P. Kimmins, a forest ecologist at the University of British Columbia. Like many foresters, Kimmins believes that public concern must reach a point where Canadians are prepared to pay the price for establishing forestry on a sound footing, including the intensive silviculture that is to the cultivation of trees what agriculture is to the cultivation of fields.

So far in Canada we have done little to help the forests grow. We rely on nature to regenerate our logged-over land. Unlike farmers, who for centuries have been sowing and harvesting domesticated crops, foresters are only beginning to contemplate the growing of man-made woodlands from genetically improved, nursery-bred plantations. Forestry being such a complex and long-term business, the challenge of introducing intensive forestry, to say nothing of the cost, is going to be immense during the next few decades, calling for a large corps of well-trained professional foresters who will be out in the field, growing trees, rather than manning desks and laboratories. Compared with more advanced forest nations, such as the United States, Germany, and Sweden, Canada has pitifully few foresters at work.

While our main competitors in world markets tend to have one forester to every 15,000 hectares of woodland, Canada has one to every 450,000 hectares. With just over 4,000 trained foresters, we have only a tenth of the number in the United States, where there are forty forest schools to our six. Only two new degree schools have been created, at the Lakehead and Edmonton, since the 1920s. Owing to insufficient funding our forestry schools are not turning out enough graduates to meet our future needs, while at the same time there are many recent graduates without jobs because of the recession in the industry.

We have urgent need of more research, since forestry cannot be imported wholesale from other countries but must be specific to our own needs. The research budget of a single company, Weyerhaeuser in the United States, is larger than the entire research and development budget of Canada's chief research agency, the Canadian Forestry Service.

And there is still much to learn. To begin with, there are eight officially designated forest regions, each with a different mix of species, soil, climate, and natural enemies. In addition, there are almost 100 subregions, divided in turn into hundreds of tracts with their own problems and potentials. Each tract requires the careful silvicultural prescriptions that foresters refer to as "site-specific" and is subject to 200 variable factors that determine the best management technique. These factors concern species, quality of soil, climate, regeneration potential, and whether trees grow on hills or in valleys, and in swamps, clay, or sandy ground. A prescription that may work well on one stand may be a disaster over the next hill.

The first forest region to be logged was the 50,000-square-mile Acadian forest in the Maritimes which lost its mature white pine more than a century ago. Having also lost much of its best spruce, it is left with a surfeit of aging balsam fir, a prey to spruce budworm, which despite its name does more damage to fir than to spruce. The mature white pine is long gone, too, from the Great Lakes–St. Lawrence forest of conifers and hardwoods, stretching through 150,000 square miles of southern Quebec and Ontario to the Manitoba border, interrupted by the small deciduous or hardwood region in southwestern Ontario. Hardwoods account for only twenty per cent of Canada's woodland and are primarily poplar, followed by birch, aspen, and maple. Of the softwoods, spruces account for a third of the total, pines and firs another third, with most of the remainder running to hemlock and cedar.

Four of the eight forest regions lie in British Columbia; the Sub-alpine and Montane also extend their lodge-pole pine and spruce into western Alberta. The Columbia region in the southern B.C. interior grows a smaller version of the coastal giants. But it is the coastal rain forest, which runs between the mountains and the sea from the U.S. border to the Queen Charlotte Islands, embracing Vancouver Island, that provides Canada's greatest source of standing timber. In the seventy-five years it takes an eastern conifer to grow, a Douglas fir, western hemlock, or cedar in coastal B.C. may grow 130 feet, with a diameter of eighteen inches and a cubic yield of wood five times as great. By the time these trees reach maturity, they may be 200 feet high.

North of all these regions, curving across Canada, is the biggest forest of all, the Boreal, which is simply Latin for "northern." It contains an estimated million and a half square miles of trees which (though they contain birch and poplar) are largely coniferous, or cone-bearing jack pine, balsam fir, and spruce. The spruce family has been dominant since early in this century when it succeeded white pine on the lumber market and also became the basic source for pulp mills. Growing to a height of 100 feet or more with a life span of 200 years, white spruce, the queen of the tribe, occurs in all regions except the West Coast; it is the slowest to grow and the most widely planted, and is used for lumber, pulp, and plywood veneers. In the east it appears most typically mixed with balsam fir. Growing best on moist, well-drained soil, a pure white spruce stand rivals a pine wood as a pleasant, silent place to be on a hot summer day, the air sweet with resin, the fallen needles a springy carpet underfoot.

Its smaller, less favoured sister, the black spruce, used mostly for pulp, tends to live in less salubrious neighbourhoods, surviving in bogs of dank moss, lichen, and fungus, where other trees may refuse to grow, or on the margins of the northern tundra, where it may be nothing more than a twisted, trunkless shrub. Its seeds small, its roots shallow, it has trouble getting started in life but, once established, can outlast its rivals. On the Queen Charlotte Islands of British Columbia the Sitka spruce came to fame when it was used, because of its strength and light weight, in the pioneer airplane industry.

Two species once regarded as weed trees have come into use now that more popular species are depleted. One is the balsam fir, used mainly for pulp but also for Christmas trees and lumber. Balsam fir has a shorter life than most—half a century or so—and lacks the strength of the spruce, which it still manages to crowd out in the early years of a new forest. In the Atlantic provinces and eastern Quebec it is the chief pulp tree, a role played in Ontario by spruce, followed by jack pine. Jack pine regenerates well, once heat releases the seed from its tough little cones, and is widely used in pulp and even in lumber these days when old-fashioned knot-free boards are harder to get. Lodge-pole pine fills a similar role in Alberta and the interior of British Columbia, though on the West Coast the pulp tree is the western hemlock.

Though it is not as common as it used to be, British Columbia still has its lordly Douglas fir, named early in the nineteenth century for the Scottish botanist David Douglas—or rather misnamed, since it is not a true fir and is closer to the hemlock family. The third major tree on the coast is the fragrant red cedar, the stuff of shingles and such.

Canadians have viewed the forest with mixed attitudes. Feared and hated by the first settlers, who hastened to clear it away with fire and axe, the forest was a treasure chest for the fur traders and lumbermen and a major source of revenue for the colonial governments. To the man at the mill the forest means raw material. To his bosses in the boardroom its value lies in profit potential. To the union leader it means jobs. As a prime resource in world demand, it is seen by economists as an instrument for correcting our balance of payments.

To a naturalist, an over-mature tree has its place in the scheme of things as much as any other living or dying thing. Foresters, who in their brief history have been primarily concerned with the industrial harvesting of woodlands rather than general land management, have in recent years been expanding their role. Many agree with at least the more moderate environmentalists that the woods are much more than just a way to make a dollar and that forests are a vital link in the complex web of life on our increasingly fragile planet.

As for the public at large, urban Canadians cling to the notion that north of our cities lies an unchanged vastness where they can go to recuperate from modern life, refusing to believe that the "north woods" are already changing, as the farm lands farther south changed years ago. For a forest nation whose economy is based on wood and whose art and poetry have long been inspired by wilderness, Canadians know surprisingly little about the forest. Despite its importance it is rarely mentioned in election campaigns. Unless there is a dramatic forest fire, it is usually ignored by the media. It is first and foremost a peaceful backdrop to a $4-billion recreation industry, or perhaps to an evocative beer ad on television. People from other countries coming to live here usually take more interest in the woods than do native Canadians, and a lot of the best work here has been done by foresters trained in Europe or the United States.

The Science Council of Canada, with no particular axe to grind in its task of assessing national resources, is concerned about just how bad the situation has become behind the green curtain that is all that most Canadians see as they move around the country. "In a resource-based economy such as Canada's, the forests are essential to our social and economic well-being, yet we have allowed them to degenerate to a dangerous point," the council has said. "We have been felling, selling, and shipping timber for so long, and at such a rate, that today a $23-billion industry is facing economic stagnation. . . ."

If we are to continue to exploit a resource that is shrinking at an alarming rate, we will have to make wiser use of it, as countries like Germany do. And not only for timber but for recreation and for enhancement of the air we breathe and the water we drink. Unless there is public awareness of what is happening and governments are encouraged to look after the trees, not once in a while but continuously, the next few decades will bring more deterioration.

It is easy enough to heap the blame on industry, or to say that forests are merely a toy of federal politicians and nothing more than a source of short-term revenue for provincial governments. The Science Council takes a harder line: "Who is responsible? We are all responsible."

*H*urling down the pine

THE STORIES OF THE WORLD'S OLD FOREST nations are sadly similar. The trees that once seemed so inexhaustible were hacked and burned and wasted until at last the people woke up, usually too late, to find them gone and their nation the poorer. For thousands of years this was the destructive pattern in China, the eastern Mediterranean, North Africa, and Spain.

In Lebanon, whose cedar forests were the greatest of the ancient world, there is rock and erosion where the Israelites felled logs for King Solomon's temple. Lamenting the destruction of the forests of Attica, Plato observed that the very streams were drying up in protest; but the city-states of Greece went on destroying trees until hardly a tenth remained. The natural seedlings that might have provided new growth were eaten by goats and sheep.

By the beginning of the Christian era, the Romans had denuded so much of southern Italy that wood had to be imported and sold by weight, like meat or cheese. State forests were rented out to influential private exploiters, as they have been in Canada. Under the onslaught of agriculture and grazing, the forests receded up the mountainsides, where the charcoal burners finished them off.

Spain, for the most part so stark and treeless now, was wooded from the Mediterranean to the Atlantic when the Romans arrived in 218 B.C. It was part of the thick forest that moderated the harsh sun and enriched the soil all the way from the Black Sea to the Gates of Hercules. With the disappearance of the forests, those lands have become dry and eroded, prone to floods. In North Africa the coastal forests have turned into desert.

The fate of northwest Europe was less dramatic, because of greater temperate rainfall, among other things. Even so, the demand for wood in England was exceeding local supply by Shakespeare's time. The problem had started during the reign of King Canute, no more able to control deforestation than he was to stop the sea. Since most of its trees were hardwood, England had long been importing softwoods from Norway, and now its native hardwood, the oak from which England built its seapower, was melting away.

In 1639 a man named Gabriel Platte, with foresight that makes his words almost as applicable today as they were three and a half centuries ago, wrote: "Now the multitude of Timber brought yearely from Norway, and other parts, doe plainly demonstrate the scarcities thereof here; also it may be conjectured what a miserable case the Kingdome will be plunged into about an Age or two hence, for want of Timber.

"There is a law in Spaine, that he that cutteth downe a tree, shall plant three young ones for it; and by this means there are builded in two Provinces, both not so great as Yorkeshire, twenty ships yearely, and yet the wood increaseth; if this law were observed here, how happie would it be. The charge is little, to wit, love manifested, by working for the general good; not ownly of all that are now alive; but also of those that shall come after. And I feel no reason why Landlords should not contract with their tenants, to put this work into practice diligently, for then their rents will be more and more improved every year; and if this be omitted, their rents will be diminished in future time."

As usual, no one heeded the prophets, though John Evelyn was to make some impact on the reading public in 1662 with his book *Silva, or a Discourse of Forest-Trees, and the Propagation of Timber in His Majesties Dominians*. Pointing out the connection between forest husbandry and general prosperity, Evelyn wrote: "Truely, the waste and destruction of our woods has been so universal that I conceive nothing less than a universal plantation of all sorts of trees will supply and encounter the defect....We had better be without gold than without trees."

Five years later Samuel Pepys, whose work at the Admiralty had acquainted him with the need for timber, reflected in his diary on why nothing was being done: "Too many land owners believe with a Restoration peer that wood was an excrescence of the earth, provided by God, for the payment of debts." Instead of growing wood, the English eventually turned to Ireland and Scotland, helping to reduce those countries to peat and heather by the eighteenth century. Large public effort to restore depleted forests was too much expense and bother. By Cromwell's time the English were importing wood from the American colonies.

Though never as badly off as England, France was complaining of local timber shortages, much as Canada does now. The forests that had awed Roman legions marching through Gaul had been reduced to a tame chequerboard of domesticated woodlands. When Jacques Cartier sailed from France into the St. Lawrence in 1534 he was amazed; though having no notion of how big the forests really were, he called them "the finest in the world."

Tacking into the west wind, Cartier would have smelled the aroma of the softwoods, that sweetest of Canadian smells, long before he sighted land. Though largely untouched by the hand of man, the fringe of the immense forest glimpsed by Cartier more than 400 years ago was no more "primeval" than it is now. Like all living things, the woods had been born, grew, and died, but they renewed themselves in cycles longer than those of most other living things. The great renewer was fire, caused usually by lightning or sometimes by the native population.

A Stone Age culture with no iron tools, the Indians were not numerous enough to make much impact, though they did set some spectacular fires to clear berry patches or provide grazing for deer. Only the Haida, living among the giant western cedars of the Queen Charlotte Islands, made great use of wood, felling trees by girdling them with fire and hacking them down with wooden axe heads edged with sea shells. They built plank lodges, sculpted totem poles, and hollowed out long war canoes; they made coffins and dishes and fashioned their clothes out of cedar bark.

To all the tribes, the forest was a friend, not the enemy it was to the European settlers, who saw it as a hiding place for hostile Indians and wild animals, a serious hindrance to planting crops and growing sustenance. Few of the French, Scots, Irish, and

English had ever seen big trees and they had to learn by trial and error how to chop them down without injuring themselves. Trees too huge to fell, stack, and burn they cut with a deep groove around the bark to impede the flow of life-giving sap. Deprived of nourishment, trees by the thousands ceased to grow, then withered and died, a target for forest fires.

The settlers learned from the Indians to coax syrup from the sugar maple. They manufactured potash from the ashes of hardwoods to make soap and to sell for export. But once their houses, barns, and fences were built and they had enough fuel stacked away, there was nothing to do with the wood but burn it. This they did with abandon, the breakaway fires causing great damage.

"*Les brûleurs de forêts* behave as if the trees were of no use in the world and as if the people will never have use for them," said the intendant Dupuis. "They are scattering fires and starting fires everywhere to clear a concession of which no more than one-tenth will ever be cultivated. They are not only endangering their neighbours' forests, but are also extending these fires over two or three thousand acres, burning without care, sometimes the *habitant* himself, his barns and churches."

Otherwise the French, preoccupied with colonizing and fur and numbering a few scattered thousands at best along the St. Lawrence and on the Bay of Fundy, made little effort to exploit the forest for commerce. The first shipment of wood from Canada to France was made in 1667, from Trois-Rivières, after Pierre Boucher, the governor, had written to Jean-Baptiste Colbert, the finance minister in Paris, that "the woods which are here in abundance should be of great profit either for marine or other construction." Since the trees were never cut or cured to the standards of the timber from the Pyrenees, one of France's few sources of big domestic logs, the trade was not successful and died out in the early 1700s. The Quebec governor, the Marquis de Beauharnois, recorded: "The irregularity with which the trees have been exploited, without observing either the moons or the seasons, the slight attention given to peeling the trees properly, to drying them and storing them in such a fashion that they can dry without rotting, can be regarded as a cause of complaint." There was a small export trade to the French West Indies and the navy built a few ships in the St. Lawrence, but that was about all.

Nor did the English do much logging during their first fifty years. The forests beyond the settlements remained undisturbed, a source of admiration for newcomers. "They have the appearance of being as ancient as the world itself," wrote a British army officer based at Quebec in the 1780s. "I was struck with the loftiness of the pines, fir-trees, and cedars, which are of a size perfectly astonishing."

The American War of Independence, depriving Britain of timber from Massachusetts and New Hampshire, forced London to look more closely at the northern colonies. In Halifax Sir John Wentworth, Governor of Nova Scotia and Surveyor of the King's Woods in all of British North America, was made responsible for supplies of pine masts and oak for the hulls of British warships. Wentworth introduced the custom of marking trees with the king's "broad arrow," a crude arrow with the royal initials, to warn settlers against cutting the tall trees wanted for the shipyards. The arrow, which had caused almost as much resentment among New England settlers as the stamp duty and tea tax that led to their revolution, was largely ignored.

Apart from an ineffectual fire-prevention law passed in Nova Scotia's legislature in 1761, these were virtually the only measures in the eighteenth century to safeguard the forests. Preservation of timberlands in the New World had no priority with government or settlers, though some of them must have recalled the consequences of deforestation in the lands they came from. If they did they saw no reason to apply that lesson in North America.

Britain, the world's biggest wood importer, was getting most of its timber from the Baltic, which was closer and where an efficient industry had grown. But logs of a length and taper useful for masts were hard to find there; to avoid the compromise of weaker masts, spliced from two shorter trees, the British were forced to go all the way to New Brunswick. William Davidson, a Scot who had been trying to sell square timber from the Miramichi without success, was awarded the first contract to cut masts in New Brunswick in 1779. This was a limited, if lucrative, trade and his men cut 400 masts, each of almost 100 feet, in a year.

Had it not been for Napoleon's war with England,the timber industry might not have been developed for another forty or fifty years, or until the United States, having used up much of its own best timber, turned to Canada for wood to build its towns. As it was, the British, fearful of losing their Baltic timber in the event of a French blockade, began in the 1790s to build up colonial imports of square timber as well as masts.

Still small, this industry had spread up the St. Lawrence to Quebec City by 1804 when Scott, Idles and Company, contractors to the Royal Naval Dockyards, were awarded the exclusive right to subcontract out harvesting and export privileges. Under the tutelage of United Empire Loyalists who had learned lumbering in New England, the Canadian industry was born. Merchants and settlers who had been rafting farm produce and barrels of potash down to Quebec City from the Richelieu River or Glengarry and the northern shores of Lake Ontario began to send down timber as well.

With so much timber to choose from, the early logging permits were extremely generous, giving a single company the run of areas as large as Switzerland or Scotland. "High-grading," which means taking only the best and leaving the rest— the antithesis of forest management—was encouraged. A standard government contract gave a lumberman *carte blanche* "to travel into and search Our woods in Our Provinces of Lower and Upper Canada where We have reserved to us the property in any woods or trees and the right of cutting them, and there to fell and cut so many good and sound trees as may answer the number and dimensions of said Contract."

White pine was what they sought, for it was strong but "workable"; most of it came from the Maritimes. East of the the Ottawa River watershed, Quebec's forests ran to spruce and balsam fir. Then, in 1806, one of the great white pine regions of the world was suddenly opened up—along the 700-mile-long Ottawa River and 1,000 miles of tributaries on both shores, in Quebec and in Ontario. In the telling, at least, this historic event seems as simple as it was inevitable. Philemon Wright, a Massachusetts Yankee who had settled a land grant in 1800 in what is now Hull, across from Ottawa, had heard that cash could be made by selling timber in Quebec City. Despite the warnings of *habitants* down-river that it could never be done, Wright ran a raft-load of timber and barrel staves down the rapids to Montreal and then down the St. Lawrence to Quebec City. It was a cheap, natural, water-propelled delivery system that was to be used for a hundred years.

Wright's contribution to Canadian lumbering could not have been more opportune: Napoleon and his allies had made good the threat of blockading the Baltic and depriving England of timber, as vital to the navy as oil and steel are now. Canada's commercial evolution from fur to timber was swift, as the export figures for 1799 and 1811 attest. From Nova

Scotia, where white pine was not nearly as abundant as in New Brunswick, exports increased from 11 masts and 607 loads of square timber to 842 masts and 17,419 loads. (Each load was fifty cubic feet, an English measure representing the amount a horse could draw in a wagon.) From New Brunswick mast exports increased from 763 to 3,151, timber from 276 loads to 75,870. But it was from Quebec City that the most spectacular increase came, signalling the opening of the Ottawa Valley. In 1799 Quebec shipped 1,069 loads of oak from the Eastern Townships and southern Ontario, but only 7 masts and 29 loads of pine square timber. Twelve years later it exported enough wood to fill 500 ships with 23,053 masts, 24,469 loads of oak, and 52,888 loads of pine.

The Baltic embargo had diverted the whole British timber fleet to Canada, and by the time the embargo collapsed, Canadians had established a foothold in the wood markets of Liverpool, Cardiff, Bristol, Cork, and London. The protective tariffs were to remain in effect for another thirty years or so, climbing to thirty-five shillings a load on Continental timber compared with one shilling a load on colonial wood.

Other companies, including those cutting Crown timber illegally for the black market, were awarded government contracts. William Price, one of Scott, Idles and Company's up-and-coming young men from England, launched Price Brothers, which now is part of Toronto-based Abitibi-Price. Price pioneered the export of "deals," three-inch white spruce planks, which were sawn into thinner lumber in England.

For the most part the British demanded their wood in the form of balks, great beams of square timber. For one thing, they were easier to load and store in ships' holds. For another, mills and sawyers in England were better, and by sawing the timber themselves British firms could maintain monopolies on the domestic market. It was none of their concern that the making of square timber was a highly wasteful process. In New Brunswick the legislature heard warnings of "very great waste of pine," "wanton depredations," and valuable timber "rotting and useless on the ground."

Having selected the very best pine, gangs of square timber makers would fell a tree 100 feet tall, "hurling down the pine," as they said on the Ottawa. Decapitating as much as a quarter of the tree, leaving the top to rot on the ground,they hewed the remainder into a smooth "stick" thirty or forty feet long and a foot or more square, discarding great slabs of wood in the process. One-third of every tree was wasted. If a tree had the slightest hint of heart-rot at the core, which could be discovered only after it was felled, it too was left on the ground. Trees with knots, crooks, or other defects were ignored, though they could have been used as eighteen-foot sawlogs in the lumber mills that came later. Perhaps one pine in a hundred was suitable for the square timber maker; the lumber industry that came later took the rest.

The only way to get timber to market was to float it down the rivers, so more wood was lost to sinkage or in the storms that smashed the timber rafts on the St. Lawrence. No one knew how many thousands of square timber "sticks" came to litter the beaches of the lower St. Lawrence and the Atlantic coast, but it was estimated that at one time one million feet of timber had been washed up on Anticosti Island in the lower St. Lawrence, a treacherous shore that claimed its share of timber ships.

By the 1820s, loggers or "shantymen"—"shanties" being the crude, crowded log shacks in which they spent the winter logging season—were "hurling down the pine" as if there would be no end to it. In a colonial industry dependent on mysterious market fluctuations in a far-distant country, keeping a company afloat left a boss no time, even if he had the inclination, to consider the future of his stock in trade. Boom and bust were part of the business. "Few people make money by getting it [timber] out," lamented the *Quebec Gazette* during the depression of the 1820s, "and many engaging in the business ruin themselves." Even Wright ran afoul of creditors, but his sons continued to send twenty rafts of timber down each summer. In New Brunswick, Bathurst, the Miramichi ports, and Saint John were dispatching thousands of masts and hundreds of thousands of lengths of pine square timber every summer. Prince Edward Island was exporting the last of its once plentiful white pine, and in Pictou Harbour, Nova Scotia, twenty-six tall ships were counted one day taking on pine for Britain.

Born in war, growing up unregulated in backwoods rough-and-tumble exuberance, the trade was rife with political patronage and a code of devil-take-the-hindmost. The Crown had continued to insist that only authorized contractors could cut Crown land. Since a government could not tax its own logging, it received no direct revenue. Governor Smythe of New Brunswick reminded the colonial secretary in London that timberlands were being lost with no public gain; eventually the province was empowered to permit commercial logging and collect royalties and taxes.

In the meantime, in 1826, the governments of Upper and Lower Canada began to collect public revenue by selling one-year licences to any qualified citizen who wished to log on unsurveyed Crown land. Royalties, called "stumpage fees," were based on the number of trees cut, which in the early days was actually ascertained by counting the stumps. Revenue was disappointing. Grants were made to political favourites, the ever-recurring custom of treating public forests as a "pork barrel" having come early to thwart efforts at forest management.

There were hardly any regulations. Like the cattle trade in the American southwest, the lumber industry had grown up lawless. Lumbermen ignored concession boundaries, helping themselves to timber not their own. Nova Scotians sailed schooners to Newfoundland to steal timber from the only colony that had not developed its own industry. American timber pirates stole from Canadian territory on the Great Lakes.

The worst of the lawlessness was the Shiners' War on the Ottawa River in the mid-1830s. The Shiners were raw labourers brought out from Ireland to dig the great industrial canals, and after finishing the Rideau Canal they had gone to work cutting oak, thereby earning the French tag *chêneurs*, or oak cutters. In the days when Ottawa was called Bytown, these Irish fought the French Canadians for jobs in the pine camps, egged on by the notorious Peter Aylen, who used them in his effort to grab control of the timber trade. Fifty men lost their lives in the Shiners' War. The Lumbermen's War in the Maritimes produced no fatalities, but bones were broken when loggers from New Brunswick and Maine clashed on the border for the right to log on the Aroostook River.

More serious were complaints that timber camps, with their promise of ready cash, were draining so much labour from the farms that New Brunswick's agricultural economy was suffering. Food that could have been grown locally was imported. Joseph Bouchette, surveyor general of Lower Canada, wrote in 1832: "The quantities of timber that have been felled, squared and taken from that part of the country are enormous and yet no one industry presents so few symptoms of improvement. The pursuit of lumbering (perhaps a necessary evil in colonizing a wilderness) seems indeed a demoralizing tendency, sometimes depriving its followers of the inclination and even the capability of consecutive and steady industry."

Efforts by the government of the United Province of Upper and Lower Canada to gain greater revenue from the forests resulted in 1842 in serious over-production. Where the government had made its mistake was in demanding that far too many trees be harvested per square mile. Poor markets in Britain left loggers with no choice but to pile timber in the woods to rot or burn. The industry virtually collapsed.

Calling for "wholesome regulations," the first of a long line of government-appointed commissions seeking "the protection of forests from unneccessary destruction" got the harvest reduced and achieved adoption of an Act for the Sale and Better Management of Timber upon Crown Lands. It was loose enough to provide an administrative framework that was to last fifty years while accommodating changes. Ground rent was introduced to supplement stumpage. The principle was established that the people, through government, would hold possession of the land, disposing only of the cutting rights.

For Nova Scotia and Prince Edward Island it was too late, but New Brunswick, which still controlled sixty per cent of its timberland, decided to hold on to the remaining land and only dispose of cutting rights. Complaints from lumbermen that the annual auctioning of timber limits was impeding the industry caused the government to grant longer tenure, of thirty years and more. This method of leasing out timberlands became the rule across Canada, differing only in detail from province to province. Stumpage and ground rent at so much per square mile remained one of the principal sources of government money up to the 1930s.

Efforts were made to achieve maximum revenue, rather than manage and perpetuate the forest. Throughout the nineteenth century, logging was a prelude to settlement; as the Royal Canadian Institute stated in 1851, the destiny of the nation lay in "the acts of opening up the wilderness and preparing the country for the pursuits of the agriculturalists."

This hardly sat well with lumbermen, who had begun to argue against the folly of handing out submarginal land to settlers. Of all the 80,000 square miles of the Ottawa Valley region, no more than ten per cent was believed suitable for farming. The Ottawa lumberman W.H. Burke condemned "the wanton, foolish and insane policy of the Crown Lands

Department in surveying [for settlement] a township where nothing but pine and rock exist." The government went right on granting forest land to settlers, including the pine-rich Huron-Ottawa tract of 13,000 square miles.

Burke, like other lumbermen, blamed settlers for spreading "fire and havoc," apparently forgetting that lumbermen left great quantities of slash and waste that dried into dangerous tinder. Because of lightning, there had always been periodic conflagrations. Clouds of wood smoke, blown out across the Atlantic by the westerlies, were seen by European seamen before Canada was settled. There is evidence that now-denuded parts of the southern prairies were once forested and were stripped of their woods by fire before settlers arrived. With colonization, the threat had grown more serious, beginning with the Miramichi fire in New Brunswick in 1825. Starting in balsam fir that had been reduced to kindling by an attack of spruce budworm, which kills trees slowly over several seasons, the fire destroyed a swath of forest eighty miles long and twenty-five miles wide. It burned the communities of Newcastle and Douglastown and caused 160 deaths.

A large fire was recorded between Lake Superior and Rainy Lake in the 1840s. Much of the "big pine" country on the Bonnechère River, a tributary of the Ottawa, was burned in 1851, the fire starting in the wadding of a lumberman's hunting rifle. Four years later an Indian burning off a blueberry patch started a fire that ran all the way from Lake Timiskaming near the Quebec border across the height of land to Michipicoten Harbour on Lake Superior. A surveyor who toured the area a few years later wrote: "Almost the whole of this district appears to have been devastated by fires at different times and at periods more or less remote, which swept away the original forests, some remains of which are still to be seen in the shape of huge trunks of pine, blackened and charred by fire. The country to the north of my line, along the height of land, has been swept over by fire and now is, for an area of 2,000 square miles, a desolate wilderness. Judging from the remains still standing, it was formerly covered with pine and other timber."

Nature's age-old method of clearing the forest of dying vegetation so that new growth can come up had become a nightmare for settlers and lumbermen. Pine is particularly flammable, and once a fire starts in dry weather it can build up into a veritable firestorm if there is any wind. The first attempt at fire legislation came when the Assembly of United Canada—

2. *In the making of square timber in the Ottawa Valley in the
nineteenth century as much as a third of a white pine was wasted in the
process of hewing it to size. Here Ottawa square timber-makers are
making "waney timber," sticks of white pine with bevelled edges to cut
down on waste.*

Ontario and Quebec—drafted a bill in 1854 "for the protection of the forests and preventing the setting of fire to the
woods for the purpose of clearing the lands." The proposal got
side-tracked, buried in the work of a committee set up to look
into the whole range of forest problems, fire included. After
hearing a great deal of contradictory evidence, the committee
failed to come up with recommendations. Not unexpectedly,
and certainly not for the last time, a committee had found itself
confused by "the varied and extensive character of the subject."

The wasteful square timber trade was starting to peter out
around this time. Attempts had been made to avoid some of
the notorious waste by producing "waney timber," with round
rather than squared edges, permitting the use of smaller trees.
But the gradual demise of square timber was due not so much
to waste but rather to the fact that the growing trade in milled
lumber, mostly exported to the United States rather than to
Britain, was more lucrative.

The industry spread westward from Ottawa to the Muskoka
region, spurring the growth of towns like Bracebridge and
Orillia, and Collingwood and Midland on Georgian Bay. Large
mills appeared, one at Peterborough being able to process fifty

logs an hour. Timber to build American towns was exported via the railways and the Erie and Champlain canals until exports to the United States equalled those to Britain. American capital supplanted financing from Britain. American entrepreneurs such as H.F. Bronson and E.B. Eddy arrived in Ottawa to join John Egan of Bytown, who had come from Ireland as a young man and was now employing 3,500 men, 1,200 horses, and 200 oxen. Lumber had become big business. The age of the timber barons had arrived: J.R. Booth, who came to Ottawa as a young carpenter from the Eastern Townships of Quebec, built an empire that covered 4,250 square miles, second in size to that of Price Brothers in Quebec.

There has rarely been much agreement on the state of the commercial wood supply at any given time, but few estimates have been so wildly optimistic as that reported in the 1850s by Charles Richaid Weld in his book *Vacation Tour in the United States and Canada*. "The question naturally arises," said Weld, "how long will the Canadian forests continue to meet the enormous demand for timber. With a view to obtaining some information on this point, the Government recently instituted an inquiry as to the probable duration of the supply in various districts; and it was ascertained that in the Ottawa forest-region alone there was timber sufficient to feed the mills on that noble river, at the present consumption, for 600 years."

Whatever the source of Weld's information, the advent of the lumber trade brought more concern for the future, rather than less. Not that there had been a total lack of concern in the past. In 1819 François André Michaux, the first botanist to make a systematic study of Canada's trees, had plumped for conservation. Thirty years later James Dawson, later head of McGill University but then a Nova Scotia geologist whose work took him into the woods, warned of "the depletion of the forests of British North America." After finance minister Alexander Galt denounced "the profligate waste of one of the greatest sources of provincial wealth," a select committee of the Canada legislature was instructed in 1863 "to enquire into the rapid destruction of the forests and the means to be adopted to prevent it, to consider the expediency of reserving as forests the extensive tracts of land which abound in exportable timber, but are unsuitable for cultivation." The committee got lost in the bustle prior to Confederation, when responsibility for the forests, and the revenue from them, was handed over to the separate provinces (except for the territory that became the Prairie provinces, which gained control of their forests in 1930).

Impatient at repeated failure to come to grips with forest renewal, Alexander Campbell, the last commissioner of Crown Lands for Upper and Lower Canada, demanded "sustained yield," a system of harvest rotation wherein a new forest is always coming back up. This had been introduced in Sweden and Germany, but in Canada Campbell was a century ahead of his time and Canada opted, in effect, for forest exploitation rather than forest management; the first of many opportunities had been missed. It is intriguing to imagine what the state of the depleted forests, pine among them, might be today had Campbell's advice been taken.

It was at this time, in the lush rain forests of British Columbia, that the greatest lumber source of all was opened up. The beginning was not auspicious. A pugnacious 53-year-old English shipmaster, with no knowledge of lumbering, built the first important mill in 1861 at Alberni Inlet on Vancouver Island only to fail; the cause, of all things, a shortage of wood. It was one of the lessons that Canadians, including lumbermen, have taken so long to learn: reserves of timber are not enough, they also have to be accessible. There were huge trees galore near Alberni Inlet, but oxen could drag them only a short distance and once Captain Edward Stamp's loggers had cleared off the shoreline there was no way of getting more distant logs down to the mill. (In eastern Canada today the problem is usually the opposite: the trees are too small.)

Stamp started up a new mill within a year on Burrard Inlet, where the city of Vancouver stands, leasing 8,000 acres at a penny an acre for twenty-one years. From such uncertain beginnings grew British Columbia's largest industry. Far from England, the eastern United States, and even the rest of Canada, cut off as it was by the mountains, British Columbia was forced to confine its market for fifty years to the Pacific Rim countries. As for the forests, the 200-foot Douglas fir, the hemlock and cedar that dwarfed even the biggest of the eastern white pine, were surely candidates for the term "inexhaustible." Though British Columbia has done a relatively better job of forestry than eastern Canada, and of course enjoys much richer forest land in the coastal rainbelt, it too has found itself faced with the same problem of diminishing supply.

For those who wished to heed the lesson, the fate of hemlock has been a cautionary tale, hemlock having been more or less wiped out by destructive harvesting. Some 10,000 acres had been felled each year, the bark stripped off for the leather-tanning industry, the trees themselves left to rot. It was a classic example of short-sighted destruction for temporary profit and ended only when the market for tanbark disappeared.

After Confederation, the level of forest policy varied from province to province. There was no centralized administration, as in the United States, the federal role in Canada being confined to those woodlands, mostly fringing the prairies, remaining within Ottawa's control. Ottawa's lack of authority was demonstrated in 1872 by Prime Minister John A. Macdonald.

For decades tremendous quantities of pine had been floated down the Ottawa, prompting Macdonald, in his home beside the river, to write to the Ontario premier: "The sight of the immense masses of timber passing my window every morning constantly suggests to my mind the absolute necessity there is for looking into the future of this trade. We are recklessly destroying the timber of Canada and there is scarcely a possibility of replacing it." He tried to get both Ontario and Quebec to establish ways of conserving it, with no success.

Not much was being done about fires, although after a series of conflagrations that swept the Gaspé and threatened Chicoutimi near Lac St. Jean, leaving 500 homeless, Quebec in 1874 was the first province to employ forest rangers, or *gardes forestiers*. Land clearing was as disastrous as ever. Years later, J.A. Gillies recalled how a settler who set out to clear an acre and a half for potatoes managed to burn enough timber to supply the Gillies mill on the Ottawa for twenty years. On the Canadian Shield prospectors were deliberately scorching the land so they could examine the mineral formations that lay beneath the forest floor. The damage they caused to the forests has never been fully documented.

The fire legislation that eventually passed in Ontario in 1878 took another six or seven years to implement, by which time rangers were being sent out into the woods, along with inspectors who were supposed to guard against "any wanton or special waste" in the logging camps. Nova Scotia and New Brunswick passed fire laws in the mid-1880s but had no way of policing them.

By the 1870s the forest management campaign of a Montreal lumberman, James Little, was gaining adherents. In one of his many pamphlets, *The Timber Supply Question,* Little said: "The most shameful waste of this indispensable material has become the order of the day, while our boards of trade, our political economists and statesmen, and the leading journals of the country, totally ignore the subject as not worthy of their slightest notice. The answer thus treated with so much indifference and neglect will, however, it is certain, before many years roll round, force itself on the attention of the whole community to such a degree as to dwindle all other questions into utter insignificance in comparison."

Concern was spreading into the business community. Captain N.W. Beckwith of a Halifax shipping firm wrote to *Canadian Monthly* in June 1872: "We are wasting our forests, habitually, wickedly, insanely, and at a rate which must soon bankrupt us all in that element of wealth....Destroying a forest because we want timber is like smothering a hive of bees because we want honey."

↑ ↑ ↑ ↑ ↑ ↑ ↑ 3 ↑ ↑ ↑ ↑ ↑ ↑ ↑

"*Woodman, spare that tree!*"

IF THERE WAS ANY ONE TIME AND PLACE THAT the Canadian conservation movement put down roots, it was at Montreal in August 1882. The conference was called, rather grandly, "the first parliament of forestry," though it had no powers beyond recommendation and persuasion. Nowadays conservation is widely looked upon as an effort to reduce waste, enhance productivity, and generally perpetuate resources, but in those days many of the delegates present tended to think in terms of simple preservation rather than wise use.

The conference was the first occasion for scientists, civil servants, politicians, industrialists, and citizens to discuss a fairly new concern—the destruction of the forests. Both site and timing were appropriate. Montreal, the centre of finance and communication, had eclipsed Quebec City as the hub of a forest industry that had provided the capital to build Canada's towns, railroads, and government services.

The initiative had come from the United States, the meeting being a continuation of the American Forestry Congress, which had convened in Cincinnati the previous spring. That had been a colourful three-ring circus, with Cincinnati draped in bunting, school children planting trees on Arbor Day, and orators in halls and on street corners preaching an optimistic age of science, technology, and conservation in a pioneer, exploitative country.

The conservation movement in the United States had been thriving since the Vermont naturalist George Perkins Marsh, whose book *Man and Nature* in 1864 demonstrated cause and effect in human interference with the ecosystem, urged that people "be roused to a sense of the dangers to which indiscriminate clearing of the woods may expose not only future generations but the very soil itself." Forests, said Marsh, were one of the planet's modifiers, checking the force of winds, anchoring the soil, equalizing extremes in temperature, absorbing excessive precipitation, preventing floods and erosion. As American ambassador in Italy, Marsh had seen the damage caused by deforestation, which he linked with the decline of the Roman Empire. He had seen the advantages of reforestation in Germany and France.

By the 1880s others were sharing his concern. The American Association for the Advancement of Science declared that "consumption and waste of the forests of the country much exceed their restoration by natural growth." The commissioner of the General Land Office, Joseph M. Wilson, declared, "In forty or fifty years our forests will have disappeared and those of Canada will be approaching extinction." Since he was talking about eastern white pine, he was not far wrong. The map of the United States was beginning to look like a large cleared farm with woodlands only around its edges, or so it was said.

It is questionable whether there would have been a meeting in Cincinnati or anywhere else had it not been for a visiting forester from Prussia, Richard von Steuben. A local judge became so interested in von Steuben's account of forestry in Germany, where it had been practised more or less scientifically since the 1780s, that he felt something similar might be done in America, where forestry was regarded merely as a minor branch of agriculture, when it was considered at all. As it happened, 1882 was municipal election year and candidates seeking a likely issue supported the congress.

The Cincinnati delegates were a mixture of bureaucrats, farmers, horticulturists, arboriculturists, botanists, environmentalists, and lumbermen, all with their separate concerns. Some wanted to plant trees to protect farm lands, some to assure clean water by preserving watersheds. One group, repelled by the ugliness of cities, brought along a silver spade for planting trees, which bore the hopeful if unscientific legend "From churlish wreck and wrong our prayer; for bloom and beauty everywhere." The only trained forester at the conference was Bernhard Eduard Fernow, a compatriot of von Steuben's, who had come to the United States to marry a Brooklyn girl he had met in Germany. There were neither foresters nor the schools to train them in the United States or Canada.

Assailed by amateurs and competing interest groups, the American organizers made an imaginative choice of keynote speaker for their five-day meeting. James Little was, to begin with, a Canadian. He was also something of a rarity, a wealthy lumberman who, in those days of timber barons and rampant *laissez-faire,* had been waging a passionate campaign for restraint and reform. Since he was eighty years old and ailing, his speech was delivered by his son, William, who was carrying on his father's battle.

An Irishman from Londonderry, James Little had come to Canada as a boy and developed timber holdings at Georgian Bay in Ontario and the St. Maurice Valley in Quebec. Settling in Montreal, he had become a major lumber exporter to the United States. In the 1860s he had begun to attack wasteful logging and short-sighted profit motives. He accused government of encouraging overproduction in order to rake in more revenue, thus causing a glut on the market, poor prices, and yet another round of boom and bust in a notoriously unstable industry.

Nor was any of this new. Once governments had realized the revenue potential of the forest, they had tended to milk it like some great, green, everlasting cow. This had begun in New Brunswick in 1817 with the introduction of timber-cutting duties. Nine years later Quebec and Ontario fixed regulations and Crown dues that established government control—and also entrenched the constitutional right of provinces to own and develop Crown forests. So began the habit, which has persisted to our own times, of swallowing timber revenue into consolidated funds and putting little back into the restoration of the forests whence the wealth had come. Revenue from auctioning, licensing, and cutting of timberlands—variously known as timber berths, concessions, or timber limits—was spent on hospitals, roads, and administration. On almost anything, in fact, except forestry. The timberlands provided a seductive byway for political patronage and were handed out in large chunks to encourage entrepreneurs to build railways. The

Dominion government alienated millions of acres in that way. On Vancouver Island some of the very best woodland on the east coast was granted to the company building the Esquimalt & Nanaimo Railway, and sizeable tracts of it are being harvested to this day by companies like MacMillan Bloedel and Pacific Forest Products.

James Little upset his fellow lumbermen by taxing them with "an inexcusable ignorance of the timber question, or an astonishing want of foresight." When he made one of his fighting speeches in Michigan, where the greatest pine forest in the world was being demolished, the American *Lumbermen's Gazette* responded complacently that "forests yet unexplored for lumbering will be made accessible when required." In his Cincinnati speech Little took issue with the assumption that when its own supplies ran out the United States could always look to Canada.

"I know the idea prevails on the American side of the line that the area of timberland in Canada is so great that supplies are practically exhaustless," he said, "but this idea, I regret to say, is not borne out by the facts. . . . There is one thing sure, that our magnificent forests of pine are about all gone.

"In point of fact, we are following the United States very closely in our efforts to get rid of forests, and fully justify the remarks of a Glasgow journal that 'Canada and the United States are busy sawing from under them the high-reaching, fortune-making branch on which, like conquerors, they are sitting and overlooking the world.' I hardly dare attempt to describe the consequences of a dearth of timber, and every effort should be made not only to protect our existing forests, but to plant new ones, for no civilized country can do without timber."

One had only to look at New Brunswick, where white pine had once been king and had dwindled to forty per cent of the total cut. Lumbermen there, as in the St. Lawrence and Saguenay valleys of Quebec, had turned to white spruce, but that too was rapidly diminishing. As for the oak that the French navy had prized in the seventeenth century, it was virtually gone from the Eastern Townships of Quebec. From the mixed forests of Quebec and Ontario, one of the world's great treasure chests of white and red pine, lumbermen had been forced to push hundreds of miles back into the wilderness to get the wood once believed inexhaustible.

Little had carried on a lonely campaign, but now was being

joined by a few of his colleagues. A.T. Drummond, also from Montreal, told the conference: "Men are selfish, and are not disciplined to go to labour and expense in regard to what does not promise immediate results, the advantage of which they will not themselves reap." Lumbermen were in the habit of regarding timber as a "one-crop commodity." Cut and move on! The time it takes a pine or spruce to reach maturity, the better part of a century, was considered sufficient reason to do nothing. Most did not expect the pine to regenerate, and it certainly would not come back fast enough to be cut in their lifetime.

As a cautionary reminder of what happens to a nation that annihilates its woodlands "through the ignorance of the people and the apathy of their rulers," David H. Bailey, American consul general based in Shanghai, described floods and droughts that had brought disaster and death to millions, "preparing a desert out of the soil which was once famous for its fertility."

Bailey's grim report made a strong impression on the three delegates from Ontario, members of the Fruit Growers' Association who, in the absence of any forestry tradition, had been trying to fill the vacuum. They had long been anxious to educate the public before Canadians found themselves "compelled to forever inhabit a dismal treeless waste." There was urgent need for reforestation in southern Ontario, which had been stripped by generations of settlement and lumbering so that fifty townships had been left with only five per cent of their forest cover. No township on the southern fringe had more than fifteen per cent left, and there were areas in half a dozen counties where the sandy soil had turned into wind-blown waste. Some 150,000 acres in Bruce, Simcoe, Lambton, Northumberland, and Durham counties had been reduced to drifting sand, half-buried tree trunks, and general desolation. Regarding the conference as an excellent vehicle for informing the public, they were successful in having it reconvene in Montreal, though the Canadian government agreed to host the Montreal meeting less for ecological reasons than because the depression of the 1870s had given the industry such a blow that a general stock-taking was needed. Because of the late arrival of the chairman, United States Commissioner of Agriculture G.B. Loring, the meeting was opened by Canada's leading forest conservationist, Henri Gustave Joly de Lotbinière.

Conferring the honorary title "Nestor of American Forestry" on James Little, Lotbinière recalled how for fifteen years

3. Lawyer, politician, and amateur forester, Sir Henri Joly de Lotbinière was one of the most effective of the handful of conservationists in the late nineteenth century advocating greater care of our woodlands.

Little had campaigned practically alone. Now it was encouraging to see that sceptics were at last admitting that Little had been right, but sad to see them tumbling to the other extreme and declaring there was no use protecting forests because there was so little left to protect. Lotbinière, who had completed the first federal effort to estimate the extent of the forests, said: "There is still a good deal worth caring for and improving. It is late, but not too late. Having no school of forestry in Canada we must educate ourselves; we have got books written on the subject by eminent and practical men, and we have got, always before our eyes, the great book of nature."

Lotbinière knew more about the forests than most. Born Henri Gustave Joly in France, where he attended the Sorbonne, he had come to Quebec to practise law and take up occupancy of the family seigneury granted to one of his ancestors by Louis XIV. He had served a one-year term as Liberal premier of Quebec and was soon to be known as Sir Henri Joly de Lotbinière, having adopted his ancestral family name and accepted a knighthood for services to Canada. In Lotbinière County, on the south shore of the St. Lawrence some thirty miles above Quebec City, he had begun to practise forestry in the European tradition, as a hobby befitting a gentleman farmer. In one of the first efforts at "sustained yield," which is an attempt to balance the number of merchantable trees cut with the new growth coming back to provide a second harvest, he cut only trees of a certain age and size, leaving smaller ones to grow. He established one of Canada's first tree plantations and introduced valuable black walnut into sites that were farther north than the regions in which experts thought that species could flourish.

His report to the federal government on "The State of the Forests" in 1875 had been of necessity more general and philosophical than scientific, because there were no means of making a proper survey. Contemplating 100,000 square miles of wilderness drained by the Ottawa and the St. Maurice rivers, he asked: "Does it begin to show signs of exhaustion? Is it possible that, in such a short time, man has been able to make an impression upon these millions of acres of forest?" Reckoned in the lifetime of a tree, logging had not been going on at any significant rate for long, but in those seventy years tremendous quantities of pine had been cut.

"If there is no sign of exhaustion," Lotbinière asked, "what is the meaning of the complaints that have come to us over the seas, every year louder and louder, about the falling off, in quantity and size, of our white pine, hitherto considered as the finest in the world?

"Look at the map of that great region, and you will see how little of it is now left untouched. . . . Those who think that there will never be an end to our timber may say: 'We can still go north.'" But they could not go very far, for over the height of land dividing the watersheds of the St. Lawrence River and Hudson Bay lay "a huge barren wilderness with little timber, and that mostly of stunted growth." The hope for the future was in the Douglas fir of British Columbia, where "the bountiful gifts of Providence are still stored up for us, and the forests have scarcely been attacked by the lumbermen."

Lotbinière recalled that he had seen manuscripts of the French governors, written two hundred years before, in which the danger to the forests had been clearly recognized, but what was the condition now of our forests? "In a very short time since the beginning of this century," he said, "we have overrun our forests, picking out the finest pine, and we have impoverished them to a serious extent, and, what makes it worse, impoverished the country too. Men are the same all over the world. They never set much value upon the free gifts of Providence, and disregard them in proportion to their abundance....What appeared to be inexhaustible becomes exhausted, it then begins to be valuable, and we must pay for our experience."

Lotbinière lamented, as foresters lament to this day, the lack of public interest. He recalled how an attempt in the 1870s to form a Quebec Forestry Association, the first in Canada, had died of lack of support. It had been composed of private citizens who had been requested to go out and plant trees.

"It is rather difficult, I admit," he said, "to induce people to plant forest trees in this province where, for generations, they have been brought up to look upon the forest as their natural enemy, to be got rid of at any cost, hacked down, burnt out of the way (for want of a better way of disposing of it), and still troubling the settler for years with its ever-lasting stumps, an obstacle to thorough cultivation.

"The children and grandchildren of the old settlers remember too well; they cannot be expected to love the forest tree, but self-interest ought to conquer instinct and prejudice. In Europe, where land is scarcer and more valuable than here, they plant, every year, thousands and thousands of acres in forest trees."

Now, at the Montreal conference, Lotbinière had opportunity to press the need for forestry. The meeting also heard from two opposing factions, lumbermen and preservationists, whose mutual suspicion enlivened the proceedings. To lumbermen, seeking to protect their investment, "conservation" meant legislation against forest fires, and laws to stop settlers from occupying land unsuitable for anything but growing trees. They complained of bogus settlers, whose farms were nothing more than disguised lumber camps, who moved in only long enough to cut the timber and thus avoid the rental fees and royalties paid by *bona fide* loggers.

The preservationists, on the other hand, argued passionately, if not always from adequate information, that indiscriminate logging and burning by lumbermen and settlers were ruining not only the beauty but the balance of nature. Things were happening that were little understood. Streams were dwindling away to sand in summer or becoming torrential floods in spring. One delegate declared: "Our springs are later, our summers are drier, and every year becoming more so. Our autumns are carried forward into winter, while our winter climate is subject to far greater changes of temperature than formerly."

The preservationists felt that nature knows best, and they ignored the needs of an industry on which the nation depended. They were sincere, and sometimes justified, in their views, even though Canada for reasons of climate and low population pressure was in no danger of suffering the destruction caused by deforestation in countries such as Greece or China.

Between the two extremes, the preservationists who wanted to turn the clock back and the busy lumbermen who merely wanted to protect their investment, were the moderates, corresponding to our present-day conservationists. Some lumbermen present were surprisingly enlightened, though believing, wrongly as it turned out, that given no more than fire protection the forest would always, everywhere, regenerate itself satisfactorily. Dr. A. Eby of Sebringville, Ontario, one of the pioneers in campaigning for the sort of logging that assists nature in producing suitable new natural growth, saw then that the time would come when the timber supply would not equal the demand.

With a bit of updating, some of the papers might serve well today, so slow has been our progress. The arguments about what should or should not be done could be heard at conferences as late as the 1970s, when consensus began to jell as to what constitutes proper management. But some of the papers would now seem dated. One of these reflected the influence of Charles Darwin's *On the Origin of Species,* which had been changing attitudes towards nature since its appearance in 1859. A paper prepared by Dr. Henry Howard of Montreal, like the naïve and impractical slogan "Woodman, Spare that Tree!" that hung above the platform, did nothing to change

4. *Bernhard Eduard Fernow, German-born "Father of North American Forestry," came to the United States as a young man. He served as chief forester for the United States government before being appointed dean of Canada's first forestry school, at the University of Toronto. As the first professional forester on this continent, Fernow introduced into Canada many of the methods developed in Germany during the nineteenth century.*

the opinion of Bernhard Eduard Fernow that forest management in Canada was still in the Dark Ages.

"An amusing incident happened," Fernow told a friend, "which although remaining without any deleterious effect on the movement, might have proved a setback but for the fact of a Canadian gentleman, the best-loved and strongest advocate of forestry, Seigneur Sir Henri Joly de Lotbinière.

"The then U.S. Commissioner of Agriculture was the chairman of the meeting. An old gentleman, a local physician, had been invited to deliver a paper and he had hauled out the beginnings of the Universe, developing in great detail the theories of evolution, and demonstrating that all things are matter and under the law of matter. He had arrived at a summing-up sentence, 'And so a gold mine is matter, a sheep is matter, a forest is matter, and for that matter, man is matter,' when down came the gavel of the chairman and up got the chairman with great aplomb, calling the gentleman to order. 'I will not allow anyone at any meeting over which I preside to utter such heterodox ideas,' and therewith left the hall, to the consternation of the large assemblage and the innocent speaker.

"Sir Henri immediately slipped into the chair, explained there must have been something misunderstood, and asked the speaker to continue. . . .The congress proceeded without a hitch."

Fernow, the only forester at work in North America, was to have great influence on the development of forestry in the United States and Canada. He was then thirty-two years old, a lean little terrier of a man, with keen eyes, an abrupt manner, and a spiky moustache grown while serving as an officer in the Prussian army. The son of a forester, he had worked for the Prussian forestry service before emigrating to the United States. After much difficulty in finding a job in a country where, as he said, even the name of his profession was unknown, he had been hired as woods manager to a smelting firm in Pennsylvania. As a graduate of one of the best schools in Germany, he was disappointed by the backwardness in North America. His assessment of the Montreal congress was somewhat scathing.

"Of the real science of forestry there was no glimpse," he wrote, "unless you allow the writer to mention his own efforts to lay down and explain those scientific principles which underlie forest growth, and the resulting general rule of forest management.

"In its literary aspects the meeting carried with it the stamp which was impressed on it by the interests of the western treeless prairie states. Tree planting and arboriculture was the

theme of most papers offered. The questions how to preserve
and how to manage extant forest resources were hardly
touched upon. The majority of the sixty-one papers may be
characterized as laborious attempts to gather information
without any critical discernment of what was important, what
unimportant, and what was required for the present, and what
may be left for the future to decide."

Fernow was the first trained forester most of the 200
delegates had ever met. Having discovered a pedagogic flair,
which was to make him the first forestry professor in North
America, Fernow regaled them with a short course in European
forestry. There was no great mystery, he said. Like farmers,
foresters sought to produce a renewable crop, but with rotations of not one but seventy years or more. Though he was
often to be linked with the conservation movement and called
a "denudiac," he believed the forests were not there to be
admired; rather they "grow and are grown to be cut and to
furnish valuable material to man." Remembering the tame
forests of his native Germany, he believed proper harvesting
was compatible with enjoyment of the woodland scene. His
message was not "Woodman, spare that tree!" but rather
"Woodman, cut the forest in such a way that it may grow green
again." Unlike the preservationists, Fernow had no objection
to logging, but only to the way it was done in North America,
where forests were treated like a non-renewable resource.
"Their influence, climatic and hydraulic, is by no means
destroyed or checked by a well-conducted, systematic forestry,
which utilizes ripe timber, taking care of its immediate regeneration for the continuity of the forest as well as the timber
supply."

Being a realist, he admitted that Canada was not ready, if it
ever would be, for the classic forestry of Europe. Though he
was later to change his mind, he said tree planting was not
advisable in the Canadian wilds except in areas in danger of
erosion. The European method of clear-cutting, or taking off
all or most of the trees from a given area followed by immediate
planting, was impracticable and unnecessary in Canada so long
as efforts were made to cut in a manner that would encourage
natural seeding from those trees left standing after logging.

"From a financial point of view this method of working for
reforestation by the seed from the original timber growth is the
only advisable one where soil and timber are cheap and labour
difficult to obtain, as in the case of our lumbering regions and

especially so as the lumberman, having taken what can be converted into cash, is not likely to make any expenditure upon the soil to provide future growth."

While believing that good forestry meant incurring expense for the sake of future revenue, he had no illusions that Canada was ready to forgo current profits so long as God-given supplies remained. People, whether in industry or government, rarely functioned that way, as the history of other forest nations had demonstrated. "The time has not yet arrived when the profit from the growing forests will induce capital to arrest the devastation of our timberlands."

He urged his listeners to study ecology and the interaction of sun, water, soil, and climate, which differed in Canada, region by region, and was little understood. "The whole science of forestry is built, or in the case of this continent, is to be built, upon a very complicated system of elementary knowledge, which can only be gathered by local observation based on correct understanding of the physical forces at work."

Among the delegates who applauded Fernow's speech, which by its very professionalism was seen as "opening the door" to forestry in North America, was Dr. F.B. Hough, chief of the Forestry Division of the U.S. Department of Agriculture, whose job Fernow was to take four years later. Hough had been advocating woods management despite lack of support from his superior, Commissioner Loring, whose indifference eventually drove Hough to quit. Noting that forestry was as yet "hardly envisaged" in Canada, Hough still believed Canada was far ahead of the United States, which, if true, was not a distinction Canada would enjoy for long. In evidence, Hough cited Quebec's ban on timber burning for land clearance in the summer months, and Quebec's offer, which in fact was never very effective, to pay twelve dollars for each acre planted with trees and tended.

Not a trained forester, Hough found himself being corrected by Fernow when he unwisely praised the "diameter limit" imposed by Quebec and Ontario, which banned the cutting of trees less than a foot around near the ground. Apart from attempts at fire protection, this had been the only notable stab at forest management, but Fernow had little use for it. The problem lay in the ignorance of the wood cutters, who knew too little about trees to make the "diameter limit" work. Small trees, like small people, were not necessarily the youngest but had been stunted due to circumstance and might actually be much older and less healthy than the taller trees that had robbed them of light and space. They were hardly good stock to base a new crop on and might as well be cut.

Hough made himself unpopular with lumbermen by declaring that Canada's greatest advantage lay in public ownership of most of the forest land. The Canadian forests were ninety-percent public land. In the United States most of it was locked into private holdings where government had no say in how it was treated.

"Unlike the people of the United States," said Hough, "Canadians will never be compelled to spend millions of dollars from the public treasury to regain title to forest lands in order to place them under silvicultural management and thus assure a continuous supply of timber. This will always give Canadians an advantage over the U.S. and many other countries."

At the end of three lively days in Queen's Hall and the St. James Street "Forestry Chambers," so named for the occasion, the delegates passed hopeful resolutions that indicated the congress had learned the inadequacy of its irrelevant slogan "Woodman, spare that tree!" The conference advocated tree planting, the study of ecology, and segregation of forest and farm land. It urged adoption of European silviculture and condemned, as enemies of the nation's greatest renewable resource, "the deadly sweep of forest fires," sloppy logging practices, and settlers who wasted forest land.

It had remarkable success, one that present-day foresters might envy, in stimulating public interest. Newspapers devoted more space to it than to the sophisticated conferences of more recent times. The *Montreal Herald*, for example, had begun its coverage with only the vaguest notion of what the congress was all about, welcoming it in poetic terms, as if greeting a gathering of Druids, with the homily "The tree brings us nearer to Divinity than we can get any other way," thus anticipating Joyce Kilmer's famous line that only God can make a tree. By the close of the meeting, the newspaper was commending the gathering for its "practicality" rather than for its poetry.

It is impossible to tell how many of the various government measures that followed could be attributed to the congress, but the "first parliament of forestry" undoubtedly helped to assure permanent forestry organizations in the United States and Canada. Where there had been scattered voices, there was now a movement. A concern of amateur conservationists had now spread to politicians and civil servants eager for revenue, businessmen and bankers who knew the value of forests to the economy, and others, including clergymen, who saw the social issues involved, such as the ghost towns created when timber supplies ran out.

Opinion-makers—for a time, at least; such is the attention span of the popular press—were suddenly looking at the forest with interest and slightly less ignorance. Admitting surprise that the value of forest products surpassed that of every other industry, a surprise somewhat puzzling in the capital of the woods industry, the *Montreal Herald* said the news that no one had devised a way to check forest waste must be "startling to the general public." It was, at least, startling to the Montreal Board of Trade, which issued a statement, too vague and general to have impact, urging the government to plant trees "on the immense wastes of the Province of Quebec."

The Ontario government passed an act promising a bonus to any community planting trees. New Brunswick went one better with a regulation that no tree should be cut that did not yield at least one eighteen-foot log, which proved more effective than the "diameter limit." All the eastern provinces, except Prince Edward Island, were dabbling in fire legislation, most of it toothless because of lack of money to enforce the laws. The fire problem was horrific, the Ottawa Valley alone losing $5 million worth of wood to fire every year.

One direct result of the Montreal conference was the creation of the office of clerk of forestry in the Ontario Department of Agriculture. As clerk of forestry, Robert W. Phipps was to collect information and educate farmers in the need for healthy woodlots. Colourful and energetic, a fifty-year-old journalist and apple grower, Phipps had no authority to change anything, but as he travelled southern Ontario he preached an important message that few had thought about: while trees of some sort might grow back, they were frequently not the same merchantable species that grew there before.

A political pamphleteer for both the Conservatives and the Liberals, Phipps did not hesitate to take both parties to task for lack of vision and commitment. "Among all the politicians who have in turn 'saved' our country," he said, "few of them have thought it worth while to attempt to save the timber. No destruction was ever more ruthless, more injurious, more lasting in its effects, more difficult to repair, than that to which

Canadians, for the past hundred years, have cheered one another on."

Seeking further evidence that serious harm had been done to land carelessly cleared, he corresponded with 300 farmers who lived in townships that had been denuded in the southern fringes of the province. "Everyone agreed that the deforestation of our country has taken away the moisture from the surface of the earth," he reported. "Those who say they formerly obtained water by digging six or eight feet must now dig thirty or forty feet or more in the same places. The reason for that is, the forest is a reservoir for water. Its base is composed of decaying branches and leaves; of roots penetrating into the earth and forming a great porous mass out of which the rain or dew does not pass. The great body of moisture feeds springs and rivulets all around, and keeps water near the surface of the earth."

Though some of his theories do not command scientific approval now, his work was useful and he preached to every farmer who would listen, telling them to keep cattle and sheep from grazing farm woodlots, the proverbial "back forty," because they were destroying thousands of young trees every year. "Leave some forest protection for your crops. Cease overclearing your land as if trees were an enemy rather than a friend."

In Ottawa, one of the organizers of the Montreal conference, J.H. Morgan, had been appointed commissioner of forestry in the Department of the Interior in 1887. Morgan's recommendations were as sensible and progressive as they were overdue. He wanted federal-provincial programs for tree plantations, to fill the widening gaps where nature was failing to reforest. He called for legislation against indiscriminate logging and for establishment of experimental stations and schools to train foresters, and devised practical ways to reduce fires, such as screens for the smokestacks of railway engines. But his deputy minister thought so little of Morgan's ideas that they were shelved to gather dust. As so often in the frustrating annals of Canadian forestry, time was lost, and with it valuable forests.

The federal government did, however, begin to set aside forest land in the federal territory in what is now the Prairie provinces, which contain more forest in their northern and western reaches than most Canadians realize. The United States had recently opened Yellowstone National Park, and a smaller version was created in the Rocky Mountains at Banff

Springs, where lumbering was permitted only under government supervision.

The idea of forest reserves was not new. In the 1670s the
intendant Jean Talon had introduced the first conservation
ordinances in North America, to protect Quebec's oak and
elm, required by the French navy. In 1864 the United Provinces of Upper and Lower Canada had asked a legislative
committee to consider "the expediency of reserving as forests
the extensive tracts of land which abound in exportable timber
but are unsuitable for cultivation." Nothing came of it, nor
from similar efforts eleven years later in Quebec, by then a
province. An act was passed in Quebec but was repealed after
lobbying by "the colonization movement," which included
nationalists and the Roman Catholic Church. They argued that
public lands were needed by settlers and should not be allocated to timber companies. Settlement, not forestry, was the
priority, as it would be until the early 1900s, when the government swung the other way and leased vast acreages to the new
pulp and paper companies.

It was in Ontario, in 1893, that the first breakthrough came,
and with it the first move towards what we now call "multiple-
use management." Concentrating its attention on a wilderness
region within reach of Ottawa and Toronto, a Royal Commission on Forest Reservation and a National Park established the
1,733-square-mile Algonquin Park on the fringes of the Canadian Shield. It was to be "a public park and forest reservation,
fish and game reserve, health resort and pleasure ground for the
benefit, advantage and enjoyment of the people of the province."

Noting that in one winter 400 men had felled 30,000 white
pines in the area, the commission took the view that while "the
reckless removal" of forest may for a limited time provide "a
prodigal profusion of wood, the waste of one generation must
be atoned for by the enforced economy of the next. To obtain
from a forest the largest amount of product that it is capable of
yielding without at the same time trenching upon its capacity,
calls for careful and scientific management, such as has hitherto been but little practised this side of the Atlantic." The
watershed was to be protected. Agriculture was banned. Logging, though permitted, was to be controlled. Hunting and
fishing were restricted.

Two years later Quebec established the 3,710-square-mile
Parc des Laurentides north of Quebec City in spruce and fir

country, though one of the main purposes of the park was to preserve the vanishing caribou rather than to save the forest.

Lumbermen welcomed these parks because they excluded settlers and promised fire suppression. That their conversion to what they called "sound forestry principles" was based on self-interest made it no less sincere; they were concerned at the rapid depletion of white pine. But they wanted more than reserves, where logging was only one of many priorities. If there was waste of wood, they said, it was not their fault but the government's. Leasing out public land for short-duration harvesting was wasteful because they felt compelled to cut it down as fast as they could before the lease ran out. "What I hold," said Senator W.C. Edwards, a leading Ottawa lumberman and president of the Quebec Limit Holders Association, "is that the best condition of all is to have a lumberman who has a permanent and large investment to sustain and maintain and one who desires to conserve the timber for the supply of the establishment." The demand for longer tenure on logging lands, which is only coming to a workable compromise now in the 1980s, had begun.

In Ontario, further efforts to set up special reserves—a move towards what might have become a viable forest management scheme, had it worked—began in 1897 with a new royal commission to look into "restoring and preserving the growth of white pine and other timber trees upon lands in the province which are not adapted for agricultural purposes or settlement." As a result of these deliberations, the government passed a Forest Reserves Act in 1898 which, more optimistically than realistically, was seen as "the initial step in establishing a rational system of forest management."

Thousands of square miles were set aside, most of it in a great arc extending from the Ottawa River westward across the north shore of Lake Superior and past the Lakehead to the 1,800-square-mile Quetico Reserve on the Minnesota border. The pride of the planners was the 6,000-square-mile Temagami Forest Reserve in northeastern Ontario, where there were millions of feet of white and red pine and the axe of the lumberman had never been heard. Established in 1901, it contained the biggest reserve of pine left in Canada. With this act the Ontario government believed it had ensured a perpetual source of timber—and public revenue. Forest rangers were appointed. Cutting was supposed to be limited to mature trees, "allowing that which is not fully developed to remain until it is at the proper stage for cutting to the best advantage." It was a brave idea, and it took a while before disillusionment began to set in, and longer still before it became clear that lack of commitment from government and industry (and insufficient knowledge of the forest) meant the reserve system would not in fact become the hoped-for foundation for forest management. As governments changed there was lack of continuity. Regulations were eroded. Settlers and mining operations invaded Temagami with the arrival of the railway. Large spruce and pulpwood concessions were leased out in an area supposed to have been devoted to pine management. It became a focus of patronage.

At all events, it was late in the day, even if the reserves policy had worked. "The first quality pine has nearly disappeared," said the Dominion statistician in 1895. "We are within measurable distance of the time when, with the exception of spruce as to wood and of British Columbia as to province, Canada shall cease to be a wood exporting nation."

Fortunately there was still a lot of spruce and Douglas fir, but even if the statistician's report was over-pessimistic there could be no doubt that pine was on its way out. Thomas Southworth, who succeeded Phipps as director of forestry for Ontario, found himself unable to share the optimism of lumbermen like Edwards who said that if cutting was limited to mature pine, young trees would come back naturally and the forests would renew themselves forever.

"In the first place," said Southworth, "I have noticed that when a forest has been operated for pine for a number of years, and where no fire has taken place, there seem to be no seedling pines coming up. True, there are pine trees still growing to take the place of the mature trees removed, but they are trees that were suppressed and stunted in their growth at the time of the previous lumbering operations and that took on new growth after the pressure on the forest was relieved, but I cannot find in a forest of this sort there is any new crop coming on; that is to say, trees that have seeded since the cutting of the original crop."

The course of forestry in Canada has often been a case of one step forward and one step (or two) back, and nowhere more than in Ottawa. But now the federal government, having failed to support J.H. Morgan's reforms, awoke to its responsibilities by appointing Elihu Stewart head of the Forestry Branch of the Department of the Interior in 1899. With Stewart, federal forestry got a start. A land surveyor from Collingwood,

5. Elihu Stewart, superintendent of forestry for Canada 1899-1907, was a pioneer in efforts to establish forest fire protection and logging regulations and the founding of what is now the Canadian Forestry Service.

Ontario, where he had been mayor and an unsuccessful Liberal candidate for Parliament, Stewart saw his duty as "conservation and propagation."

He built the organization now known as the Canadian Forestry Service, established tree farms in Manitoba and Saskatchewan to create shelter belts for farmland, and developed the federal government's enduring role as the nation's centre of forest research. He also organized the layman's organization that has done so much to draw attention to the danger of fire: the Canadian Forestry Association. It was founded in 1900 by educators, politicians, and businessmen, including a surprisingly large number of bank managers, who found it a way of keeping in touch with the vagaries of an industry they were called upon to finance. Some of the biggest lumber czars of the Ottawa Valley—J.R. Booth, H.F. Bronson, and Senator Edwards—were active members. "There was a time," observed Lotbinière, CFA president and by now federal minister of revenue, "when lumbermen, if they had heard of forestry, would turn away in disgust and consider it only a nuisance, but they have begun to find it quite the reverse." Their attendance was hardly surprising, since the organization was dedicated to fighting fire and to reserving forest land unsuitable for farming. Belonging to such an organization could do their public image no harm, expressing as it did support for "the preservation of the forests for their influence on climate, fertility, and water supply."

The CFA carried out practical demonstrations to show that settlement was not necessarily the best use of land. It commissioned a survey of Pontiac County in western Quebec, where the government and the church had promoted colonization. With four million acres under cultivation, the yield from hay, oats, and cattle was $4 million. Had the marginal soil been developed for lumbering, said the association, it would have brought in seventy per cent more money. If it had been used for the new pulp and paper industry, the yield would have been even greater, allowing the county to support a much larger population.

"The time seems to have arrived for a more systematic and scientific study in Canada of the conditions of reproduction and development of the forest, so that the data may be available on which to base plans of management," the association said. "Public interest in the subject is growing in a gratifying manner, but in order that wise action may be taken in silvicultural operations, the information at the disposal of the authorities should be much more exact and definite than is now available."

S.N. Parent, a member of the association and Quebec's commissioner of lands and forests, had declared: "The settlement and opening up of our vacant lands and the consequent increase of our population constitutes our chief aim. All our energies are directed to that end, for from it comes the political influence we now have and which we must possess in the future." Nevertheless, when he became premier his views changed, and with the emergence of the pulp and paper industry the Liberal administration began to pursue a policy of inviting big business into the forest. Criticized for this by those who supported the agrarian movement, the Liberals appointed a colonization commission that supported government policy and recommended that expansion of the pulp industry be encouraged. Both Parent and his successor, Lomer Gouin, were to follow this advice. By 1905 Quebec had begun to separate farm land from that which would be retained permanently by the Crown as industrial forest.

During the next few years Quebec built up one of the biggest forest reserve systems in the world in an effort to form a base for a forest policy, rationalize land management, and keep bogus settlers from grabbing cheap timber without paying for it. (Such people had been a nuisance in the white pine days and had become even more so now that black spruce, much more prevalent in Quebec than pine, had become of commercial value to the new pulp mills.) Expensive to administer, and politically controversial, the Quebec reserves were to founder on many of the same problems encountered in Ontario. It was not enough to create reserves on paper yet otherwise do little but attempt to suppress forest fires. Commitment and funding were also necessary, along with a cadre of trained foresters. Both were lacking.

There were neither foresters nor schools in Canada to train any, though a move was afoot to establish a Canadian school. Fernow, who had resigned as chief of the Forestry Division in Washington to found the first American forestry school at Cornell in New York State, was invited in 1903 to give ten lectures at the School of Mining and Agriculture at Queen's University, Kingston, which had hopes of establishing a forestry faculty. Publicized as "the beginning of a new outlook upon one of our greatest industries," the lectures dealt with silviculture, regeneration, botany, ecology, forest history, and economics and were printed in an eighty-page English and French booklet that was to serve as a manual for students.

Two decades had passed since the Montreal conference at which Fernow had launched his ideas, but he had found no reason to change his belief that Canada was not ready for sustained yield, the systematic management of the same land for successive timber crops, common in his native Germany.

No matter how many forest reserves might be created on paper, more investment would be needed than government or industry were prepared to provide. Canadians would first have to come to believe in the advantages of permanent, well-planned investment as opposed to speculation.

Speculation had been the norm. The same year Fernow delivered his famous Kingston lectures, the Conservative government in British Columbia had set off a veritable "gold rush" in timberlands by opening them to all comers. In a short-sighted grab for quick public revenue, the number of leases rose from 1,600 to 15,000. Large areas were sold outright to Americans who had exhausted timber in the eastern United States and had moved on into the Pacific northwest states and thence into British Columbia. The rush went on for four years until the government, fearful of losing control of the forest completely, ended the speculation and put the remaining timber on reserves.

There had been similar patterns in the east. In Ontario hundreds of square miles on the north shore of Lake Huron had changed hands periodically, making profits for speculators without a single tree being cut. The Conservatives, then in opposition, said northern Ontario was "ruthlessly exploited by timber barons aided and abetted by a revenue-hungry government." Nationalists in Quebec had a similar story. The tug of war between current revenue and future supply would have to end before forests could be properly managed. But in forestry the future is long. The short life span of government and the long life of the forest are always incompatible, although there have been politicians who have been aware of the gap while being able to do little about it.

"It is a natural thought that we shall live to see the young generation of trees at their full growth," Prime Minister Sir Wilfrid Laurier said, "but we must not think alone of ourselves; we must think of the prosperity of Canada in the days when all of us shall be sleeping in our graves."

Coming from the Laurentians north of Montreal, Laurier knew what the forest meant to people's livelihood. In 1906, with the help of the Canadian Forestry Association, he convoked the first all-Canadian forestry conference. Senators, members of federal and provincial legislatures, delegates from boards of trade, railway companies, and the Canadian Society of Civil Engineers attended, along with lumbermen. Delegates numbered 267, an attendance that Laurier said, much too optimistically, "was manifest evidence that the Canadian people at last, at long last, realize the great importance of all the problems connected with forestry." The Canadian people realized nothing of the sort, nor is it likely many do to this day.

After pointing out that Canadians were making no effort to replace the trees they had cut, while Germany and France had been replanting for generations, Laurier estimated that logging consumed only ten per cent as much as the quantity of timber destroyed each year by fire. "The forest, unfortunately, has many enemies. Man is bad enough, we all agree; but man is not so bad as the insects, and the insects are not as bad as fire."

After this brave rhetoric, Laurier disappointed those hoping for solutions by fudging the whole issue. "I am not prepared to say that such drastic conditions should be imposed on lumbermen," he said, "though I am not prepared to say on the other hand that a plan of this kind should not be taken under advice." Laurier was a politician, well aware that in the end responsibility lay with the provinces, but his government did pass a federal Forest Reserve and Parks Act aimed at maintaining timber supply on federal land, including forests of the Prairie provinces, where, prior to the transfer of natural resources to those provinces in 1930, the federal government was responsible for 30,000 square miles of forest. It was an advance in federal forestry, even if somewhat blunted by the provision that land already licensed was exempt from federal control.

Fernow, teaching at Cornell, attended as a representative of what he called "that small body of early reformers who laid the cornerstone and began building the foundation walls of the great structure that we are going to erect into the forestry system of the Americas." He was as outspoken as ever. "The Dominion government has confessed through its Prime Minister that it has neglected its duty," he said, adding that Ottawa now appeared ready to make amends, though the provinces with the possible exception of Ontario "as a rule have not done very much."

For the first time, Fernow was not the only forester present. Judson F. Clark, a thirty-two-year-old Maritimer who had taken his degree under Fernow at Cornell, had been appointed chief forester for Ontario in 1902, the first professional employed in Canada by either government or industry. For Clark, a forceful man with decided opinions, the conference was a forum to vent his frustrations. He was to leave government service the next year to become an industry consultant in British Columbia, convinced nothing would be done in Ontario except for fire protection.

Clark made himself unpopular with lumbermen by demanding they be forced to clean up the mess they left on the ground after logging. "Logging may be conducted so as to be ruinous to a forest or it may be merely injurious," he said. "Or it may be beneficial. It all depends on how it is done and what happens afterwards. Unfortunately a combination of destructive lumbering and its all-but-certainly-following slash fires has proven so disastrous to American forests that the popular mind has come to associate lumbering as necessarily an evil of the forest. As commonly practised it has been, and is, exceedingly detrimental to both future wood production and water conservation."

Lotbinière, now eighty years old and lieutenant-governor of British Columbia, believed the birth of the pulp industry in the 1890s lent urgency to the need for a forestry school. Immensely more complex and costly than a sawmill, a pulp mill required such large long-term reserves of spruce or balsam fir that the hit-and-miss methods of the pine era would no longer serve. Moreover, there were already ten university forestry schools in the United States, and American companies now starting to invest in Canadian pulp mills were getting into the habit of hiring foresters for their American timber limits.

Early in 1907 the first Canadian school was opened, not at Queen's, as that university had hoped, but at the University of Toronto. Fernow was dean, having been left jobless when the school he had founded at Cornell had been forced to close. Practising clear-cutting at Cornell's experimental forest, the strong-willed Prussian had run afoul of neighbouring landowners who had managed to have the school deprived of its grants for a time. He anticipated better treatment in Canada. Providing the Toronto school with his personal library of 2,500 books and pamphlets, most of them of European origin, Fernow devised a four-year course in silviculture, biology, mathematics, surveying, physics, chemistry, political economy, French, and German.

In New Brunswick, where Premier L.J. Tweedie had convoked the first provincial forestry congress, in which he said the woods had far too long been allowed to look after themselves, a forestry department was opened at the University of New Brunswick in 1908.

In Quebec Monseigneur J.C.K. Laflamme, a botany profes-

6. *Monseigneur J.C.K. Laflamme, professor of botany and founder of the school of forestry at Laval University, Quebec, in 1910. Because of his influence, Quebec was to take an early lead in forestry in Canada.*

sor and a founding member of the Canadian Forestry Association, established Laval University's department of forestry in 1910, a government forest service having been set up a year earlier under Jules Allard, minister of lands and forests. With initiative and foresight, the government had sent two promising young men, G.C. Piché and Avila Bedard, to study forestry at Yale, and under Laflamme they helped establish the school, where Bedard remained as director while Piché went on to become provincial chief forester.

There were now considered to be enough foresters, if barely

enough, to establish a professional association, and at a meeting in the Montreal Board of Trade offices on March 13, 1908, the Canadian Society of Forest Engineers was formed (renamed the Canadian Institute of Forestry in 1952). Fernow, who chaired the meeting, was disappointed when the word "forester" was omitted from the title, while admitting few people in North America knew what "forester" meant, confusing it perhaps with the name of a fraternal body flourishing at the time that had nothing to do with forestry.

Among the founding members were Piché; Ellwood Wilson, an American who had become the first forester hired by a wood products company in Canada; and H.R. MacMillan, who had taken an MA in forestry at Yale and was working for the federal government. MacMillan went on to become chief forester of British Columbia at the age of twenty-six and eventually built the biggest lumber company in Canada. Established at first to promote an *esprit de corps* among a small band of foresters, the society was to grow in fits and starts into a national body of well over 2,000 from coast to coast. Along with forestry schools, it provided a focus for the study of Canada's forests.

The early years of the century brought some progress in forestry in Quebec and Ontario, but nowhere as much as in British Columbia. Having become alarmed by the rapidity with which speculators were grabbing up Crown land at sacrifice prices, a worried government had in 1907 put an end to the rush of speculation. It was time, said Lands Minister W.R. Ross, "to substitute a constructive forest policy which should make a radical change and revolutionize conditions in the province." Government concern about the future of the forests was increased the following year by a rash of forest fires that swept the southern interior, destroying several communities including Ross's own town of Fernie, which he represented in the legislature. In 1909 a Royal Commission was established, out of which came the best forest act to date in Canada. The act was to take timber sales out of the political arena to a considerable extent and guarantee the orderly disposal of forest lands, while guaranteeing that most of the productive forest remained under control of the Crown. Having hired H.R. MacMillan as chief forester in the Forest Branch formed in 1912, Ross declared: "We are trying to compress into a few short years the constructive work that in older countries has been the labour of generation after generation."

In Quebec and Ontario progress was made in programs for tree planting, if not in the sort of legislation achieved in B.C.

7, 8. North of Lake Erie, generations of land clearance and logging had reduced large areas to desert by the early 1900s, some of the worst being in this area of Norfolk County around Normandale. It was here that E.J. Zavitz, later Ontario's chief forester, began land reclamation work that restored the wasteland to productive forest.

Fernow at the University of Toronto had changed his mind by now about the value of man-made forests. He had come to believe that failure to plant would leave areas that would "never produce anything worth having by natural regeneration, after having fooled away valuable time and energy." Land that had been cut over or burned, at least in areas where it could be more or less protected from forest fires, should be restocked immediately with seedlings, young trees that had had a start in nurseries. His studies had indicated, over-pessimistically as we now find in most areas, that only one-fifth of an original stand could be expected to regenerate naturally.

At the urging of the Association of Fruit Growers, Ontario purchased 100 acres of wasteland north of Lake Erie and commissioned E.J. Zavitz to plant pine. A farm boy from the Niagara peninsula, Zavitz had been teaching forestry under Fernow at Toronto and at the Ontario Agricultural College in Guelph, where forestry had been encouraged among agricultural students. Zavitz, who later become chief forester of Ontario, moved his small nursery from Guelph to St. Williams in the deforested wastelands north of Lake Erie and eventually produced a million seedlings a year. Slowly he began to rehabilitate townships where, as the dead stumps testified, there had once been green forest.

In Quebec a Sulpician priest, Father Lefebvre, had planted trees at Oka, near Montreal, in the 1880s. Having no nursery, he set out 65,000 wild spruce and pine seedlings gathered from the forest, reclaiming eighteen acres of eroding sandy soil. In 1908 the government also began to take a hand in planting, establishing a tree nursery at Berthierville, on the St. Lawrence east of Montreal, and furnishing seedlings to reforest 15,000 acres of Argenteuil County that had been ruined by logging and were threatening farms with blowing sand. Near Lachute 350 acres of incipient desert were purchased and planted.

An even greater need was for forest information. "There is no country that I know of where it is more urgently necessary to the public interest that the natural resources should be tabulated and inventoried than it is in Canada," said Clifford Sifton, the former minister of the interior. In an effort to find out at least how much wood was being cut, Robert Campbell, Elihu Stewart's successor as head of forestry, wrote to 3,000 lumber companies requesting their annual production figures. Sifton, whose father had farmed and logged out of Brandon, Manitoba, and who had enthusiastically supported Stewart's afforestation efforts on the prairies, set up a forestry section in the new federal Conservation Commission in 1909, with Fernow at its head.

Growing out of the North American Conservation Conference organized in 1909 by wilderness enthusiast President Theodore Roosevelt and Chief U.S. Forester Gifford Pinchot, the commission attracted representatives from the provinces as well as from organizations such as the Canadian Society of Forest Engineers. Fernow's section did a long-needed study of the forest fire menace and undertook surveys in the Trent watershed area of southern Ontario, where over-cutting had been causing floods and soil damage, and in Nova Scotia, Saskatchewan, British Columbia, and Quebec. It began a research program, collaborating with the provinces and industry.

Reporting directly to the cabinet, rather than to any one ministry, the commission was well supported at first, in large part because of the ability and commanding personality of Sifton. Its freedom was to be its undoing. When it moved from information collection into policy making it fell foul of certain cabinet ministers. It died in 1921, a victim of "politics," but not before it had played a useful role, including efforts to raise public awareness of the need for forestry. Its research projects were taken over by the Dominion Forestry Service.

It had come, at any rate, much too late to save the white pine. In the year of the commission's formation, the last of the great timber rafts had come down from the Ottawa to Quebec City. It had contained 150,000 board feet, worth $100,000, from J.R. Booth's camp on the Coulonge, an Ottawa tributary. For a century these rafts, some of them a quarter of a mile long, had been a colourful scene on the St. Lawrence, 400 a season in good years scudding down to Quebec under home-made sails. Now the pine loggers had moved on to the northern shores of Lake Huron and on west to Thunder Bay. Lumbermen would go on cutting white pine where they could find it, shipping it out by rail, but the glory days of the pine trade were finished, much as James Little had foretold.

The paper forest

WITH ITS APPETITE FOR HUGE AMOUNTS OF CAPI-
tal, costly and permanent mills, and sophisticated marketing,
the pulp and paper industry brought the American corporation
to the forest. The timber barons, who had boasted of running
businesses "out of their back pocket," were a dying breed, their
traditional methods of "hurling down the pine" a growing
source of public criticism.

"I do not think that people are prejudiced against lumbermen as individuals," said J.R. Booth at the age of ninety in
1923, "but they do feel some bitterness toward men who are
dealing in the leased property of the state. They are ready to
exclaim: 'That man has established a big industry founded on
public-owned timberlands,' forgetting that for every dollar the
lumberman takes out for himself, the workers, the merchants,
the railroads, the public treasury, all take many dollars."

Progress in forest management was long overdue and it came
in with the development of the pulp and paper industry and
with foresters like Ellwood Wilson who were hired by the new
corporations to protect their resource investment. Wilson was
to typify the new generation of foresters, ready to temper
European teachings with practical local experience. They were
aware that European forestry practice was based on high-

9. *Ellwood Wilson, the first forester employed by industry in Canada, was hired by the Laurentide Paper Company of Grand'Mère, Quebec, in 1905. A leader and innovator in all fields of forestry, in 1918 he helped pioneer the use of airplanes in fire protection and aerial photography, and he established one of the first industrial tree nurseries, his plantations containing 300,000 trees by 1914.*

quality woodlands in countries where timber prices were high and labour costs low and where there was usually a shortage of wood. There was no place for this in Canada, with its large pulp forests, relatively low return, and stumpage prices so low they militated against the practice of forestry for years.

Lean, energetic, sandy-haired, a practising Quaker, Wilson shared Eduard Fernow's sense of the sweep and range of forestry. As a boy in Philadelphia he had read Fernow's books and every other book about forest husbandry he could find. After studying at Yale he had served in upper New York State before coming to Quebec at the age of thirty-three to work for the Laurentide Paper Company of Grand'Mère in 1905.

"Lumbering had always seemed to me to be conducted in a very hand-to-mouth way," he said. "The waste, the rule-of-thumb method, the way-father-used-to-do-it attitude of mind ...and when the forest was exploited and destroyed in one sector the lumbermen would move on to another. My first trip into the woods in Quebec showed me that Canada was still playing with zest the old game of killing the goose that lays the golden egg."

He was appalled by the way lumbermen, who would not dream of buying a $300 piece of mill machinery without inspecting it, leased a tract of forest sight unseen. He recalled how one large company had invested in 100 square miles on the say-so of an old-time "timber-looker," a man with no formal training, who had spent barely a week in the area. "All he did was to paddle up streams and if he saw timber he would guess at its amount and make no effort to see how far back from the stream it extended." The following year when Wilson surveyed the area he found that beyond the margins of the streams ninety per cent of the timber had been ruined by fires.

In the days of small sawmills, such slapdash methods were not necessarily disastrous. If a "timber-looker" were mistaken in his estimate, a lumberman could always move his mill saws on to a more promising site. But such casualness would hardly do for a pulp company, anchored to one place by a costly plant designed to run for a lifetime. Wilson was dismayed to find that his own company, Laurentide, for all its progressive attitudes, had invested $3 million with no notion of what the timber lease contained. The company's maps were so poor they failed to show where the boundaries ran; the government's maps were worse, even though the lease was Crown land.

Travelling by canoe in summer and dog sled in winter,

Wilson set out to survey a trackless rectangle 100 miles long and 60 wide. "Just as a general cannot hope to plan and carry out a campaign successfully without accurate maps and information about the country in which he is fighting," said Wilson, "so a woods manager cannot hope to carry out intelligently and successfully his logging operations without accurate maps and information about the woodlands."

Over the years foresters have frequently been frustrated by bosses whose only aim has been to get cheap wood—cheap wood this year, next year, and for the life of the mill to keep things running at a profit. If they employed a forester, it was to facilitate that policy. In the absence of laws demanding that forestry be practised, a forester's job consisted of surveying and mapping, measuring merchantable stands and measuring the wood after it was cut—in other words, only about half of what he had been trained, or had hoped, to do.

At Grand'Mère, Wilson was fortunate in working for George Chahoon, who looked beyond the ledger books. Nor did Wilson let Chahoon down with impractical schemes, for when he planted trees it was for the definite purpose of "bringing the forest back to the mill." It made more economic sense to plant on 100,000 acres of company land ten miles from Grand'Mère than to lease ten times as much 100 miles away. On home ground forest fires could be detected and controlled; trees could be nurtured to greater growth; waste could be minimized, at a time when twenty per cent of a log harvest might be left lying on the ground or lost in river drives through sinkage or log jams.

Compared with a lumber mill, a pulp plant required quantity more than quality. Merchantable pulpwood trees averaged between 300 and 400 per acre, each tree containing a little less than a quarter of a cord and weighing about 225 pounds, its average diameter about six and a half inches. A single mill might consume 3,000 square miles of spruce, balsam fir, or jack pine during its lifetime. Since the new industry needed longer tenure than the usual yearly contracts that had been negotiated with lumber companies, the first of the twenty-one-year pulp leases was signed in Ontario in the 1890s at Sault Ste. Marie.

With the expansion of newspaper advertising in the United States the industry grew quickly. Americans looked north for paper as they had for lumber in the 1850s, and no area equalled Quebec and Ontario for supplies of the long-fibred black spruce. Ignored for lumber so long as white spruce was available, the smaller black spruce grows in wide swaths that encourage economical clear-cutting. For pulp mills, which can use trees three inches at the butt, size does not matter so much, though bigger trees are cheaper to log and transport.

Although a few small mills had begun transmuting softwood into pulp in eastern Canada in the 1860s, there was little industrial growth for thirty years and most of the pulpwood harvest had been exported to United States mills in the form of logs. Speculators had cornered hundreds of thousands of acres of pulpwood forest with no intention of building mills; of the four original pulpwood concession holders in coastal British Columbia, not one built a mill.

By the turn of the century, eastern lumbermen, who had themselves supplanted the old square timber makers, realized the challenge of the new pulp technology. Price Brothers in Quebec, E.B. Eddy and J.R. Booth in Ottawa, and E.W. Backus in northwestern Ontario all diversified by building pulp mills. Cutting spruce for pulp supplemented the pine lumber trade that had grown up in communities between Sudbury and the Manitoba border since the decline of the pine trade in the Ottawa Valley in the 1880s. A new breed of entrepreneur appeared, men with no timber background but with a talent for raising financing. Francis H. Clergue, an American, built a mill at Sault Ste. Marie and F.H. Anson from Montreal founded the Abitibi Pulp and Paper Company at Iroquois Falls in northern Ontario.

Usually a mill was financed on the promise of future earnings, collateral at the bank being enhanced by the size of a company's timber holdings. Thus began the controversial practice of granting huge Crown timber limits, much bigger than needed for current use, thereby relieving a company of the need to practise expensive forest renewal. When timber ran out near the mill there was always more up-river. It was not uncommon for a company to hold a lease for 3,000 square miles or more. The largest were about 6,000 and today there are some two or three times that size.

No one knew how much timber such limits contained, and one of Wilson's self-imposed tasks was to find out, at least on Laurentide's limits. To get knowledgeable help, and to provide students with practical experience at a time when old-time lumbermen still regarded them with disdain as interfering "bug-hunters," he invited Fernow at the University of Toronto to look upon Grand'Mère as a "department" of his school.

Apart from the work at Laurentide, Fernow found few signs that the wood products industry had changed. Addressing a Canadian Club luncheon in Montreal, he said people should not imagine that Canada was immune from the ravages of deforestation experienced in older nations. Even in neighbouring Wisconsin the practice of clear-cutting virtually all the trees had created "a desert of four million acres, made by man in less than fifty years." Nor, he added, was it necessary to leave Canada to find destruction. "If you want to study the effects of denudation in your own country, visit the Sudbury or Muskoka districts and you will see how a rock desert is started....I repeat, now is the time for abandoning the politician's method, who works for the day and to please his party, and to substitute a statesman's broad view, who works for all time and to please the country, now and forever." His plea, unfortunately, went unheeded.

Fernow had experienced at first hand in Ontario the incompatibilities of forestry and "politics." When Conservatives ousted the Liberals in 1905, their campaign had included allegations that lumbermen had been raping the forests, aided and abetted "by a revenue-hungry government." But the new administrators were not doing much better. As Fernow bluntly told the minister of lands, forests and mines, Frank Cochrane, government policies were doing more harm than good. Cochrane, a northerner who had once sold equipment to the industry, angrily showed Fernow the door. It might have been coincidence, but none of Fernow's graduates was able to find a government job for many years thereafter. As Fernow lamented to his friend G.C. Piché, who was struggling to get a forestry school established in Quebec, there was little call for professional foresters.

Fernow had been joined on the faculty by another of that small band who did so much to advance forestry before World War II. Clifton D. Howe, who had learned the value of woodlands from his father on a Vermont farm, was a specialist in ecology and natural regeneration who had taught at the Biltmore Forestry School in North Carolina, the first experimental forest on the continent. Howe had set out early in his career to demonstrate the futility of always expecting nature to come back, unassisted, with the same species that had been cut. And when Robson Black, secretary of the Canadian Forestry Association, contended that the forests of central Canada "are probably not thirty per cent as well stocked as in 1800," Howe took the opportunity to test what otherwise would have been one of the countless generalizations that have caused as much confusion as enlightenment over the years.

On a ninety-seven-acre sample plot of cut-over forest in Quebec, Howe found that indeed only a third of the original forest was regenerating to commercially useful species. Where an average of twenty-six spruce trees had been cut on each acre, only seven were growing back. The sample plots were being invaded by scrub and poor, unusable hardwoods.

Howe's investigations were backed by the federal Conservation Commission, which, before it fell foul of political infighting in the cabinet, had begun to tackle the massive question of what the forest actually contained. In the past only the crudest estimates had been made, based on arbitrary decisions as to how many cords there should be on a given number of square miles on the map. Most of the areas had never been inspected.

Attempting to supplant guesswork with reality, Fernow, while head of the forestry branch of the commission, personally directed the first survey attempted in Nova Scotia since Titus Smith, secretary of the Provincial Board of Agriculture, had tramped the woods in 1808 at the behest of Governor Wentworth. (One of Smith's strongest impressions had been the tremendous amount of timber blown down by windstorms and going to waste.)

The forests of Nova Scotia had been badly mauled by loggers, ransacked and high-graded for export and for shipbuilding. Almost half the province's forests were softwoods, spruce and balsam fir, with a mixture of red and white pine, hemlock, and larch. The remainder were hardwoods, mostly maples and birch. The degradation due to high-grading, which delayed growth of new vigorous stands, had gone unnoticed. Fire had also retarded growth. Submarginal land incapable of supporting agriculture had reverted to scrub and brush.

Fernow's 1909 survey was so poorly funded by the provincial government that he had to pick up his information from farmers, lumbermen, and trappers. Even so his "reconnaissance" was to serve Nova Scotia for forty years. He concluded, over-pessimistically, that the province would run out of exportable wood within a quarter of a century, and with this in mind he recommended increased use of the little-used balsam fir. Though it was vulnerable to spruce budworm and prone to butt rot, and not then considered as good as spruce for pulpmaking, he concluded that under the circumstances fir could prolong the industry on which Nova Scotia depended. By the

1920s balsam fir was being widely utilized in most of eastern Canada. (In recent years the high concentration of balsam fir on Cape Breton Island has been the scene of Nova Scotia's most disastrous forest problem, a massive attack of budworm that has replaced green forest with a mantle of death that looks like grey lace.)

Other provinces were mounting inventory surveys, although the results were questionable. Such surveys should be more or less continuous, or at least kept up to date, because of depletions due to logging, fire, disease, and land alienation for uses other than timber harvesting. Unfortunately the surveys were frequently discontinued for lack of government funding. It was not until after World War II that the country began to get any grip at all on what the forests contained.

Fernow believed there was far less useful wood—as distinct from mere trees—than people realized. He had no patience with Canadian folklore, the myth of inexhaustible timber that has been embraced by politicians, editorial writers, school teachers, after-dinner speakers, poets—and lumbermen who might be expected to know better. He surprised people by asserting that Canada, known around the world as a land of trees, held only half the amount of merchantable timber possessed by the United States. In this figure he included hardwood; as a softwood nation Canada actually ranks second, though a poor second, after the Soviet Union.

Anticipating by seventy years the conclusions of present-day forest economists, Fernow said much of Canada's "inexhaustible" timber would always be economically inaccessible, growing as it does in swamps, on mountain heights, or too far north. He had put his theory to the test by surveying a 200-square-mile area in the Boreal west of Cochrane, Ontario, and decided that only forty-five per cent of that area contained merchantable trees, even if there were an economic way of getting at them. South of James Bay, timber reserves were even worse. Of nine million acres, seventeen per cent appeared to contain commercial timber; the rest had been ruined by fire or was in muskeg, where horses could not work. In all that vast area, there was not enough pulpwood in a continuous economic block to support a single mill!

For the most part, however, the Boreal contained splendid supplies of untouched pulpwood, and after years of speculation and false starts the industry was taking advantage of Boreal black spruce. There had been a phenomenal increase in mills, particularly in Quebec and Ontario, after the U.S. government, pressured by an American newspaper lobby seeking lower newsprint prices, allowed Canadian newsprint into the States duty-free in 1913. New towns appeared and old ones that had been dying with the closing of lumber mills were rejuvenated. Communities on the north shore of the lower St. Lawrence that had known nothing but fishing grew into large towns.

In British Columbia, which made pulp from western hemlock rather than black spruce, an American lumber company built a mill at Powell River, on the coast seventy miles north of Vancouver; it was fast becoming the largest in the world. A mill was built at Grand Falls, Newfoundland. New Brunswick lumbermen, faced with depressed lumber sales, were transferring their timber licences to pulp and paper companies.

Between 1918 and 1922 pulpwood production had quadrupled. The shantymen of the timber camps had been succeeded by a new generation of lumberjacks, equipped with short, bow-like saws for cutting pulpwood into bolts four or eight feet long. "Matchsticks," the old-timers called them, but in eastern Canada pulpwood had become more important than lumber. Instead of masts, timber for industry, and boards to build homes, eastern Canada's prime wood-products export was to be newsprint and cardboard. There was not much alternative, since so much of the timber large enough for lumber had been depleted. Exports of pulp and newsprint, valued at $2 million in 1900, had increased to $13 million, the single most important wealth producer, followed by food produce. Lumber had slipped into third place and came increasingly from British Columbia.

The pulp mills' need for black spruce and balsam fir—which had been ignored by lumbermen—gave Canada, in effect, a new commercial forest relatively untouched. While this circumstance diverted attention from the passing of the white pine, there were those who feared that history might repeat itself, the spruce following the pine.

In tones not unlike those of James Little fifty years earlier, the secretary of the Canadian Pulp and Paper Association in Montreal, Arthur L. Dawe, said: "Unless steps are taken at once to ensure more reasonable use of our forest wealth than in the past, and adequate provision is made for their replacement by either natural or artificial means, there is bound to come a time when the industries dependent on them will run short of raw material."

The provinces were still spending most of their money and effort in merely administering the revenue-producing timber licences, with not much attention to forest renewal, though most were trying to deal with fire. In this, Quebec was in the forefront, having introduced in 1911 a system of co-operative associations, established by the various companies and partially funded by government, to protect their timber limits. The best known of these, the St. Maurice Protective Association, introduced aircraft for spotting fires in 1919. In northeastern Ontario a series of conflagrations that took almost 300 lives and destroyed the towns of Matheson, Cochrane, and Timmins had caused such a public outcry that a new Forest Fires Prevention Act was adopted in 1917.

Industry complained that for every tree logged, twenty were destroyed in forest fires. A quarter of the nation's timber was going up in smoke. Railways had joined lightning, settlers, and lumbermen as major culprits, and in the summer of 1920, 150 fires started along the tracks of the Transcontinental, twenty-five of them from the sparks of one particular engine, the notorious No. 313. An average of two million acres were burned annually across Canada. Frequently an area burned more than once, destroying seed sources and in some cases organic soil, so that no commercial forest growth could be expected there for a century.

"There are close to a million acres in the Maritime provinces on which the possibility of natural regeneration of the original pine forests has been destroyed by repeated burnings," Clifton Howe told the Conservation Commission. "The areas are now covered with an inferior growth of birch, poplar, and maple. Quebec is reported to have about two-thirds of a million acres of brushlands, where once pine and other valuable trees grew.

"Ontario has a million acres or more of brushland once covered with luxuriant pine forest, once supporting many thriving communities now completely deserted or merely existing in that state of industrial stagnation popularly designated as 'dead' because successive fires have destroyed both the merchantable timber and the young growing stocks on which future supplies depend."

Ontario also had political problems. The election campaign that ousted the Conservatives and put Premier E.C. Drury's United Farmers party into power in 1919 had included a promise to reform forest administration. Few doubted there had been political patronage, maladministration, and scandal. Just before the election, at a time it obviously needed funds, the Conservative party was accused of disposing of 1,200 square miles of northern timber without tender, auction, or any other form of statutory public competition. The *Mail and Empire* in Toronto referred darkly to "crooks and grafters."

Ontario was certainly not the only province in which politics and timber had become entwined in questionable liaison, but because of a hearing invoked by Drury in 1920 its dirty laundry was more public. R.T. Harding, counsel to the Ontario Timber Commission, which was presided over by two jurists, attacked the government forest record with enthusiasm. "They seem to have given away most of the north country not already disposed of," he said. Harding himself was not immune to charges of influence peddling in the industry and resigned soon after.

In political terms the prime target was the erstwhile minister of lands and forests, G.H. "Boss" Ferguson, an ebullient lawyer whose enthusiasm for northern economic growth, on whatever terms, prompted charges that he played fast and loose with timber regulations. Under his ministry the Ontario lumbermen known as "the old Tory timber ring" had been allowed to make a mockery of the ban on pulpwood exports from Crown lands that was supposed to protect the province's domestic industry. Of the various irregularities investigated, the most blatant was the evasion of timber regulations by staking mining claims with no intention of seeking ore but every intention of mining the timber without paying for it. It was, said commissioner Justice F.R. Latchford, "the merest pretext in order to get pulpwood."

The commission gave Ferguson's department a slap on the wrist for failure to enforce regulations, but Ferguson's part in the affair did nothing to prevent him from becoming premier a few years later. Robson Black, secretary of the Canadian Forestry Association, suggested that Drury take advantage of the hearings to eliminate political patronage in the industry, whereupon the lumbermen on his own executive informed the premier that Black had exceeded his authority by not consulting them on the matter.

The Ontario commission had failed to come to grips with the future, treating the question with the bland lack of specificity that can easily be ignored. Acknowledging that the forest had environmental, ecological, and aesthetic values, it piously hoped that logging would not be permitted to destroy those values altogether, "or more than absolutely necessary." The commission concluded with the thought that "a thing of beauty should not only be a joy but a source of revenue forever," but this was hardly forest policy.

"In spite of the assertions of so-called practical men that nature will look after the replacing of the forest," said E.J. Zavitz, now Ontario's chief forester, "the following is certain, that on large areas where no seed trees exist it will be impossible to obtain satisfactory new growth within a reasonable time." With the aid of Premier Drury, who owned a farm in Simcoe County which had been wasted by over-cutting and erosion, he renewed the campaign he had started in 1908 to reforest the province's southern counties. Because of the frequency of wildfires, nothing was done in the northern forests.

Plans were made to reforest 1,000 acres every year for the next sixty years, all within 100 miles of markets and mills. The Ontario government, like Wilson at Grand'Mère, believed 600,000 acres of man-made forest close to mills was better than "eleven million acres of timber limits scattered from one end of the province to the other." Like other forestry plans of the 1920s, the scheme was to be shelved by the Depression and war.

A hopeful sign in the 1920s was the tendency of a few companies to start planting trees; Wilson of Laurentide planted millions every year from the largest private nursery in Canada. Riorden Pulp and Paper, later part of Canadian International Paper, had started a nursery and planting program. The Spanish River Pulp and Paper Company, soon to be incorporated into the Abitibi Company, was planting burned-over land where there was no hope of natural regeneration.

The Ontario government had 2,000 acres of plantation and was producing nine million seedlings, mostly pine. Quebec's nursery at Berthierville had distributed enough seedlings to plant 5,000 acres. A New Brunswick nursery had been set up and on the federal experimental station established in 1917 at Petawawa, near the Ottawa River, planting had begun. In relation to what was obviously needed, none of this government effort was more than tokenism.

Four universities were turning out professional foresters, those at Toronto, Quebec City, and Fredericton having been joined in 1921 by the University of British Columbia. In the beginning all the graduates had been hired by government, but now they were finding jobs with pulp and paper companies, though few found practical use for the forest management and silviculture they had learned in school.

Foresters working for government were hemmed in by civil service regulations, by accounting systems, and, inevitably, by what they called "politics." They were frequently deskbound. In industry, where they enjoyed somewhat more opportunity to get into the woods, they were limited to doing inventory surveys, building roads, or, as logging supervisors, getting out the timber. Regretting that he had no opportunity to grow timber as well, C.D. Orchard, later chief forester of British Columbia, described what was expected of a forester when he got out of college.

"My day developed into a program of eight hours of sleep and sixteen hours of fire organization, stumpage prices, outstanding accounts and what have you. I wanted to keep in touch with all new developments but...I found it a losing battle....Perforce I was happy to see a timber sale completed without worrying too much about problems of regeneration, or to see my ground fire extinguished without caring whether it was *arctostaphylos* or *chrysoplenium* that had been consumed. In other words, I was probably a fair example of the average forester in Canada who has no time to practise forestry."

Clifton Howe maintained that when a forester did occasionally get a chance to practise silviculture he was regarded "as a physician to attend a sick patient, and worse than that, he is not called in until the patient is very ill indeed; in fact, the patient is usually in the first stages of rigor mortis when the forester is summoned. And then he is often criticized by the forest owner because he cannot effect an immediate cure."

What a forester's responsibility actually consisted of in the 1920s was not always clear. The question was much debated in the *Forestry Chronicle*, the organ of the Canadian Society of Forest Engineers, which played a key role in keeping foresters informed and forestry alive. One correspondent, in an effort to define industrial forestry, called it "an attempt to give an expression to a type of forest practice consistent with the business interests and the problems of the undertaking of the timber operator." Another saw a forester's role as much more positive. "No forester is living up to the ethics of his profession unless he makes an honest attempt to keep the forest under his jurisdiction growing repeated crops of merchantable timber."

R.D. Craig, one of Fernow's Cornell graduates and the first to make a forest inventory in British Columbia, believed foresters could do a more reasonable job if they were given professional recognition as doctors and lawyers are, or as foresters traditionally have been in Europe. The Quebec professional body, now known as l'Ordre des Ingénieurs forestiers du Québec, had already moved towards such official status. Craig believed it would help foresters in their most important duty— "the reforestation of cut-over and burned-over land not suitable for agriculture."

For F.D. Mulholland of the British Columbia Forest Service, the confusion lay in the comprehensive nature of forestry. "Perhaps because its results are so slowly obtained many people have only a partial conception of it. In treeless lands it is thought of as tree planting and silviculture. In densely wooded countries it becomes synonymous with logging and fire fighting. To most of us on the Pacific Coast a forest means trees that can be sawn into lumber. The land is said to be 'deforested' when the last load of logs has gone, and logged or burned lands are considered valueless by our forest industries. Yet the completion of logging does not justify the abandonment of a forest any more than a single harvest is the end of a farm. . . . The primitive nature of the forestry practised is accounted for by the seemingly inexhaustible supply of timber, by reluctance to forgo any present advantage for the benefit of posterity, and by the belief that future markets will not pay for reforestation because there will always be cheaper timber somewhere else."

Ellwood Wilson argued that industry must realize that current profit should not always be its sole aim. When necessary it should defer to the long-term requirements of reforestation and silviculture rather than "the bottom line." "A company, having drawn a dependent community around its plant, has a moral responsibility to guarantee permanent woods operations," he said, recalling the ghost towns stranded in the woods in the eras of square timber and lumber. "Located, as the mills are, far away from other centres of population and often in the wilderness, they must make their own towns, and many of these, from 2,000 to 8,000 in population, have grown up and are thriving. They are all dependent upon sustained yield from our forests and we must see that these towns are protected and will not be abandoned in thirty-five to sixty years by the burning or over-cutting of the woodlands."

But in the hive of industry, the mill was the queen bee. Everything revolved around it, for better or worse. It was the "profit centre," whereas the woodlands, despite their increasing value as timber became harder to get, were a "cost centre." Mill managers, who inevitably took precedence over woodlands managers and foresters, showed scant interest in the forest, rarely visiting it except to take company bigwigs and customers out to the ornate hunting and fishing camp most companies maintained on their limits. Few showed interest in the costly business of linking the harvest process with planting (and tending) a new forest; most believed the first priority was profit. Only then could silviculture even be considered. Meanwhile industry would have to range further into the Boreal for its pulpwood, though even in the 1920s surprisingly little was known of that vast region.

To master the immense distances of the Boreal, Wilson in 1919 helped pioneer the use of aircraft and aerial photography, which brought a quantum leap in the making of forest inventories. Wilson had thought of using hot-air balloons, but managed instead to get his company to purchase two war-surplus U.S. Navy Curtiss seaplanes. Whereas on the ground a party of men might take a month to cover 50 square miles, 200 square miles might be reconnoitred in one day from a plane. Air surveys revealed unexpected gaps in the forest, and flying over northern Quebec, Wilson saw "many hundreds of square miles completely burnt in recent years, which had apparently never been reported."

From a seaplane base on Remi Lake, the Ontario Department of Lands and Forests began to photograph and map northwestern Ontario. In 1920 the Air Board of Canada inaugurated an airplane patrol over those forest areas, particularly in the western provinces, in the charge of the Forestry Branch of the Department of the Interior. One of the civil duties of the pioneer Royal Canadian Air Force was to survey the forests and detect forest fires from seaplane bases. By 1929 the RCAF was using twenty-three aircraft from nine bases for forestry work and that year covered more than sixty million acres of forest land.

Holly Parsons of Toronto developed the art of sketching the forest in contrasting colours from the open cockpit of a Curtiss amphibian flying at 3,500 feet. On a fine day he could cover

125 square miles, sketching exactly what he saw—the feathery, pale spike crowns of immature trees less than fifty years old and not yet ready for cutting, or the darker green table-top crowns of mature timber. It is a lost art now, but at a time when aerial photography was being developed, Parsons' method was fast and effective.

"The colour and density of the crowns of the trees," said Parsons, "not only tell you the species but the age class and in many cases the quality of the timber underneath. You could not see much of what was under the crowns but the various intensities of green would tell you whether it was spruce, white pine or red pine, hard maple or tamarack. As to the heights of the stands, if the crown cover was fairly consistent you knew it was a mature stand. If you could see holes in the stand you knew it was over-mature. If the crown cover was flat but coming up almost to the height of mature stands you knew it was an advanced second-growth stand of timber, usually the result of a forest fire."

These were "operational" timber cruises, aimed at harvesting specific areas, but as far as the country as a whole was concerned, information on the size and condition of the forest was scanty. This, as M. B. Morison of the Dominion Forestry Branch explained, was largely because of lack of government commitment: "The depleted state of the forest has been known by forest authorities for some time. Both government and forest industries have recognized the necessity of having complete, detailed inventories of their forests, and most of the provincial governments have made an attempt to have these surveys completed. A comprehensive forest survey covering large areas, however, necessitates a heavy expenditure for a number of years, which in many cases shows no immediate visible return; and when budgets have to be curtailed, projects of more immediate importance generally receive preference."

Dr. J.H. White, professor of forestry at the University of Toronto and formerly with the Ontario forestry department, expressed another concern of foresters in the 1920s. "I think it is time we were changing our cutting methods if this province is to forge ahead," he said. "We can only enjoy prosperity with permanent expanding industries, not rapidly dwindling ones. On the whole, as individuals, we have not felt the shrinkage of the lumber industry in the province to one-half its volume in less than twenty years largely because of the development of the pulp and paper industry."

For forty years, as Clifton Howe, Fernow's successor as dean at the University of Toronto, pointed out, there had been much talk but little action. As Fernow said, "The trouble with you Canadians is that you have forestry everywhere but in the woods." It was one of Fernow's last pronouncements, for he died in 1923 at the age of seventy-two. His influence on North American forestry, particularly in Canada, had been immense, and as Howe recalled, his proselytizing had been immensely difficult. "Few can realize the discouraging and deadening effect of a stupendous public apathy, both in Canada and the United States, toward the conservation of natural resources. For years he was a lone voice in a wilderness of ignorance, opportunism and complacency." He had served concurrently as president of the Society of American Foresters and the Canadian Society of Forest Engineers and as an associate of the Swedish Forestry Association, and he had received several honorary degrees. He was called "the father of North American forestry."

Disappointed that Canadians had failed to learn from the mistakes of other countries, Fernow conceded in his book *The History of Forestry* that forestry was "an art born of necessity"; only when wood supplies began to disappear, in a way that all could see, would forestry make its appearance. "We have embarked upon the road to the exhaustion of our timber supplies," he said, "squandering our capital instead of living on the interest which our forest, if properly managed, might yield forever." He urged government and industry to study new uses for wood, "since from the cradle to the grave we are surrounded by it."

In 1924, the year after Fernow's death, the first intensive study of Canada's woodlands was mounted by the Dominion Royal Commission on Pulpwood, formed to recommend whether the federal laws should be changed to halt export of raw pulpwood. Canada was exporting $13 million worth to the United States every year that, had it been manufactured into pulp and paper in Canada, would have been worth seven times as much. The commission had been organized largely at the insistence of Frank J.D. Barnjum, a Nova Scotia pulpwood operator, who maintained that every cord of unprocessed wood shipped from Canada shortened the life of Canada's timber industry. In a campaign that reached into Parliament in Ottawa, he demanded a strong federal policy to halt depletion of the forest "because of the greed, carelessness and indifference of our people."

The commission's mandate included a study of how the timber was managed and produced "with a view to the recommendation of measures which would more frequently ensure the maintenance of the forest resource in a state of continuous productivity." It found cause for concern.

In Nova Scotia it deplored the complete lack, at that late date, of a government forest service. "Undoubtedly, the apathy on the part of the government and of the people of the province is due to the fact that such a large portion of the forest estate is now under private control," it said. It urged the government to take more interest in the provincial forests and not leave everything to private entrepreneurs, such as Barnjum.

The commission found the government of New Brunswick putting too little revenue—less than a quarter—back into the forest. Despite an active forest service, an impressive forest act, and some efforts to limit annual harvesting to the rate of forest growth, the commission found the province had failed "to arrest the serious depletion in forest resources which is taking place."

Quebec, the commission reported, was maintaining its reputation for frugal administration at the expense of its forests. Like other provinces, it was using capital "from the forest bank" for a multitude of expenses other than forestry, "effecting in this manner a serious reduction in the capital growing stock of the forest." Extracting $4.5 million annually in revenue, it returned a scant $400,000, mostly in the administrative expenses designed to extract logging revenue.

The commission was not impressed by Ontario's policy of planting trees only in southern wastelands instead of trying to manage the existing forests of the north. It contended that the province had simply drifted along without any clear conceptions of forest policy. "There is ample evidence that the government of Ontario also has followed the practice of extracting too great a toll from its forest resources, without returning thereto, by way of protection and competent administration, the amount which proper conduct of the forest business would demand."

In British Columbia it found what was, on paper, the best forest act in the country, but concluded the province was otherwise oblivious to the need for forest management. Since

10. In British Columbia, steam mechanization came into the woods early in the 1900s due to the great size of the timber. By the 1920s logging sites resembled outdoor factories, with steam engines and "high-lead" lines hauling logs into piles that dwarfed anything seen in the east.

1912, when the Weist Logging Company first moved logging steam engines into Alberni Valley on Vancouver Island, British Columbia's dense coastal forests had begun to look like outdoor factories. By the 1920s Lidgerwood skidders, weighing 250 tons and costing $100,000 each, were hauling logs over "skyline" rigs that looked like giant clothes-lines. At least 800 of these steam engines were operating, each cleaning off a clear-cut of one or two hundred acres every few months. More than 700 miles of logging railway had been built, and it was not unusual to see one of the 148 locomotives, especially constructed for steep grades and sharp curves, hauling eighty cars loaded with ten-ton logs. "Those were the days of highball," said the *British Columbia Lumberman*, the organ of the B.C. Timber Industries Council. "To hell with the land—clear-cut right to the back and get out!" There was nothing comparable in the east. Since World War I, B.C. had exceeded the lumber production of Quebec and Ontario.

As for the rest of the country, apart from scattered logging in the western foothills and areas near Prince Albert, Saskatchewan, and around The Pas, Manitoba, the industry had not developed much in the Prairie provinces. Wood was cut only for local consumption in the river valleys of the Northwest Territories. In Newfoundland the forest was more or less the fiefdom of two English pulp and paper companies, to feed the presses in London's Fleet Street.

In all of Canada, lumber, pulp, and paper were earning $500 million a year in the mid-1920s. Of this, the various governments, including Ottawa, took $12 million in revenue, putting very little back into the forest. The federal government, spending $1.5 million a year for agricultural research, paid a miserly $35,000 for silvicultural research.

The commission found "a glaring lack of detailed knowledge regarding the extent of timber supplies," while finding that more timber was being destroyed than was growing back, because of logging, fire, and natural depredations such as budworm. The spruce budworm had deprived eastern Canada of 200 million cords of fir and spruce between 1910 and 1920.

The Canadian Pulp and Paper Association, whose awareness of forest problems has sometimes been ahead of that of the conservative industry it represents, supplied a note of urgency. "The rate of forest depletion is now dangerously high," it said in its brief to the commission, "in the sense of involving an imminent and certain period of great hardship to the Canadian pulp and paper industry, and in market increases of advantage to its competitors, not a hundred years from now, not fifty years from now, but in ten or fifteen years, or even less."

Though not sharing the CPPA's transitory sense of urgency, the commission agreed some modicum of conservation was needed, including limits on the export of pulp logs needed for future consumption in domestic mills. "If we are to any appreciable extent to improve what is, over vast areas, a sadly depleted and deteriorated forest estate; if we are to permanently maintain in a flourishing condition a gigantic industry that has been built up, we must approach the question of forest destruction in a positive and vigorous manner," the commission said.

Almost the only focus of such a positive approach at the time was the Dominion government, which still controlled 33,000 square miles of national forest in the Prairie provinces and the railway grant lands in British Columbia. In a policy declaration in the House of Commons in 1926, the minister of the interior, Charles Stewart, said federal forest reserves were to be extended so as to include all non-agricultural land suitable for timber production, though regeneration was to be sought through natural means except in areas that were so denuded that artificial regeneration was absolutely necessary. With the transfer of these forest lands to the western provinces in 1930, this policy was dropped, and the federal Forestry Service began to concentrate on research and compiling a national inventory of forest resources.

By the 1920s many of the problems we face today—lack of forest renewal above all—had been clearly identified. That they were so widely ignored or discounted was largely a matter of motivation and short-term economics. Canadians were unaccustomed to paying for something they expected nature to provide free.

Cutting blind

THE GROWTH OF THE PULP AND PAPER INDUSTRY in eastern Canada, coupled with the swift expansion of the Douglas fir lumber trade in British Columbia, had the effect of masking the loss of the eastern white pine. The old pine-producing towns, from New Brunswick to Ontario, certainly had reason to regret the passing of white pine, but the impact on the national economy was muffled.

Perhaps if the issue had been more dramatic there would have been public awareness of the need for forest renewal; a vigorous program of tree planting and silviculture would have provided mature wood today when we need it. But there was no drama. The glory days of pine just withered away, first in New Brunswick, then on the Ottawa, until the last frontiers were reached in the wilds of northwestern Ontario. Pine was still being cut in shrinking quantities, as it is to this day for a specialized market, but as a major industry it was done for, a victim of over-cutting, fire, disease, ignorance, and public apathy. Having exhausted the pine, Canadians turned to other species.

In more recent years, with scarcities emerging in spruce and Douglas fir, the lesson of the white pine has grown clearer. But in the Roaring Twenties there was enough of both to encourage the belief that Canada was uniquely blessed: a country that could never run out of timber. Through luck rather than planning, the pulp and paper industry had given Canada another chance—and an excuse not to practise forestry. The companies and politicians who had no wish to spend money on the uncertain rewards of reforestation and silviculture took comfort in the thought that when quality raw material grows scarce, a way is usually found to replace it with material of lesser quality. The harvest had declined in eastern Canada from majestic, 100-foot masts to forty-foot balks of square timber to spruce and balsam fir pulpwood for newsprint, boxes, and toilet paper. When James Little had predicted in the 1870s that pine would disappear within thirty years, or when his son William suggested that spruce would go the same way in another thirty, they were thinking of the lumber industry as they had known it. For them a commercially useful tree was two feet around, not a skinny log like those now being cut for laths, boxwood, and pulp.

Since the arrival of the Europeans here, an area estimated at 150,000 square miles, three-quarters the size of France, had been burned and cut, its trees destroyed. The pineries had been reduced to anaemia, logged over first for big trees and then for the leavings. New pine struggling to come up had been killed by white pine weevil and blister rust or choked out by faster-growing hardwoods that were of little use. (Hardwoods were utilized, for furniture and the like, by only six per cent of the wood products industry.) Nature tended to fill gaps in the woods with uncommercial trees whose seed trees the loggers had left undisturbed. Forest renewal was mostly a matter of chance.

Once the best trees were cut, the lumbermen, who financed their operations solely to "liquidate" a choice bit of timber, lost interest in the site and moved on to a fresh one, leaving the flimsy mill to moulder or burn down. If a settlement had grown up around the mill, it probably became a ghost town, a melancholy cluster of abandoned shacks. In a period of twenty years, 200 mills had been abandoned in the Eastern Townships of Quebec alone.

In a rapidly changing world it is surprising to discover how little things had changed in the logging industry. "We go on practically treating our forest as inexhaustible, and in the face of the yearly-increasing distances to which lumberers have to go back from all our main streams, we have as yet taken no steps towards preserving what remains to us." Thus an Ontario lumberman, John Langton, lectured a Quebec City audience in 1862. Sixty years later the warnings sounded more or less the same: "We still regard the forest as something that must necessarily be destroyed in the process of utilization—as a mine and not a renewable resource capable under intelligent care of yielding successive crops," said Dean Howe at the University of Toronto.

However inexact the comparison, this habit of equating a renewable forest with an unrenewable mineral deposit has been common. Lumbermen themselves frequently spoke of "high-grading," a mining term that means taking only the best. Like prospectors, lumbermen cut only the best "veins" of pine, which grows in clumps, leaving poorer trees as well as less valuable species to propagate their own inferior kind, grow old, and die.

Even in the 1980s, when it has become abundantly clear that Canada is using up its commercial woodlands faster than they can adequately restore themselves, the impression has lingered that the forest does not fall into the category of renewable resource. Not long ago an economic review issued by the National Bank of Canada casually lumped the forest among such patently "wasting" resources as coal, copper, and oil.

In a nation where four-fifths of the productive soil is suited for nothing but the growing of trees, there is no question but that we must harvest wood. The problem has lain in how we have gone about it. As Frank Barnjum in Nova Scotia said in the 1920s, spruce and balsam fir of such tender age and small size was being cut that the province was depriving itself of a second crop. The chief forester of Quebec reported that the heavily logged St. Lawrence basin was growing an average yield of seven cords per acre, "whereas in Europe twenty to fifty cords per acre was not uncommon...and on soil inferior to ours." In British Columbia Howe found that because of repeated fires in the slash and stumps left by loggers only half the cut-over was growing back to merchantable trees.

Nonetheless, B.C. lumbermen were complaining that the Forest Act was "an academic system" the industry could ill afford. M.A. Grainger, an architect of the act and a provincial chief forester, had stated that industry knew so little about the forest that they were "cutting blind" 160 square miles of timberland on Vancouver Island and the neighbouring coast every year. Two-thirds of the cut was Douglas fir. "Our logging

11. Alexander Koroleff, one of the several European-trained foresters to introduce, in the years before the Second World War, an awareness of the need to renew our woodlands as well as log them. Koroleff was the first woodlands manager for the Canadian Pulp and Paper Association and sought to teach lumberjacks how to log so that the forest would renew itself.

methods are extravagant," a British Columbia lumber commissioner admitted, "and visitors from Europe are apt to hold up their hands at the amount of waste left in the woods."

Alexander Koroleff, a Russian-born forester hired to head the woodlands section of the Canadian Pulp and Paper Association in Montreal, deplored the practice of viewing reforestation as completely unrelated to logging. In Europe a forester was simultaneously a logger and a silviculturist. In Canada he was one or the other, never both, and Koroleff felt the Canadian forester was suffering from a split personality.

"Unless logging and silviculture are united in a common purpose," said Koroleff, "their relation may be antagonistic. It should be the main object of commercial forestry to bring logging and silviculture together and make them both work harmoniously for the purpose of continuous wood production in order to derive maximum benefit without diminishing forest capital." Unfortunately this advice was not much acted upon until the 1970s.

After graduating from the Imperial Forestry School at St. Petersburg, Koroleff had worked in Siberia. He emigrated to the United States where he did postgraduate study and laboured as an ordinary lumberjack, exercising a knack of combining the theoretical with the practical. Like Fernow and most of the European foresters who have enriched forestry in Canada, he was a cultured man with an interest in history and philosophy.

Teaching efficient logging in camps from Newfoundland to British Columbia, Koroleff tried, with considerably less success, to teach the principles of silviculture. "It is strange and unfortunate," he said, "that lumberjacks, the men who actually handle and often badly maltreat our forests, are left in complete ignorance of the simple fundamentals of silviculture."

For Koroleff, the most important silvicultural tool was the axe rather than the planting spade. "Grow trees with an axe," he said. Proper logging could be more effective than planting, and certainly cheaper; and by a timely thinning of trees too thickly grown, it was possible to triple the yield. "It is a surgical operation upon a forest that may be beneficial or ruinous to its future depending on how the cutting is done," he said. "The percentage of spruce—the most desirable pulpwood species—is diminishing. Balsam fir and jack pine reproduce in most cases readily. . . . With rare exception the role of planting is negligible. . . . While readily accessible forests are often overworked, in distant regions great losses of wood are sustained through over-maturity or the impossibility of salvaging timber killed by insects or fire."

Reforestation was not helped by the practice of hiring contractors, or "jobbers," to do the logging. With no vested interest in woodlands owned by a government and leased by a timber company, a jobber's concern was to get wood out as cheaply as possible in the hope of making some profit. Ellwood Wilson, by now president of the Canadian Society of Forest Engineers, criticized the system in an article in *American Forestry*.

"For the most part the areas to be cut," he wrote, "are chosen from year to year by men who are not familiar with the ground and who lack technical knowledge. Their only idea is 'Where can the logs be cut and delivered the cheapest?' The jobber system has been responsible for enormous waste, but owing to the high prices asked by jobbers and the realization of how their lands have been butchered this will gradually disappear and cutting will be done by company camps. . . .It is high time that intelligent plans were made for logging, not for one year ahead but for the next ten years."

As cutting in Quebec had pushed north from the St. Lawrence and into the Boreal, where trees were smaller and grew more slowly because of harsher climate and poorer soil, the government in 1922 had passed an important law, the first of its kind in Canada. It stipulated that lumbermen opening up new areas send the government a working plan of how they proposed to operate, which the Forest Service would rule on. It was to include a statement of inventory that indicated the volume of wood actually growing, thereby requiring growth studies to be made. While only some of the companies complied, it was a start.

There had been varying amounts of reforestation in Quebec, Ontario, and British Columbia, though considerably less than the attendant publicity would suggest. It was estimated, specific figures being hard to come by, that 200,000 acres had been planted in Canada by the late 1920s. There was no estimate of how much of that had survived. Only a fifth of the planting had been for timber production, the rest to halt erosion, protect upland water sources, or provide shelter for prairie farms.

Silvicultural work, what there was of it, had been tentative, experimental, and controversial, mostly carried out by the federal forestry service. Tree-growth studies undertaken by Clifton Howe and a few others had been too limited to give any idea of forest growth in general. There were no methods of forecasting destruction by insects, disease, and windstorms.

Measures against fire had much improved in Quebec and New Brunswick and on federal lands, including parks and the northern fringe of the prairies. Fire protection was fair in British Columbia, in need of much improvement in Ontario, and poor in Nova Scotia, where a forest service was finally established in 1926.

In the end protection and renewal came down to money. For more than a century the wild forests had supplied cheap wood. Now government and industry were being asked to pay for the past, the present, and the future all at once. Since the public owned the land, or most of it, industry felt the government should pay, much as the tenant expects a landlord to pay for the upkeep of a house. This has been a long argument, still not fully resolved, and it was Ellwood Wilson's impression that most companies "were more or less hostile" towards any spending to increase forest productivity. There seemed always to be some reason why forestry was shunned, whether because of lack of fire protection, lack of inventory, or lack of research. "Before these things are accomplished, incredible harm is being done by improper cutting," Wilson said.

Apart from the erroneous belief that investment in forestry was unprofitable, Wilson said two things were impeding it: politicians with no knowledge of the industry and "a lack of courage on the part of foresters to lay their jobs on the line in their advocacy of better forest management." Though proud of a profession that contributed to the growth of the pulp industry, he felt foresters must learn to play a greater role and shoulder a greater responsibility as they did in Europe or, for that matter, as he did himself. "We all know in our hearts that there is only one way to handle our forests profitably and that is by following good silviculture practice, and we should have the courage to say so to our employers whether they be in governments or wood-using industries. We are trying to do the impossible by concentrating on cheaper logging and by 'yes-yessing' the men in authority. Worse still we are encouraging them to carry on to the detriment of their business and the interests of the stockholders and of the country at large."

But there was really not much foresters could do. Theirs was a new profession in a conservative industry; eastern loggers, if not their B.C. counterparts, were felling trees and hauling them out with horses much as their fathers had done. Like their grandfathers, they were intent on "letting daylight into the swamp." Their job was to cut trees, not to grow them. In a

12. Men and horses harvested the woods with muscle power in eastern Canada right up to the 1950s, though by 1929 power saws like this heavy two-man contraption had begun to appear in the St. Maurice Valley in Quebec.

decade pulpwood production had increased threefold. Camps were bigger; a camp of 100 men produced 100,000 cords each winter. (A newspaper could consume 2,000 trees in one edition.)

By the late 1920s, there were more than 100 pulp and paper mills in Canada, supporting new company towns from Corner Brook, Newfoundland, and Liverpool, Nova Scotia, to Ocean Falls, on the coast 200 miles north of Vancouver. The first mill to appear in the Prairie provinces was at Pine Falls in Manitoba, where forests were better suited for pulpwood than for lumber. A score of mills were operating in Ontario, more than half of them in an arc extending from Sault Ste. Marie up to Iroquois Falls, Kapuskasing, and Long Lac and around west of Thunder Bay. Quebec boasted even more, ranging from the Gaspé and the shores of the St. Lawrence to Lac St. Jean. The St. Maurice Valley with its rich store of spruce and its burgeoning mills had turned Trois-Rivières, site of the first timber exports to France 250 years earlier, into the "Newsprint Capital of the World." Quebec and Ontario between them accounted for three-quarters of the nation's annual pulp production and eighty per cent of its newsprint. The lumber trade was dominated by British Columbia, producing forty per cent of the country's lumber from one-third of Canada's 100 large and medium-sized mills. There were also an estimated 4,000 small sawmills in Canada.

By the time the Great Depression struck in the early 1930s, Canada ranked second (after the United States) among the world's pulp and newsprint producers and was first in terms of exports. The industry in Canada was not, however, in any fit condition to ride out an economic crisis. Financed on timber limit collateral and the promise of future earnings, in fifteen years it had mushroomed from infancy into over-production, causing a decline in newsprint prices of almost fifty per cent. Even before the Depression, mills were operating at less than capacity and were facing virtual collapse. Forestry programs were the first to go. Laurentide, under a change of management, abandoned planting and Wilson went back to the United States to teach at Cornell, though he was to return later to set up a consulting practice out of Knowlton in the Eastern Townships.

In British Columbia the Forest Service was severely reduced, depriving the province of fire protection. "The government already was beginning to feel the pinch when I came to the Chief Forester's Office in 1930," said C.D. Orchard. "And shortly thereafter it began to fall apart like a leaderless mob, one minister after another resigning as the going got rough. It was nearly impossible to get decisions where a dollar of expenditure was involved."

The Ontario government fired half its forestry staff on short notice, demoralizing those remaining and prompting an angry demand from the Lakehead section of the Canadian Society of Forest Engineers that "the present policy (or rather lack of true forest policy) be thoroughly overhauled by competent foresters and economists." The CSFE called for a non-political, non-partisan forest service vested with full authority to administer all public forest lands in the province.

Clifton Howe, protesting this abandonment of forestry all across Canada at a time when some progress was finally being made, said: "The governments have apparently lost interest in it. In some cases governmental grants for the maintenance of forestry have been reduced far out of proportion to reductions in other public services. The cynic might say this was done because the governments knew that it could be done with less public protest than in any other field of public endeavour. Forestry controls few votes. . . . The public should be led to such an appreciation of the importance of our objectives in terms of intelligent and orderly development of land use and of the forest industries, that it would not endure without protest the abandonment or serious curtailment of great reforestation projects, the reduction of fire protection services to a dangerous limit, and the wiping out of practically all investigative work upon which any sensible policy of handling our forest resources must be based."

Quebec by now had the best fire protection, had attempted at least some worthwhile replanting, and was trying to get companies to submit logging plans for government approval, though in fact few were doing so. In twenty years its forest revenue had increased six-fold and its forestry outlay twelve-fold. Realizing now that this progress was in jeopardy, l'Ordre des Ingénieurs forestiers, the province's professional body, urged the government to take special measures. It wanted all logging placed under the responsibility of licensed foresters, as it was in Europe, and urged that inventories be kept up to date and that silvicultural measures be increased. None of this was done, for the government felt it had no funds for such work, which, at any rate, it considered up to industry. But industry in Quebec as elsewhere was simply trying to stay alive. Mills were closing down and going into receivership. Whatever forestry had evolved in the 1920s was melting away.

No legislation requiring long-term management had been passed, and now, the depths of the Depression, seemed no time to start. This view was not entirely shared by the United States, which accomplished some excellent Depression-era forestry in make-work projects carried out by the Civilian Conservation Corps. In Canada a National Forestry Program was eventually set up to provide jobs but was not as effective, though federal experimental forestry stations were established in New Brunswick, Quebec, and Manitoba.

If the Depression years gave the forest a rest from over-cutting—a dubious advantage, given the fire damage in the unprotected woodlands and the fact that proper logging is a form of forest management—the war years had the opposite effect. The industry revived, with sawmills producing lumber for everything from military camps to wooden Mosquito bombers, and pulp mills producing gun cotton and surgical dressing as well as paper and cardboard. Everything was geared to production. Harmful practices such as high-grading were not only tolerated but even encouraged; any logging standards that had developed were forgotten, so that immature trees that needed another decade's growth to reach proper merchantable size were being cut. The industry again was "cutting blind."

Through the Depression and World War II, or almost fifteen years, forestry was allowed to lapse. There had been insufficient tradition, commitment, and foresight to keep it alive. After sixty years of agitation and effort, Canada had little to show in the way of policies to guarantee forest renewal. H.R. MacMillan, who served part of the war as Canadian timber controller, noted: "Forty-nine years after the first forest reserves were established in Canada, there is practically no forest land in Canada managed deliberately on a sustained annual yield basis. . . . There has not yet been in Canada an inventory of forest resources. Now, if one considers how important the forest reserves are in the economy of this country, it is an appalling fact that there is no province in Canada concerning which it can be learned what is the actual amount of forest that might be made commercial, or brought into some form of production within, say, the next fifty or the next hundred years. . . . There can be no support by the Canadian people of sound forest management in Canada, if they do not know what is the inventory and what are the proper results of management and what is the need for it."

The investigators

FOREST MANAGEMENT KNOWS NO WORSE ENE-
mies than lack of commitment and continuity. Along with lost
time and opportunity during the long hiatus in forestry during
the 1930s and early 1940s came a break in the slow curve of
learning and experience. The new generation of foresters coming in after World War II had to start again virtually from
scratch. Most of the few experienced practising foresters who
had been pioneering forestry in the 1920s had retired, moved
on to other things, or become disillusioned.

These Dark Ages of forestry were not a total loss, however.
For one thing, the economic crisis in the Thirties had drama-
tized Canada's dependence on wood. When sawmills fell silent
and pulp companies foundered into bankruptcy, few communities in eastern Canada or British Columbia escaped the blow.
The ensuing wartime demand brought another, more hopeful
lesson, illustrating new ways wood fibre might be used in
postwar development, from plastics and cattle food to compos-
ite building board. Long before the war was over, timber had
become a buzz-word for postwar planners.

Increased timber consumption and the introduction of
mechanized logging after World War II put tremendous pressure on our few commercial species, for apart from building

materials and pulp, the vast range of products made from wood, numbering in the several thousands, runs from alcohol to xylophones. From its cellulose come rayons, explosives, film, and cattle fodder; from its resins drugs, insecticides, and printing ink. A hectare of mature conifers can produce thirty tons of cellulose, thirty tons of glucose, and 15,000 litres of methyl alcohol. The possibilities are still being explored.

The Canadian Society of Forest Engineers took the initiative with its first "Statement of Policy." The theme is well worn, even frayed, by now, but in 1943 it had a fine, fresh ring: "To ensure the perpetuation and improvement of the forests...to encourage their wise use as a source of raw materials for the creation of new wealth; and to promote fuller recognition of their value for recreation, and their importance in the protection of drainage basins, regulation of stream flow, encouragement of tourist traffic and maintenance of wildlife." Thus it recognized the importance of "multiple use," long before that phrase gained common currency.

A year later the foresters hosted a conference of senior officials from federal and provincial ministries. An industry representative, admitting that companies had expanded on unsound principles before the war, suggested the best way of guaranteeing forest renewal would be to give longer tenures, of fifty years or more, but otherwise it was apparent that not one government department had managed to put together a long-term postwar policy. Most of the delegates were civil servants, so the speeches were cautious and generalized, though the Dominion forester, D. Roy Cameron, reminded his colleagues that "we as foresters have our own responsibility to insist, in public and private, that adequate attention be given to the proper management of Canada's forest estate."

Fortunately in every generation there have been foresters ready to speak out, though as E.C. Manning, when chief forester of British Columbia, was to say, this could be risky if they "rocked the boat."

"I state with regret that in Canada reports on forest resources and forestry measures needed, appear to be too often edited, not with the sole idea of accuracy and completeness of statement, but having in mind the reaction of the business and political interests affected," wrote Manning. "The forester who forgets to tread softly in any public presentation will undoubtedly be reminded of his omission. Any presentation of the forestry situation showing that conditions are unsatisfac-

tory and that certain remedies are needed is apt to be inter-
preted by political opponents to the disadvantage of the government of the day. Where remedies that cost money are
involved, finance ministers do not look kindly on such situations which are largely in the interests of a generation not yet
represented at the polls. Influential business interests watch
any policy that may affect their profits."

Manning, who had been seconded to Ottawa during the war
as assistant timber controller, was on his way to deliver this
message to a meeting of the Canadian Society of Forest
Engineers in Vancouver when he lost his life in a plane crash
near the logging community of Armstrong, Ontario. He had
written a speech in which he urged foresters to ensure that "the
public has been accurately informed by those competent to
interpret the many misleading factors involved." Then as now,
a major concern among foresters was to convince an increasingly urbanized population of the value of the public forest
lands, which most people are only vaguely aware that they own
and which are administered for them by their provincial
governments.

Manning's speech was read to the meeting by his successor, C.D. Orchard, a bespectacled, scholarly-looking New
Brunswicker with a master's degree from the university in
Fredericton. Then in his early fifties, Orchard was to make a
significant contribution to West Coast forestry. Having
worked for the Forest Service since 1920 in the field and as
deputy chief forester, he agreed with many of Manning's
beliefs. "Forestry, in simple language, means the replacing of
crops," Manning had said. "I contend that in that respect
forestry in this province has been more of a fancy than a fact.
We have been so engaged in collecting revenues and protecting
present values in mature timber that a new crop has received
insufficient attention through lack of funds and staff."
Orchard himself was convinced of the need to get the principle
of sustained yield into legislation. He had written a twenty-
five-page memorandum plus seven pages of draft legislation,
which he thought would ensure a continuous, even perpetual,
timber supply.

There was nothing new about it. Germany had been practising sustained yield, a continuous operation described as
Nachhaltiskeit, ever since it had lost its natural forests. At its
most primitive, this meant that foresters had simply measured
annual tree growth to determine how many trees could be cut

without destroying a reasonably prompt renewal. The cut was not supposed to exceed the growth. They found sustained yield profitable. The American Forestry Service had dabbled in it, and minor attempts had been made here and there in Canada. In Quebec the American-owned Brown Corporation experimented with it at Lac Beauport. At Eagle Depot on the lower Gatineau one of the predecessors of Canadian International Paper claimed it had achieved sustained yield by practising careful cutting over a period of seventy-five years, though sustained yield really has to be carried out over a much larger area to have much meaning.

In 1929 the Ontario government had written the concept into law with its Forest and Pulpwood Conservation Act. Its aim was to place 20,000 square miles under management, balancing consumption and production, but it was one thing to make a law and another to establish the research and techniques needed to guarantee a merchantable crop on the same site every sixty or seventy years. Sustained yield not only remained elusive, but amid the vastness of the wild forests of Canada it seemed irrelevant.

Canadian forestry students heard about it in class but found hardly any opportunity to practise it when they graduated. Industry was not much interested. Orchard remembered trying to sell sustained yield to the veteran head of the Canadian Western Timber Company, Henry Makin. All morning they argued in Makin's Vancouver office. "On parting Mr. Makin set on his desk some bulky tomes with the observation that *there* was the reason why his company could never seriously consider a sustained yield program. The books were his financing contracts, bonded debts, etc. . . . ."

Orchard encountered the usual confusion over what sustained yield means. Sir William Schlich of the Imperial Forestry Institute at Oxford had defined it in 1912 as "continuous yield, brought about annually in equal or approximately equal quantities." Some had the idea that sustained yield meant planting a tree for every one cut, which was too simplistic to have much meaning. One otherwise competent forestry journal in the 1920s managed to confuse sustained yield with selective logging, which is another thing entirely. Even experienced foresters tended to use the term so loosely it meant different things to different people. In the end, sustained yield is a theoretical objective, a goal to be sought if not achieved.

It can become a meaningless exercise in areas of the Boreal

where there is a surplus of aging timber, for sustained yield is predicated on making use of growing trees reaching maturity in some sort of orderly fashion. The large number of trees that come to maturity all more or less at the same time in the Boreal have to be dealt with first before the forest can be managed for the future, and this is still a problem. Like all forestry slogans, such as "annual allowable cut" or "intensive forestry," sustained yield if taken literally can be misleading and disappointing. It is subject to a variety of outside pressures, such as economics, market conditions, and changing mill technology, which can make lumber from smaller timber of pulp species heretofore ignored. It has been a victim of politics and vulnerable to the removal of perfectly good forest land for other uses and to environmental pressures both valid and otherwise.

More realistically, sustained yield equals the amount of timber a forest can provide continuously at any given intensity of management while still maintaining a balance between rate of growth and rate of logging. In essence it works like this: if your trees are ready to harvest at age seventy, and you divide your timber concession into seventy squares, like a chess board, you can cut one square each year so that at the end of seventy years you will be back again at square one, where the trees are seventy years old and ripe for cutting. In reality it is much more complicated. Nature by itself may not come back with the species you need, whereas if you plant the cut-over square to the desired species you may get more wood for your second crop than you were able to harvest the first time around. This is now being called "augmented yield," which aspires to improve on nature through greater fire and insect protection, weeding, planting genetically improved trees, and in some cases fertilizing.

When Orchard made his proposal, sustained yield had already been tried in British Columbia. It had been suggested and then forgotten in 1912 when the Forest Service was born. It had been attempted in the Kootenays in the southeastern interior in the growing of Christmas trees. In 1928 a pilot project, decades ahead of its time, had been started under a twenty-five-year management plan but broke down because of administrative headaches. P.Z. Caverhill, chief forester at the time, had opposed it. Though educated, like Orchard, in New Brunswick, where he had directed the first inventory survey in 1916 and had reason to be aware of the mess that lack of planning can make of the forest, Caverhill felt that so long as there was more old growth than the mills could use, there was no point in trying for sustained yield.

This was a prewar view, and World War II had brought a change. Markets were expanding. European competitors had been crippled. The question now was whether there would be enough wood to meet postwar demands. Because of high-grading, over-cutting, and fire, millions of acres of productive land had been lost, with only one-tenth of one per cent successfully replanted. With 100,000 acres being logged off every year on the British Columbia coast, the forest was being cut beyond any hope of natural sustained yield. Loggers who had grown accustomed to the relatively easy terrain and access of the east coast of Vancouver Island, close to mills, were having to push into difficult mountain slopes or to the wilds of the island's western shores.

"The process of deterioration had been insidious," Orchard declared. "The resource had been so great that the fiction of inexhaustibility readily gained credence. Generation after generation has accepted conditions as they found them as being normal, and a single lifetime of busy pioneer life failed to note the progressive failure of the wood supply."

Better utilization was needed. Trees 150 feet tall and three feet around, which should rightly have been used to make lumber, were being cut up for the pulp machines, wasting half the tree. Reforestation and better protection were needed, and Orchard foresaw that the burden of securing regeneration on the 1,000 logging operations in the province would, sooner or later, fall on government. So he urged his policy of sustained yield.

"It seemed to me the only satisfactory answer," Orchard said. "It would, inevitably, tramp on a few corns, but every year of delay would make the problem worse until it would be politically impossible."

He was not hopeful. The government consulted with industry. A year went by. He had done his duty, Orchard said, and if nothing came of it the blame must rest with the politicians. Nor was Orchard alone in his concern. H.R. MacMillan, erstwhile chief forester of British Columbia, wartime timber controller in Ottawa, and owner now of the biggest lumber export firm in Canada, had expressed alarm at "this mass attack" on the forests. With his knowledge of all aspects of the industry, MacMillan said: "It is generally known amongst the few well-informed that the forest is being over-cut at a devastating rate in every forest province in Canada; that Canada, an essentially forest country, lags far behind India, the U.S., Norway, Sweden, Finland and France in forest policy; that forestry schools and forest departments in Canada are half-starved, are failing to lead or influence the Canadian people, who are still bent on exploitation rather than conservation of their resources. . . .

"There has been in Canada practically nothing accomplished, considering the fact that we have had forest schools for forty-five years and forest departments for almost fifty years. There has been practically nothing accomplished, available to the general public or the profession, respecting the growth rates of our timber on various sites. . . ."

In British Columbia Colin Cameron, a member of the opposition Co-operative Commonwealth Federation (CCF) in the Legislative Assembly, had also taken up the issue. Cameron's pamphlet *Forestry. . . B.C.'s Devastated Industry* said the province was living off its forest capital "like an exiled Russian princess selling off her jewels one at a time."

"There is no possible solution to the problem of preserving our major resource and industry unless private ownership of forest land is abolished or unless the private owners are prepared to operate under the complete control and supervision of public officials in a compulsory and integrated state scheme," Cameron declared.

Whether to defuse the opposition's socialist sentiments or for some other reason, the government came to life. On December 8, 1943, well over a year after he had submitted his proposal, Orchard happened to be visiting the office of Premier John Hart on other business. "The Premier took the occasion to tell me that the government was quite in accord with my brief and proposals," Orchard said, "but that they were so radical that he would have no chance of getting the legislation through the House without some prior education and preparation; he therefore intended to set up a royal commission—he hoped it would be [headed by] a judge—to canvass the question and give everyone an opportunity to state their case."

Within three weeks the royal commission was established, its sole member a lawyer, Gordon McG. Sloan, soon to become chief justice of the Appeal Court of British Columbia. He was to investigate all matters relating to the resource, including "establishment of forest yield on a continous-production basis in perpetuity."

Orchard, who would appear before the commission as a witness more than twenty times, was Sloan's adviser, travelling

13. *Chief Justice Gordon McG. Sloan conducted royal commissions on the British Columbia forest industry in the 1940s and again in the 1950s. "We had to change our thinking and establish our forest resource on a more enlightened basis," Sloan concluded.*

with him throughout the province and visiting the United States and eastern Canada, where he was disappointed by the lack of progress. "In 1944 in eastern Canada I had seen beautiful working plans in offices but had failed to find any rational forestry in the woods," he reported, "and had been told by one highly placed and influential Quebec forester, 'Our first and primary interest is cheap wood—we give lip service to other interests.' In Ontario I was told that if they were to enforce sustained yield management in that part of the province tributary to the St. Lawrence...they would not be able to cut one tree for the following thirty years."

He believed his proposals might lead to sustained yield forestry not only in British Columbia but in all of Canada. Forest management at last seemed possible because of the increased value of wood, improved world markets, and the involvement of large, well-financed corporations. "If our fathers had instituted such a policy at the time, British Columbia today could be cutting an estimated 1,300 million cubic feet, or a safe fifty per cent more than our actual present cut of 880 million feet, which is bordering on the danger line."

Sloan, who had headed other commissions but never one on forestry, conducted the hearings like a court. There were rules of evidence and witnesses were sworn. Anyone with something to say was encouraged to come forward, though some of the smaller operators shunned the hearings rather than subject themselves to cross-examination by high-powered corporate counsel. At the opening session a representative of the Society for Preserving Wild Flowers shared the witness stand with the secretary-manager of the B.C. Loggers' Association. Cameron, the socialist forestry critic, argued his case cheek-by-jowl with the capitalist H.R. MacMillan, who like most of his colleagues welcomed the commission as a chance "to clear the air." His influence was immense, if not always as great as gossip suggested; rumour had it that he was not only a principal actor at the hearings but also "co-producer," helping Sloan to formulate recommendations.

No one knew the coastal forests better than MacMillan. He had cruised them as an undergraduate in 1907, run the Forest Service in 1912, managed logging operations for the Victoria Lumber Company at Chemainus, advised the government on marketing and supply in two world wars, and fashioned his own company out of nothing save skill and a $10,000 loan.

Tall, beetle-browed, intimidating, "H.R." in his testimony ranged the coastal forest, which then accounted for eighty per cent of the province's production. Most of what he said could apply to all Canada: there was too much guesswork; efforts to get companies to abide by logging regulations were laughable.

93

14. *One of Canada's pioneer foresters, H.R. MacMillan was concerned all his life with the fate of Canada's timberlands. From 1912 to 1915 he was chief forester of British Columbia and in 1919 founded one of the biggest woods-products companies in the world.*

"It is admitted that there can be no orderly management of British Columbia forests to attain annual crops in perpetuity until it is possible to produce and administer working plans," MacMillan said. "It should therefore be made clear that there are probably not five foresters in British Columbia who have ever seen a working plan. Furthermore a dependable working plan cannot be produced without classification of the site qualities of the area for which the plan is required, together with ample knowledge of growth rates and the silvicultural habits of the tree species on the respective sites. To accumulate such facts requires years of field work by trained foresters, which has not yet been started."

As the only forester heading a major wood products company, MacMillan did not hesitate to criticize his fellow professionals, as he criticized his fellow capitalists and the government. Logging had been going on for decades, he said, but foresters had displayed neither the curiosity nor the ambition "to collect and publish such elementary growth studies as could have been got together with a minimum of expense and effort." He did not bother to single out the exceptions.

"The fact that the present crop of commercial timber will sustain forest industry on its present scale for another two generations or so should not lull us to sleep," he said. "It is still as necessary as ever to provide the next crop. Barely enough time remains to do it. We can afford no more losses of either immature forest by fire or of existing crop by skimming off only the cream when reaping it."

MacMillan estimated it would take fifteen years to divert industry from exploitation to sustained yield. In a province where half of every dollar earned came from the forest, the public had to do its share. It was not enough to expect industry to sacrifice profits to obtain a new crop; the public, through government, must make sacrifices too.

"In nature the old forest produces the new forest. In public finance the revenue from the liquidation of the old forest must be used to the degree necessary to produce the new forest. It is community suicide in the Coast forest district to expect the mature forest to employ the people, supply the revenue for building the roads and public works, produce the money for the educational and defence systems, carry the social services and full employment projects and at the same time reproduce itself automatically without expense. . . .The public now regards such an investment policy as an unwelcome diversion of money that could be used to satisfy present-day personal desires."

MacMillan refuted those who said it was too late. "What Sweden has done in putting her forest on a sustained yield basis in the hundred years since she adopted the objective in 1845, this province can accomplish in the next sixty-five years if we accept the task now. Nature is on our side."

To those inclined to regard timber barons with a jaundiced eye, MacMillan offered surprises. He was a capitalist, and a tough one, who demanded profit and drove a hard bargain. He was also a forester who had never completely forgotten his youthful concern for the forest, or how, as chief forester of British Columbia, he had twice blocked politicians from gobbling up choice timber for their personal profit. He was, he used to say, a "socialist" in those days.

But on the other hand he insisted that if companies were expected to manage for sustained yield, they must be given better control of the land. Since the Forest Service had been created in 1912, logging had tripled. Companies like MacMillan's had grown into giants, increasing their private timber holdings by swallowing up competitors. But on Crown land, tenure policy had hardly changed. "The practice of forestry depends upon being absolutely confident that title conditions will hold for such periods as are required to produce a crop, which is not likely to be less than eighty or a hundred years on the best coast forest sites," he said.

As things stood, lease holders felt no wish to plant a second crop. Once an area of Crown land was logged, the land reverted to the government, which left it to nature to restore. There was hardly any control over the harvest. As for investment in reforestation, the recommendations of the 1910 royal commission had been forgotten. At a time when the U.S. Forest Service was reinvesting more in the forest than it took out in direct revenue, the B.C. government was returning only a quarter of the $4 million it derived from timber. Worse, only $150,000 of this was being spent on reforestation, making B.C.'s the smallest program of any important forest province save New Brunswick. MacMillan told the commission that the backlog of land ruined by logging and fire should be replanted and land currently being cut should be reforested immediately.

"It may be that the Sloan commission will suggest to the government important improvements in these fields and enlist the loggers, both large and small, in better conservation methods," said the *Vancouver Sun.* "With the field now controlled by a few giants, the government must recognize both the increased necessity of a firm approach and the increased opportunity for an efficient program of reform."

Sloan found that most of the industry wanted a change. "Responsible operators, with large investments in sawmills and pulp and paper plants, realize that this process cannot keep on indefinitely. They feel that the time has come when, for their plants, a new industry must be created—the use of the productive capacity of the lands for the growing of forest crops. To permit the owners of Crown-granted lands to log them off and leave them without taking any steps to secure the growth of a

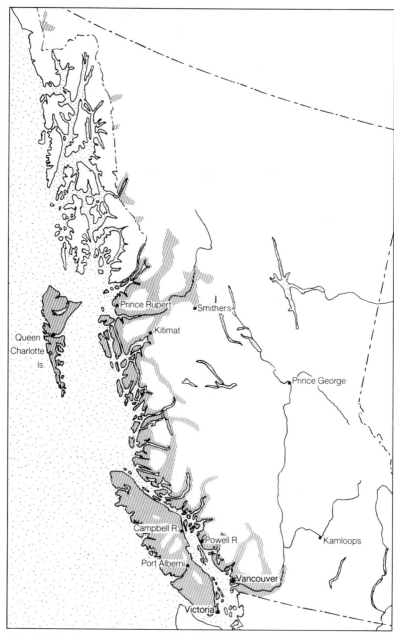

The British Columbia rain forest. Although it contains less than a fifth of Canada's total forest land, British Columbia boasts forty per cent of the nation's merchantable timber. More and more, B.C.'s timber is coming from the interior, but for more than a century the chief source has been the rain forests of the coast, ranging from Victoria to Prince Rupert and containing the great Douglas firs and red cedars which have made West Coast lumber famous.

new crop is to jeopardize seriously the future development of our logging industry. This, in turn, will lead to unemployment and the decline of communities into ghost towns." Ghost towns such as Lumberton had appeared already in the south corner of British Columbia.

Premier Hart's Liberal-Conservative coalition government had two alternatives, having already discarded a suggestion by S.G. Smith, one of the most experienced and respected loggers on the coast. Sid Smith wanted nothing less than private ownership of forest lands, as in the United States and most of Nova Scotia. His company, the American-owned Bloedel, Stewart and Welch, which was soon to become part of H.R. MacMillan's empire, had purchased considerable land since starting operations in 1911 and had pioneered industrial reforestation on Vancouver Island, planting three million trees in the 1930s. But Smith's proposal would have reversed a policy that had been entrenched in British Columbia since the 1890s —that only *trees* were for sale and the land they stood on must belong forever to the people of the province.

Of the alternatives left, one would have involved costly publicly financed reforestation, while retaining the old tenure system, with the government replanting once the lease holder had cut the trees down and the land had reverted to the Crown. The second, more lenient on the public purse, would provide a licensee with such lengthy tenure that he would be motivated to plant trees, or at least to make an effort to protect Crown land from fire and misuse until nature got around to establishing a new crop. The latter was the path Sloan recommended in 1945, after seventeen months of hearings and deliberations. A new act, passed two years later, was an effort to translate sustained yield from theory to practice for the first time in Canada on any significant scale.

Since sustained yield, like beauty, is in the eye of the beholder, there are many who claim that it has never worked in British Columbia or anywhere else. They point to how we are losing our reserves of commercial forest. But in British Columbia the act designed to attain sustained yield did make the industry more efficient, since it rationed out forest land so that the companies that dealt best with their timber were the ones that prospered. Smaller, wasteful lumber mills were bought out by larger ones.

To accommodate the host of small, independent loggers who complained that the big outfits were pushing them out of

business, two types of sustained yield management were set up
to replace the short-term leases. Owners of private forests—in
B.C., mostly large companies—were invited to apply for additional Crown land on condition they pool their own holdings
into new units to be known as forest management licences or,
later, tree farm licences (TFLs). Under the supervision of the
Forest Service, TFLs were to be managed by a company according to sustained yield principles. While taking some of the
burden off the government, this assured that private lands as
well as public ones would be managed. The company, in turn,
was assured a long-term wood supply. TFLs contributed a
disproportionately high amount of wood to the mills, though
they encompassed a relatively small part of the forest. Crown
forests not incorporated into TFLs were doled out to smaller
outfits, though not exclusively so. These were directly
managed by the Forest Service, which sold ten-year harvesting
rights, with licensees required to reforest after logging.

The new scheme meant fewer companies would control
more and more land, a trend Orchard regarded as an inevitable
concomitant to "progress." "The small operator is on the way
out," he said, as the water-wheel had succumbed to the steam
engine.

The independent loggers fought back, none harder than J.
Gordon Gibson, who with his brothers had built a patch of
cedar and a few cross-cut saws into a thriving business on the
western rim of Vancouver Island. A logger of the old school,
Gibson reckoned that trees were there for only one reason—to
cut. Pooh-poohing testimony at the Sloan hearings that the
forests were in jeopardy, Gibson saw the new tenures as a plot
to turn public land over to big corporations. "It was on this
false premise," he said in his autobiography, *Bull of the Woods*,
"that the timber of British Columbia was delivered into the
hands of the few companies who are now in control of our
resources and who are in a position to make vast fortunes out
of a heritage that rightly belongs to everyone."

Orchard had foreseen that the corporations would buy out
smaller licensees to increase and rationalize their own holdings
and create economies of scale, but he confessed that neither he
nor the government realized just how attractive the new tenure
arrangement would be in terms of capital gain and share values.
To his surprise the new licences drew scores of applications
right from the start. Big or small, companies were tired of
living hand to mouth amid a shrinking timber supply.

The first licence was certified in the spring of 1952. The second, interestingly enough, went to the company headed by Henry Makin, who only a few years earlier had assured Orchard he was not interested in sustained yield. Although most of the licences went to the big outfits, licence no. 4 was taken up by a small independent intent on seeing that the big companies were not going to be the only ones to benefit. He sold out soon after.

Foresters, meanwhile, were pointing out that just because the European policy, or objective, of sustained yield had been adopted, that did not mean the day had yet arrived when the forests were actually sustaining the yield. "It doesn't help to pretend you are at the top of the mountain when you are only half-way up," commented F.D. Mulholland, now working for industry after a long stint with government. "The fact is, of course, that we are just entering upon a period of conversion, gradually changing a forest unit here and another there from the long years of unregulated, liquidation type of exploitation. Foresters should have all the help they can get from governments, investors and taxpayers, in order to have a measure of success in this conversion during the first rotation, or even the second rotation, of the forest they are trying to convert. There should not be any pretence, while asking investors, operators and taxpayers for patience. Nor at this stage is there any merit in complacency. To replace the dwindling virgin old growth we must grow trees. . . ."

There were other, more pressing problems. Five years after the act was passed, Premier Hart's coalition was defeated by W.A.C. Bennett's Social Credit party. Though the government supported the new measures, Orchard, doing double duty as deputy minister and chief forester, found his new minister, R.E. Sommers, a schoolmaster from Castlegar, less than sympathetic.

Not long after the Social Credit party had settled into office as custodians of the richest softwood forest in the world, complaints of favouritism began to surface, particularly from the west coast of Vancouver Island. Independent loggers who had hoped their remote timber would remain safe from the big companies had got wind of a government decision to grant a large licence to British Columbia Forest Products, which E.P. Taylor, the Toronto entrepreneur, had pieced together from several aging outfits around the island with the help of his friend H.R. MacMillan. This was an issue the independents could get their teeth into, and they were a force to be reckoned with, having a tradition of tenacity and toughness going back to such forerunners as the "hand-loggers," who made a hard living by falling choice stands of fir and cedar from high ground right into the sea, whence it was towed to the mill.

Gordon Gibson carried the battle into the legislature by getting himself elected on a Liberal ticket. Rebuffed by Sommers and Bennett when he tried to find out what they were up to, Gibson delivered an angry speech in which he said, among much else, that when it came to dispensing woodlands, "money talks."

Suddenly the whole carefully constructed sustained yield program was under fire. A commission was convened under Justice Lord at the Vancouver Court House in March 1955 to investigate charges of scandal. For want of evidence it was dismantled within three days. Two months later BCFP got its licence, to the chagrin of Orchard, who said it had been disposed of without his approval although he was the chief administrator of the Lands and Forests Department.

In the aftermath, Sommers, after being defended by his colleagues in government, was to resign his post, having made an interesting speech in which he questioned the ways of free enterprise. "Unfortunately," he said, "the term is used at times when 'freebooter' would be more appropriate....The free enterprise system is justifiable only as long as it serves the public interest." Eventually Sommers, his career in ruins, was to serve a prison term, convicted of bribe-taking in the management licence affair.

This sad story, of course, was not without precedent, and recalled the whiff of scandal clinging to "Boss" Ferguson's administration in Ontario a generation earlier. In Quebec government and industry had been so chummy that one civil servant in the forest ministry, Thomas Maher, had attacked the government in the 1920s for failing to control industrial logging. The Liberal patronage system had never suffered from lack of lubrication, and government business with the big companies was conducted behind closed doors—in later years in the office of Premier Maurice Duplessis.

In British Columbia the Sommers incident did not weaken government determination to push on with its effort at sustained yield. In the coastal region, wood production had increased by 150 per cent since the war. Pulp and paper companies were beginning to appear in the interior, an area that had previously confined itself to sawmilling on a small scale, and in all there were ten pulp and paper mills, eleven plywood plants, fifty shingle mills, and four of the largest sawmills in Canada. No other province supported a forest industry of such size: its income was sixty per cent higher than mining and agriculture. Almost every community had its wood mill, and often that was all it had to sustain itself.

Twenty-three management licences had been awarded by the early 1950s, ranging in size from 4,000 to 664,000 acres. More than 100 applications were being processed. The Forest Service, embarked on the seemingly impossible task of putting every productive acre under sustained yield, was itself managing twenty sustained yield units (SYUs) without adequate staff; these lots were popular with small operators who could not take on management responsibilities themselves.

For eight years the government had been breaking new ground because Sloan had not attempted to suggest in his report how sustained yield should be achieved or how land should be apportioned. It was apparent that the program was favouring the bigger companies, and Orchard found himself increasingly dealing with criticism from independent loggers like Gibson. It was time to take another look at the program, and in 1955 Sloan was appointed to mount a second investigation under terms similar to those ten years earlier. While upholding the original principle, Sloan's second report, two years in the making and running to 900 pages, found government policy "inconsistent" and "lacking in clarity" and noted there was no legal limit to the size and number of management licences that might be granted to any one company. "The Act gives great power to the Minister and his department in the awarding of Crown timber and also in the control of management in these licensed forests afterward," he said, "but it expresses no general policy, and gives little guidance as to the vital question of what qualifications justify the award of a licence to an applicant. . . ."

Despite the need for control, Sloan shied away from trying to impose the solution he himself had suggested in his 1945 report: that an independent commission administer public woodlands. This would provide a way of keeping party politics out of the woods, but the politicians had argued that it would deprive the legislature of its rightful say in forestry matters. Since the turn of the century, government had been accustomed to regarding the forest as an excellent source of revenue;

the forest had proved a handy tool for general economic development that they had no wish to tamper with. Sloan's reason for dropping the proposal seemed somewhat lame. "An impressive number of important witnesses still favour such an independent commission," he acknowledged, "but my own feeling now is that developments in the intervening years have passed the point where the efficient functioning of such a commission could have had the most beneficial effects."

Instead he urged improvement of the under-manned, under-financed Forest Service to provide better supervision of industry. Citing testimony that Douglas fir, the most valuable species on the coast, was "in critical balance" between rate of growth and rate of harvest, he advised planting be increased from seven million trees a year to ten million, half by government and half by industry.

Tree farm licences, initially granted "in perpetuity" but later amended to twenty-one-year renewable, or "evergreen," tenures, covered twelve million acres, of which one million were privately owned; only a portion were under sustained yield working plans, however. Orchard was pleased with his brain-child.

The government had boosted its investment in the forest to one third of its direct revenue, but the supply of Douglas fir was clearly not being sustained. Nor, for that matter, was the harvest being sustained in other parts of Canada. An official of the Dominion Forest Service, W.M. Robertson, estimated that Canada was losing 7,000 square miles of forest every year, through cutting, fire, and other causes. "Canada's timber situation is uncertain, perhaps serious," he said. "It is a certainty that a hiatus will occur, in some regions at least, between the time of exhaustion of the present supply and the merchantability of the new supply."

Despite evidence to the contrary, a paper delivered at the Canada's Tomorrow conference held at Quebec City in 1953 insisted that "nearly all pulp and paper companies are today practising sustained-yield logging. . .no longer merely a paper concept but an operational reality in an ever increasing number of cases." Had this in fact been the case we would now be much better off than we are, but perhaps the confusion was understandable. It was a question of what was meant by a much misunderstood term: whether sustained yield meant merely an operational yield sustained by the fact that pulp companies with vast limits could always count on pushing farther north, or a yield actually sustained on biological principles that would guarantee a supply no matter the size of the timber limits. The former concept was the one in common use, though most provinces were making an effort to improve their yield, under the economic impetus of postwar expansion. Quebec was spending fifty per cent of its direct forest revenue on forest administration. Professional foresters had begun to take charge of harvesting operations, becoming more than theorists. Nova Scotia, in addition to its efforts to buy back thirty per cent of the land alienated into private hands, passed a Small Tree Conservation Act restricting cutting of immature trees on private land, which unfortunately had the effect of encouraging high-grading of the best trees and leaving the smaller and poorer ones. In New Brunswick a committee on reconstruction demanded controls and a start to reforestation, since the province was spending less than thirty per cent of forest revenue on the woods. Saskatchewan, worried about losing its white spruce, set up a royal commission that recommended a reduced rate of harvest.

Seven royal commissions were mounted after World War II to deal with forestry, the most notable in eastern Canada being that appointed by the Ontario government. Not much progress had been made in sustaining the Ontario yield, because the Crown Timber Act, which governed licensing and logging, had been based on the outdated notion that forests were inexhaustible. The 1929 Pulpwood Conservation Act, which required all companies to supply the government with inventories and to plan management on a sustained yield basis, had been smothered in the Depression. The practice of granting tracts of forest so much greater than needed had resulted in over-mature timber going to waste, because of old age if for no other reason, while younger timber was harvested. Efforts to get the government to build roads into areas of over-mature timber to relieve the strain on woodlands nearer to the mills had been in vain.

The Depression and World War II had halted plans to improve management, but by 1945 the provincial government did make an effort to implement a sustained yield policy on a company level. The Abitibi Power and Paper Company had been one of those in receivership during the Depression, and as one condition of getting back on its feet, Abitibi agreed to provide the government with an inventory of its leased lands along with operating and forest management plans. Within a year or two, other companies were required to do the same, under law. The Conservative government of Ontario proposed that a forest resources commission administer Crown lands, running into the same sort of opposition as British Columbia had. Industry was opposed; politicians objected it would deprive them of power over a vital resource. While the government dithered, the CCF opposition demanded action, as did the deputy minister of lands and forests, Frank A. MacDougall.

Pressured to make a decision, the government opted for the usual course of governments that are unsure. It established a royal commission, headed by Howard Kennedy, who, unlike Sloan in Vancouver, knew the industry at first hand, having been vice-president and woods manager for a major pulp and paper company and manager of the Quebec Forest Industries Association. An engineer by profession, he had served during World War II with the rank of major-general.

Kennedy began hearings in May 1946. Aided by six foresters, the commission was to look into everything from the nature, value, and extent of forest resources to the working conditions of lumberjacks. One of the most impassioned briefs came from the Lumber and Sawmill Workers Union, then headed by Bruce Magnuson, who wrote the brief himself.

"The present political form of forest administration is antiquated and intolerable," said the bargaining agent for thousands of woods workers. "The unsound short-term business practices are products of a bygone era. The outright stupidity of our present method of forest administration is revealed in the way in which we grant concession after concession to private industry for use of resources, the extent of which is a greater puzzle to the administration than it is to the corporations which get the concessions."

Tulio Mior, Magnuson's successor as head of the union, said that when he went to work in the woods in 1936 he was surprised to find no efforts to replant the clear-cuts. "I realized then that we would lose our spruce and jack pine and our forest would be depleted if we did not regenerate it artificially. The cut-over woods closest to the mills were not regenerating.

"The white and red pine, which you used to find as far west as Lake of the Woods, was already gone. I remember they used to have white pine around Kenora that was so beautiful it would knock your eye out. But by my time we were cutting white and black spruce, for pulpwood and for lumber.

"The government seemed to have the belief that two-thirds of the cut-over was regenerating naturally, and that would be enough to sustain the mills and keep them running. But my observation was that less than a third was regenerating naturally to spruce. I concluded that by the year 2000 we would be running into serious shortages. It was obvious even then that the forest would not sustain the pressure being put on it. The Boreal is not as big as many think, because north of the Trans-Canada Highway it begins to peter out into bog and barrens."

For a year Kennedy heard submissions, then wrote a report critical of government and industry and also of the public, who he said had failed "to insist that government policy demand a more rational development of our forest resources."

Kennedy found "tremendous, almost incredible, waste." The practice of logging trees before they reached full growth was like slaughtering calves rather than full-grown beef cattle. Sawmill residue that should have gone to pulp mills in the form of chips was being burned. Valuable sawlogs were locked away on pulp concessions where those who needed them could not get at them. "If the lumber industry is to continue to exist these sawlogs must be diverted to it, instead of being converted to pulp and paper for which smaller logs serve equally well," he said. Otherwise within twenty-five years sawmilling would become a minor industry and "a major tragedy."

Finding little evidence of sustained yield—a slogan that union leaders like Mior said merely lulled people into complacency—Kennedy called for prompt regeneration "equal or better than that removed, both as to species and density." As one witness had testified, "If it were true, as is often claimed, that we cut less than the annual growth and that cut-over land will produce a new crop of merchantable timber in less than 100 years, we should now have fair timber stands in large areas of cut-over land. This, as everyone of course knows, is pure fantasy without any foundation in fact."

Kennedy sided with those who opposed creation of a forest resources commission. "After all," he argued, "the administration of the day is responsible for the care of provincial resources and it cannot escape its responsibilities for the forests by delegating matters of policy and management to a non-elective commission." He proposed an advisory committee instead, with delegates from industry, labour, and the universities.

"After an exhaustive study of prevailing conditions I am convinced it is necessary to protect a probable majority of operators against their own folly in wasting forest resources," Kennedy said. "To those who are well satisfied with forestry matters as they are, it may come as a shock. I believe such people need a shock."

Kennedy's "shock" consisted of a proposal so extreme it had no chance of approval. Coming from a veteran industry woodlands manager, his recommendation was all the more controversial, for he suggested nothing less than starting all over again from scratch: that existing licences, agreements and permits be cancelled for a period of ten years so that twelve co-operative forest operating companies could handle all logging under the joint control of government and industry.

Unlike Sloan, he did not believe in a system that would lead to more public forest land in fewer corporate hands, since companies were harvesting less than a quarter of the potential of their best growing sites. There would be enough wood for all, Kennedy said, if it were better apportioned. Foreseeing the inevitable rebuff from industry, Kennedy added: "All Crown forest resources having been pooled, their sensible redistribution becomes simple and the major defects of the present system can be eliminated."

The *Forestry Chronicle*, representing professionals hungry for leadership and reform, called Kennedy's report "an outstanding contribution to the cause of forestry. Many of the basic ills, irregularities, anomalies and inconsistencies analysed with such acuteness and clarity throughout the 196 pages of this report are national rather than merely provincial in scope." Professor A.R.M. Lower, author of *The North American Assault on the Canadian Forest*, said Kennedy "points the way, if we wish to take it, to the salvation of our heritage and of poor battered mother earth itself." His study of history had not left him optimistic. "It is too much to expect that many of the recommendations will be adopted; they are too wise and far sighted for a democracy such as ours. We shall go on burning up our heritage, or giving it away to be wasted, until it disappears...."

In fact Ontario did adopt most of Kennedy's proposals, while rejecting the revolutionary idea of concentrating the harvest in operating companies. An Advisory Committee was formed under Dean J.W.B. Sisam of the University of Toronto School of Forestry. The drain on the forest caused by the export of unmanufactured pulpwood, which had been resumed in Ontario as an anti-Depression measure, was largely discontinued. The government, which had traditionally confined itself to the role of fireman and administrator to an exploitative industry, began the long task of overhauling outdated legislation. Efforts began to strengthen the Forestry Branch, which had been so seriously weakened during the Depression and war that there were barely fifty foresters in the field. A Forest Management Act passed in 1947 required that all companies, under statute and not just within the terms of individual licence agreements, submit cutting plans and take some responsibility for managing leased lands.

By the end of the 1950s the various governments, federal and provincial, were putting back only two and a half cents of every dollar of forest revenue into woodlands protection and renewal, but there was reason to hope the Cinderella of the resource world might at last be getting recognition. What was really happening, however, was that the myth that Canada was actually practising an adequate level of forestry was merely replacing the myth that the country enjoyed an unlimited wealth of timber.

↑ ↑ ↑ ↑ ↑ ↑ *7* ↑ ↑ ↑ ↑ ↑ ↑

The regeneration gap

"FROM PLANES, ROADS, RAILROADS, WE SEE THE green forest and think all is well. Nowhere else in the free world has so little been done for so large and valuable a permanent forest area as in Canada." H.R. MacMillan, The Profession and Practice of Forestry in Canada, 1907-1957.

THE POSTWAR BOOM IN CANADA'S NATURAL resources—oil, minerals, and wood fibre—did a lot to make forestry fashionable. British Columbia took the lead in its determination to test the theory of sustained yield. Ontario was struggling, however unsuccessfully, to get a reluctant industry to restore the logged-off land. Even Prince Edward Island, its forest of pine and spruce mostly reduced to potato fields and woodlots, had established a department of forestry to save what was left. The twelve founding members of the Canadian Society of Forest Engineers had grown to 1,000, located in ten provinces, split more or less evenly into two camps representing government and industry.

One of the more promising changes was in Ottawa, where forest priorities have always been well behind those of agriculture and fisheries, for constitutional reasons; but the federal government had been severely criticized by the provinces for failing to meet even the limited priorities it had set. There were at that time a dozen federal agencies involved in the forest industry; their quality and resources uneven, their promise of more than piecemeal progress doubtful. In 1949 Ottawa began to change its priorities, putting back some small portion of the revenues it took out of the woods. Its Canada Forestry Act, while not a national policy, promised "to promote cooperation between the federal government, provincial governments and industry in conservation of Canada's forests."

Ottawa entered into what was to be a series of shared-cost programs with the provinces for reforestation, fire protection, and an overdue scheme of five-year funding so that the vital forest inventories, without which talk of forest management and sustained timber yield was meaningless, could be brought up to date. A forest inventory is essentially a survey to determine such data as area, condition, volume, and species of timber.

Though five-eighths of Canada's forest was suitable for logging, it might as well have been in Siberia for all that was known about it. In northwestern Ontario, for example, the Dryden Paper Company, as it was still called before it was taken over by the Reed Company, had received an additional 1,110 square miles so as to double its mill production. While on paper this doubled its holdings, the company could not be sure if the land contained enough fibre for mill expansion. If Canada's forests were ever to be managed properly, it would be necessary to establish what species were growing where, what percentage was mature enough for cutting, the growth rate of immature trees, and the general health of the woodlands. Fortunately aerial photography had been vastly improved with military use during the war, to the point that an expert with a stereoscope could identify species, age, and forest density, and probably even get an idea of soil capability as well, though some sampling on the ground remained necessary.

Quebec and Newfoundland did their own surveys; the other provinces, except for Prince Edward Island, participated in a federal-provincial $10-million inventory of a million square miles. The results were alarming. There on photos was unarguable proof that thousands of square miles had deteriorated into scrub, hardwoods, and unsatisfactorily regenerated land. A new phrase was heard: "the regeneration gap." In essence this meant that a dearth of mature forest by the end of the twentieth century would cause a serious shortfall in commercial wood production. It was to be some time before this warning began to sink in.

The prospect was no more promising in Quebec. Eighty-five per cent of the spruce forest accessible to mills was growing back to balsam fir, or to "weed trees" currently useless to industry, such as aspen, birch, and other hardwoods. New Brunswick loggers were cutting into undersized, third-growth timber, and suffering a serious budworm epidemic that was exacerbated there and in southeastern Quebec by the growing dependence on budworm-prone balsam fir.

In British Columbia's coastal forests, where four million acres had been logged or burned, only one-quarter was regenerating, and cut-over areas were producing fifty times more useless hardwood than before. The problem had increased since the 1920s with the growth of mechanized logging and the growing size of clear-cuts.

At the University of Toronto, where he received an honorary doctorate, H.R. MacMillan compressed the problem into one sentence: "It is doubtful whether Canada, with its present attention to forest management, can sustain today's annual cut in perpetuity, even by going farther north each decade into virgin forest (at a greater cost for logs) or by using a high proportion of inferior species (thus reducing our competitive ability in the foreign markets on which we depend)."

By the 1950s mechanized logging had spread into eastern Canada. Until then few machines had made their way into the woods east of B.C., and the change-over was primarily due to problems of manpower, the traditional use of farm labour in the woods having been disrupted by World War II. Farm workers were taking town jobs, an attractive alternative to the hard and lonely toil of remote camps. Labour costs had mounted since the unions had got a foothold in the camps.

Mechanical wheeled skidders supplanted horses. The colourful old spring log drives on a score of rivers were replaced by logging trucks on thousands of miles of dirt roads. With a power saw a lumberjack could cut as much wood in fifteen minutes as two men with a cross-cut saw could produce in an hour. The "horse camps," with their stables, teamsters, and blacksmiths, gave way to industrial compounds complete with gas pumps, maintenance garages, and gleaming kitchens. Lumberjacks, earning wages that would have astounded their

1

2

Clear-cutting, which accounts for more than eighty per cent of the timber harvesting in Canada, is often in disfavour because of the large size of the desolate-looking sites and the time it takes for them to grow over. The key factors are the suitability of the site to this method, and proper regeneration; if the latter can be achieved most foresters find nothing wrong with clear-cutting. The top photo shows clear-cuts near Skidegate on Moresby Island in the Queen Charlottes, where environmental groups, including the local Haida band council, fear the effects of widespread logging on slopes prone to erosion. The sad scene below is damage from mechanical skidders in the peatland of the Quebec-Ontario Clay Belt.

3

4

Since the Second World War giant tree harvesters have replaced the lumberman with his axe and horse. "Feller forwarders" like this one, almost forty-eight feet long and weighing nearly fifty tons, shear off whole trees and trundle them out of the forest. Massive Douglas firs (left), the tallest trees in Canada, have largely disappeared from the coastal forests of British Columbia, much as the white pine vanished from eastern Canada early in this century. This fir, felled by George Read near Sooke, contained enough wood to build a small house.

5

6

7

Though most forest management has consisted of little more than logging the timber, there have been examples of progressive forestry, such as this 60-year-old plantation at Kirkwood east of Sault Ste. Marie. Here the provincial government reclaimed hundreds of square miles of poor farmland and virtual desert and turned the Kirkwood Management Unit into a research centre. (Foresters no longer believe trees must be planted in such orderly rows.) The alternative to proper management is environmental damage that retards regeneration to commercially useful species. Shown below is a clear-cut (left) that was swept by fire after logging and (right) "junk forest." Perhaps one quarter of the forest land logged or burned has been growing back to junk forest of no use to industry and little attraction to nature lovers.

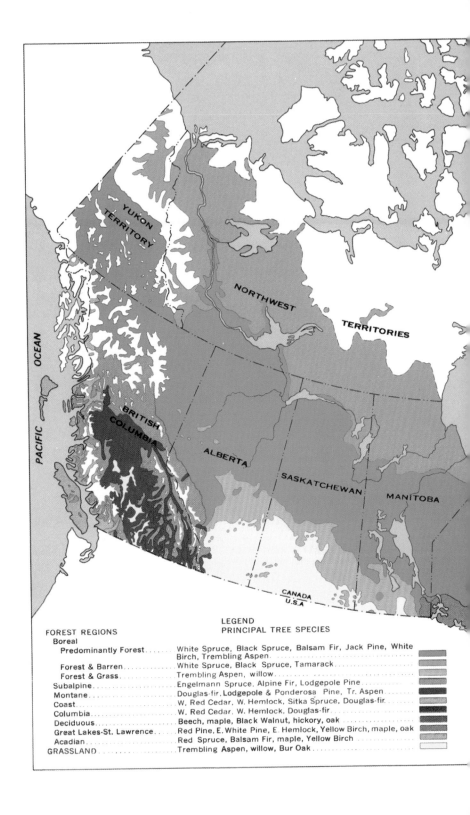

LEGEND
PRINCIPAL TREE SPECIES

FOREST REGIONS

Boreal

Predominantly Forest.......	White Spruce, Black Spruce, Balsam Fir, Jack Pine, White Birch, Trembling Aspen.
Forest & Barren............	White Spruce, Black Spruce, Tamarack............
Forest & Grass............	Trembling Aspen, willow............
Subalpine.................	Engelmann Spruce, Alpine Fir, Lodgepole Pine...
Montane..................	Douglas-fir, Lodgepole & Ponderosa Pine, Tr. Aspen.
Coast...................	W. Red Cedar, W. Hemlock, Sitka Spruce, Douglas-fir.
Columbia.................	W. Red Cedar, W. Hemlock, Douglas-fir............
Deciduous................	Beech, maple, Black Walnut, hickory, oak.........
Great Lakes-St. Lawrence.....	Red Pine, E. White Pine, E. Hemlock, Yellow Birch, maple, oak
Acadian.................	Red Spruce, Balsam Fir, maple, Yellow Birch.......
GRASSLAND.............	Trembling Aspen, willow, Bur Oak............

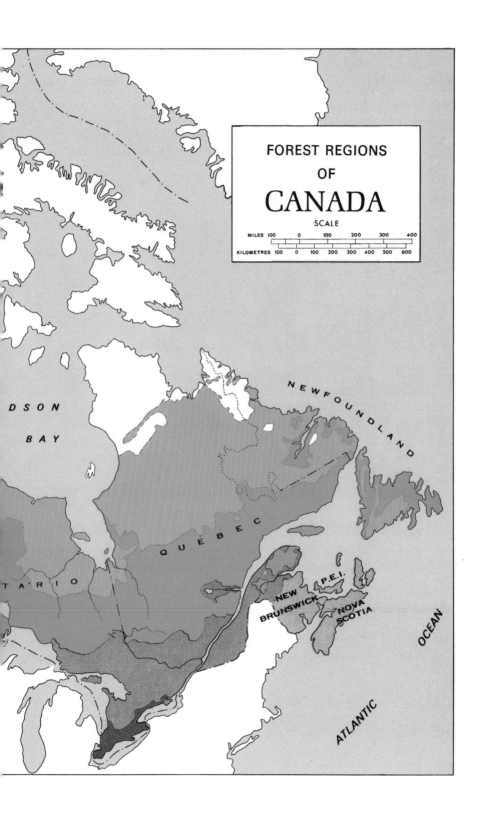

FOREST REGIONS
OF
CANADA

SCALE

MILES 100   0   100   200   300   400
KILOMETRES 100   0   100   200   300   400   500   600

HUDSON

BAY

NEWFOUNDLAND

QUEBEC

ONTARIO

NEW
BRUNSWICK

P.E.I.

NOVA
SCOTIA

OCEAN

ATLANTIC

The spruce budworm (Choristoneura fumiferana) *is eastern Canada's most persistent and harmful forest pest, often killing eighty per cent of a balsam fir and spruce forest within a dozen years. The only antidote has been the aerial spraying of insecticides. Since the Nova Scotia government banned spraying, the budworm has destroyed Cape Breton's mature balsam fir forests (below), leaving defoliated, dying trees except for strips of fresh green growth coming up as a result of clear-cut salvage operations.*

8

9

10

Forests damaged by the budworm are prey to fire, as are the piles of slash(left) sometimes left by loggers. Despite the development of scientific forest fire suppression, the toll is still enormous, averaging more than $35 million a year in damage and control costs. As well as destroying standing timber, fire can damage rich soil (opposite) built up over centuries so that it may be generations before it can again support a productive woodland.

12

13

It can be done! These two photos, taken from the same spot near Cowichan Lake, B.C., show an area logged in 1956, planted with seedlings but swept by fire six years later and planted again. The second picture was taken in 1984.

15. If loggers get to them before they die, woodlands ravaged by forest fire can still be salvaged. Here teamsters recover timber scorched by fire at Flame Lake, Chapleau, Ontario, in November 1948.

fathers, commuted to work from their homes, logging all the year round instead of only in the fall and winter. Equipped with two-way radios and industrial hard hats, they were becoming "forest technicians" with skills that would have baffled the old white pine shantymen.

Mechanization, while increasing production, brought the inevitable problems Alexander Koroleff, manager of the Woodlands Section of the Canadian Pulp and Paper Association, had predicted. Though a supporter of mechanization, impatient that logging was one of the last industries to be mechanized in eastern Canada, he expressed regret that "silvicultural requirements too frequently were neglected even when they could have been considered." (Thirty-five years later, and long retired, Koroleff found no reason to change this opinion. Mechanization had by the late 1970s brought monsters into the woods that could cut 100 trees an hour, snapping them off at the butt with hydraulic shears and lugging them off bodily.)

Horse logging had tended to preserve the vulnerable "advance growth," anywhere from a few inches to ten feet high. Horses stepped around the young trees that would assure natural forest regeneration, whereas machines crashed through and flattened everything in the way. In northern Ontario, they chewed up the swampy Clay Belt, criss-crossing the land with deep tracks that collected water, aborting natural growth.

With mechanization came ever larger clear-cuts. As Koroleff observed in 1950: "The common practice in large-scale pulp-wood operations in Canada is to rapidly cut a large area, usually clear, and then move on, coming back only when nature will have produced a new crop. Thus logged-off areas are often abandoned for eighty or a hundred years."

The obvious antidote to lack of natural regeneration—mass planting and seeding—failed to gain much support. It was convenient, and cheap, to keep on believing that nature would provide. The pittance the federal government had granted the provinces for artificial regeneration, enough for sixty million trees, hardly made a dent in the backlog classified as NSR, "not satisfactorily restocked."

In the St. Lawrence Valley alone, it was estimated that a billion and a half plantings were needed to get the land back into production. Since Ellwood Wilson's project at Grand'Mère had been abandoned in the 1930s, reforestation in Quebec had been limited to a few hundred acres here and there. The government now began to plant twenty-five million seedlings a year, which meant it was reforesting about 25,000 acres.

Of the few companies attempting reforestation in Canada in the 1950s, the most notable was Irving Forest Products of New Brunswick, which owned nine sawmills and a pulp mill. Better known for his oil products, K.C. Irving controlled two and a half million acres of forest, of which nearly two million were owned outright. Irving decided that natural regeneration was too slow and inefficient and grew back to the wrong species. He wanted to reduce the amount of balsam fir and hardwood on his land, for a new cycle of budworm infestation was starting up and he remembered too well the havoc the last one had caused in the 1920s, including such serious unemployment in Kent County that people had to move away to find work. Industry had never been required to replace the forest it had cut, even on Crown lands, but Irving decided the time had come to invest in the future.

He established his own 350-acre nursery to grow seedlings at Juniper, in the centre of the province, incidentally giving new life to a town that had been suffering from lack of sawlog timber for its mill. In 1957 he began to plant spruce—most of his planting was in spruce or jack pine along with some red pine —at Black Brook Hill. By the 1960s Irving was running the biggest private reforestation program in Canada, rehabilitating nineteenth-century railway grant land that had been sporadically high-graded for its best timber before deteriorating into junk forest—pin cherry and the like, as well as budworm-prone balsam fir, which tends to deteriorate after fifty years of growth. Through trial and effort he developed timberlands as a farmer prepares a new crop, though not without problems. White spruce plantations in particular were vulnerable to spruce tip moth and to competition from hardwoods.

Niels Kreiberg, a Danish-born tree genetics expert who ran Irving's nursery program for nine years, recalled: "People had been talking for a long time about what should be done, but Irving actually did it, and sustained the effort." Even at a planting cost of more than $100 an acre, his man-made forest proved a shrewd investment. On tens of thousands of acres, from Boston Brook in northern New Brunswick down into the heavily logged areas of the south, he was getting back three times what the old forest had provided. He was growing the same amount of wood on one million acres that three million acres produced elsewhere in the province. He was blessed with good soil, adequate rainfall, and a private company with no shareholders to whom dividends might be more important than future forests.

Though it was a public corporation answerable to shareholders, H.R. MacMillan's firm, MacMillan Bloedel, began what it called an "intensive forestry program" in British Columbia, aimed at increasing coastal timber production by fifteen per cent, enough timber to build 14,000 homes or run a pulp mill. The company also cut down on timber waste by integrating its lumber and pulp operations. Pulp mills by now were getting at least a portion of their furnish from the residue of sawmills, particularly in the form of chips, and the burners that adjoined every sawmill, shaped like giant beehives and sending useful fibre up in smoke, had begun to disappear.

But integration was no substitute for forest management, as was recognized in Ontario in 1954 when the Crown Timber Act was passed. This put responsibility for forest renewal on industry, thereby setting off considerable activity. Inventory surveys were made, forest management plans drawn up, and sample plots laid out to determine timber growth rates. Tenures were standardized at a renewable twenty-one years.

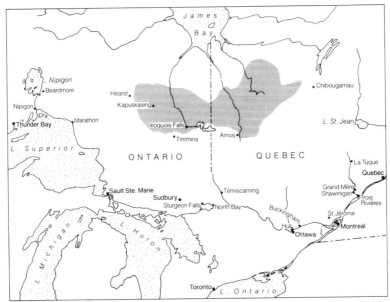

Running 500 miles from central Quebec almost to Hearst, Ontario, the Northern Clay Belt varies in width between 100 and 200 miles. It is the home of Canada's most valuable pulpwood species, black spruce, but is particularly vulnerable to machine logging, which ruins sensitive wetlands.

This approach was heralded as the start of a new era of sustained yield management, but it proved to be mostly an academic exercise to satisfy statutory requirements. The government, partly because of manpower shortages, did not police the act effectively and most companies failed to take sustained yield very seriously, exploiting the forest more or less as they always had.

One of the notable exceptions was the Kimberly-Clark Pulp and Paper Company of Wisconsin, which held licences on Crown forest land at Long Lac and around Kapuskasing and whose woodlands manager was Gordon Cosens, one-time dean of forestry in Toronto. At Kapuskasing, where it ran a pulp mill and a stud mill to make two-by-fours, it controlled thousands of square miles of Crown land plus 289 square miles of its own. These lay in the Clay Belt where, because of heavy soil, extremes of temperature, and lack of information about the growth of black spruce, the classical forestry that came from Europe did not work. They established a nursery at nearby

Moonbeam and began a planting program that grew to a million and a half trees a year. They believed that if they planted twenty-five per cent of their cut-overs, the rest would grow back naturally—which to some extent proved true since this was still in the horse-logging days, before mechanized skidders came in to chew up the muskeg, make regeneration difficult, and reduce large areas to grass and bulrushes for years after the cut.

Here and there were smaller efforts. At Atikokan, in north-western Ontario, the Ontario-Minnesota Pulp and Paper Company was one of the first to experiment with ploughing, or "scarifying," its cut-over to prepare, as the farmer does, for planting. It ran into difficulties: the disc plough cut the roots of such weeds as hazel and Labrador tea; where one weed had grown, ten sprouted up to compete with spruce and jack pine. (No herbicides were available then to keep weeds at bay.)

The Abitibi Paper Company, while not doing much planting, had started a nursery as early as 1919 at Twin Falls, had laid out sample plots for the study of tree growth, and was doing some jack pine thinning and a bit of muskeg drainage to enhance spruce growth. Now, at a whistle stop called Raith, sixty miles northwest of Thunder Bay, Abitibi established what it called a woodlands laboratory—an experimental forest—in a typical Boreal mix of spruce, balsam fir, poplar, and jack pine. Leopold Vidlak, a Czech refugee who had once managed the largest private forest in his native country, was hired to operate it with a crew of twenty-five men. "My instructions were very simple," Vidlak recalled. "I was to be responsible for regeneration and silviculture on 3,000 acres. 'Do what you want, nobody will stop you,' they said."

Vidlak worked at unlocking the secrets of the Boreal until in 1962 the Ontario government, after nine years of trying to get industry to undertake replanting and silviculture, took over responsibility itself. Companies like Spruce Falls and Abitibi, freed of responsibility for forest renewal, lost interest. Vidlak retired and was not replaced. One day, with no one there, the woods at Raith caught fire, and later a freak tornado destroyed whatever of Vidlak's work had not been ruined by fire. Vidlak, at the age of sixty-five, began a new career, teaching at the new forestry school at Lakehead University.

The 1962 amendment to the Ontario Crown Timber Act, assigning responsibility for all management of Crown lands to the minister of lands and forests, pleased industry and established a firm objective for government. It also took a step backward by divorcing logging from regeneration. While certainly not a course favoured now, it made sense at the time to the chief of the Ontario Timber Branch, A.J. Brodie, who in recommending it said, "This will permit logging to develop along purely economic lines and silviculture to develop along biological lines, as it certainly must."

The Ontario government retained the right to make cooperative regeneration agreements with licensees, but otherwise gave industry *carte blanche* to go on cutting timber at the lowest possible cost, leaving the taxpayers to foot the bill for regeneration. This split between harvesting and regenerating did nothing to alleviate the adversarial relationship between government foresters and those who worked for industry.

Spending more money on forestry than ever before, the government tripled its force of foresters and launched "Project Regeneration." Between Sudbury and Dryden, it opened half a dozen tree nurseries, and it began to look into rehabilitation of degraded forests, such as those around Beardmore on Highway 11 bordering Lake Nipigon, north of Lake Superior. The forest here was in poor shape. Cutting had been going on for half a century or more, first for jack pine railway ties, then for pulpwood; moose maple, alder, birch, hazelnut, and raspberry bushes had been taking over the sites, making them into "silvicultural slums." No forest management had been practised, but the last company to log there had agreed to pay twenty-five cents towards reforestation for every cord cut. With government contributing an equal amount, a fund of half a million dollars had built up—a practical example of what could be done to solve the interminable wrangle over who should pay for reforestation, government or industry.

To take charge at Beardmore, the government hired George Marek, a countryman of Vidlak's. Brought up in Bohemia east of Prague, the son and grandson of foresters, Marek was in forestry school when World War II began. Emigrating to Canada after the war, he worked at forest jobs around Marathon, Ontario, while picking up extra credits needed to make him a registered forester in Canada.

A man who has dedicated his life to forestry, Marek was responsible for regenerating and tending 44,000 acres, setting himself the task of achieving timber yields in fifty years that had previously taken a hundred years. Like Fernow, his rigorous standards and outspoken impatience with government were to get him into trouble with his superiors. "In Europe you cannot

16, 17. By the 1940s fire and poor management had reduced some areas near Beardmore, Ontario, once a thriving lumber town, to virtual wasteland. In the 1950s the provincial government took steps to rehabilitate this land by planting, a program George Marek was to build into one of the showplaces of man-made woodlands in northern Ontario. Marek, shown above planting, is one of many European-trained foresters who have enriched the woodland heritage of Canada.

get away with poor forestry," he said. "There are laws and regulations which can strip you of your profession, or where you can even be jailed for poor forestry practices. In Bohemia a forester was a powerful man. So I grew up with the idea that as a forester I would do my best and practise the rules of the forestry profession. So I got into trouble.

"The battle started when I began at Nipigon in 1957. I immediately ran up against the bureaucratic set-up where they said, 'OK, you may need this, but you cannot have it.' To practise silviculture you need staff, but they had no money, they said. So I was on my own. I set to work planting trees with 150 Indians, doing all the book work, the planning, building access roads, and at the same time being called out to other areas to fight forest fires when they needed me.

"Little was known about regeneration. There were no precedents. I had no expert to turn to. I started fighting for quality nursery stock, but the bureaucrats said, 'That's all right, that's all right.' But the stock was not all right, and I told them, 'I don't want to live to see my work degenerate to the point where people will call it Marek's disaster.' The bureaucrats were not really interested in quality. They were just interested in target numbers, whereas the man in the field wants the best quality and a good survival rate. That's where the clash occurs."

In pursuit of quality he was gone for months from his white cottage in Beardmore, camping in the bush, supervising the planting. "Some people laughed at me for my preoccupation with the forest," said Marek. "They thought I was crazy. There were foresters who said it was all a waste of money, that we had so much forest we would never use it all up. All they were worried about was fires. Then, when it became clear the forest was not regenerating, they said, 'OK, technology will supply the answer, with ways to use these hodge-podge forests of spruce mixed with fir, poplar, etc. Dump it all down at the mill and the mill will sort it out.' Boy, did they ever have a surprise. They found problems with that stuff from the 'junk forest,' impurities in cooking up the pulp and bleaching. If you want a good product to sell in the U.S. it has to be good, pure stock."

Marek's handiwork was part of the man-made forests that, by the 1950s, totalled 1.8 million acres across Canada—at least, that acreage was known to have been planted; just how much survived the critical first few years after planting was unclear. Few growth records were kept. Since World War II Ontario had renewed 100,000 acres, two-thirds of that planted and the rest treated in various ways to encourage natural regeneration. British Columbia, with 400,000 acres, had made a promising start for a province whose industry was still young. Quebec had planted 150,000 acres. On the prairies, 84,000 acres had been planted, much of that by the federal government and including shelter belts for farm land. The four Atlantic provinces lagged behind, with a total of 31,000 acres reforested. It was certainly clear that reforestation was minor compared with the three million acres logged off every year or mutilated by fire.

Industry was making good money in those postwar years and no longer had an excuse for not spending on forestry. Nevertheless not much got spent; while paying lip service to forestry most companies went on mining the forest and not many people thought to question the practice. Any blame usually landed on those perennial whipping boys "the politicians," and by extension the people of Canada who had voted them into office without ascertaining their views, if any, about the forest resource.

In its brief in 1956 to the Royal Commission on Canada's Economic Prospects, the Canadian Institute of Forestry, as the Canadian Society of Forest Engineers was now called, blamed government for lack of effective legislation, short-sighted tax measures that hampered industry, and inadequate tenure on Crown woodlands—all arguments that the companies themselves used to excuse their lack of forestry commitment.

There was still disagreement among foresters themselves. Gordon Godwin, an executive of the Canadian Forestry Association, believed there was only enough mature timber to guarantee an adequate supply for fifty years. On the other hand, W. A. Pepler, manager of the Woodlands Section of the Canadian Pulp and Paper Association, asserted that by the time the mature wood ran out, Canadians would be happily harvesting three times as much from a second crop—an assertion based on the misguided notion that there was a decent second crop of trees in the ground.

The CIF itself stated that the country did not face any imminent timber famine, but certainly faced the danger of impoverishing the most economical supplies of timber, and it recommended that a committee of foresters, economists, tax experts, businessmen, and politicians draft a national policy. It is indicative of the low priority given forestry that it was not until 1970 that anything resembling a national committee appeared, in the guise of the Canadian Forestry Advisory

Council, and then only with the role of advising the federal minister, with limited impact.

It seemed that government officials felt enough was already being done, and a senior official of the Ontario Department of Lands and Forests made the questionable assertion that "industry and government have cooperated closely in building a management program in Ontario that is second to none." On the books, many provinces had impressive legislation, and a layman might well be excused for believing Canada was practising adequate forestry. Yet the June 1960 edition of the *Forestry Chronicle* said: "We are presiding over the liquidation of natural resources and, in many cases, do not even provide a decent burial. We are accepting a very real loss as the price of logging in the way to which we have become accustomed. Our next crop will be much poorer than it need be."

How to explain the dichotomy? For one thing, wrong questions were being asked, evoking wrong answers. Forestry, if it is anything, is "site specific." Conditions change from area to area, but generalities were being paraded as universal truths. A public relations campaign launched by the pulp and paper industry did nothing to clear the confusion. One ad in May 1962 assured newspaper readers that the mills "will continue to produce Canada's most important crop in perpetuity. . . . with surveys, nurseries, roads, communications and scientific harvesting, they [the companies] conserve the woodlands. . . . they cut less wood than they grow. . . ."

Since most companies were doing no such thing, the *Forestry Chronicle* dubbed this "Madison Avenue forestry," adding: "We believe that foresters employed by companies whose public statements grossly exaggerate the level of forestry they practise have the unpleasant duty of protesting. . . . It is intolerable that while this Institute [the Canadian Institute of Forestry] strives for badly-needed improvements in forestry practice. . .some large forest operators deliberately mislead the Canadian public with inflated boasts about their forestry achievements and soothing assurances that all is well on their forest holdings."

In the midst of this battle for public opinion, Ottawa's conversion to the cause of forestry was heartening, as long as it lasted. For years the Forestry Service had been shuffled carelessly among various federal departments: the Ministry of the Interior up to 1936, then the Department of Mines and Resources and the Department of Northern Affairs and National Resources. It had long taken responsibility for research, unhampered by short-term concern for profit. In 1960 it had received recognition, being elevated to full ministry status and incorporating the Division of Forest Biology from the Department of Agriculture, which had conducted research in pathology, entomology, and ecology. Parliament, whose forestry debate—a rare occurrence—filled seventy pages of Hansard in June 1960, unanimously supported creation of the ministry.

The next six years were to be a high point in federal-provincial forestry relations, with the federal government funding reforestation, fire protection, silviculture, and, above all, inventory surveys. There were seven regional research centres (St. John's, Fredericton, Quebec City, Sault Ste. Marie, Winnipeg, Edmonton, and Victoria), two forest products laboratories, in Ottawa and Vancouver, and the Forest Fire Research Institute, the Forest Management Institute, the Chemical Control Institute, and the Petawawa Forest Experiment Station.

There was considerable emphasis on forestry in the Agricultural Rehabilitation and Development Act (ARDA) passed by the federal government in 1962. In 1968 ARDA would come under the Department of Regional Economic Expansion (DREE), which would make grants to the provinces and to industry to create jobs based on the forest resource.

In an effort to improve co-operation between Ottawa and the provinces, in 1963 the federal government convened the first conference of government forest ministers. A year later Maurice Sauvé, a Montreal lawyer, was appointed minister of forestry. He believed in provincial autonomy and saw Ottawa's role in forestry mainly as an "activator," and his job, as he saw it, was as "federal minister of provincial relations."

In February 1966 Sauvé called a three-day forestry meeting of government and industry delegates at Montebello, Quebec, half-way between Montreal and Ottawa, a region once famous for white pine. Unlike previous conferences it avoided generalities and concentrated on a central question: Would there be enough commercial timber thirty-five years down the road?

The answers were not comforting. In less than ten years, logging was expected to increase by sixty per cent to meet mill demands, but already many areas were being over-cut. At that rate, commercial wood supplies would be running out by the year 2000. "At the present time, there is no government policy that assures that wood harvesting and timber land management will be conducted in the best public interest," said a Newfoundland delegate.

It was in an address tabled at Montebello that a young resource economist who was to have a considerable influence on the course of forestry began to publicize his ideas. F.L.C. "Les" Reed was then an employee of the Council of Forest Industries of British Columbia.

He had been asked to contribute a paper on markets and wood consumption at Montebello and as he did his research he came to the conclusion that the greatest problem would be not markets, but supply. He had begun to focus on a problem receiving too little attention: the vital difference to the economy between trees in general, the woodlands we enjoy on holiday or that painters celebrate, and merchantable timber that is economically accessible and will thus be competitive on the world market.

"I told them we had already used our best timber supply," he said. "We were having to search even farther afield for good sawlogs twelve inches in diameter. The technology of making a two-by-four stud out of a five-inch log was still in its infancy. The timber inventory was so poor it was almost comical. There was really little information. I began, in short, to look at the question from a different point of view, and from that time on I began to worry about timber supply."

Reed's paper at the conference was largely about markets, however, and his reference to the probability that "we may be a lot closer to the margin of profitable expansion than is realized" made little impact. More attention was afforded an unexpectedly pessimistic speech from R.M. Fowler, president of the Canadian Pulp and Paper Association.

"You can go on as you are," said Fowler, "live on in the happy assumption of the past that we have unlimited forest assets to draw on, and close your eyes to the fact that assumption is no longer, or will no longer, be valid—continue with a lot of individual and rather half-hearted efforts to improve silviculture, and do a bit of research and train a few scientists, and build some roads and tinker with forestry laws and so on. If this is done, most of the people in this room will probably get by. They can work on and take their pensions, but sometime our sons or successors—perhaps fifteen or twenty-five years from now—will feel the pinch of wood shortages, and they may wonder why we were so blind and inefficient and unimaginative today."

The road would not be easy. Industry's co-operation in the past had been more evident in words than in deeds. People would have to learn that "the old happy, easy, affluent days of unlimited forest resources are nearly over." Governments would have to commit themselves to long-range forestry, "and the fact is that a politician is not good at making long-range decisions."

The Montebello conference was the first of several over the next fifteen years that tried to spread the message of impending timber shortage, the "regeneration gap." In itself, it was disappointing and lacked follow-up, and plans to hold a second Montebello conference within a year were scrapped because there were too many unresolved problems arising from the first. Members of the conference steering committee lost interest and it was dissolved.

For reasons beyond Sauvé's control, a few months after the Montebello meeting the minister of finance announced that the shared-cost forestry programs that had started after the war would not be renewed, "as we feel the provinces are quite able to carry on themselves." There was, however, no indication that the provinces were prepared, or able, to supply the $8 million Ottawa had been providing every year from federal tax money. There began a slow decline in federal participation in forestry. By the late 1960s forestry had lost its status as a ministry, merging into a new Department of Forestry and Rural Development where money was used for other things, such as marshland reclamation. By 1968 it found itself in a secondary position in the Ministry of Fisheries and Forestry, fish having a much more important priority in Ottawa's scheme of things. Scores of Forestry Service employees were laid off.

Federal forestry was clearly on the decline, reduced first from ministerial to assistant deputy minister level, and ultimately to be represented at the diminished level of director general after it was merged into the big new Ministry of the Environment in 1971.

Just when the pressing need for forest renewal was finally being recognized across the country, Ottawa was relinquishing its leadership. But forestry has rarely been much of a political issue, despite its importance, for the penalties of inaction are never immediate or spectacular. Forests do not disappear overnight, nor do mills close dramatically from one day to the next for lack of wood. The danger, rather, lies in the whole thing running down almost imperceptibly, while governments come and go and other timber-exporting nations seize the softwood markets that have contributed so much to Canada's economy.

Des Crossley's obsession

"AS THE SORRY STATE OF FOREST MANAGEMENT, OR lack thereof, across our nation became increasingly evident, I slowly became obsessed with the desire and the professional responsibility to do something about it." Desmond Crossley, retired chief forester, St. Regis (Alberta) Ltd., Hinton, Alberta.

TO MOST PEOPLE, ALBERTA MEANS OIL, CATTLE, and wide-open spaces, but it is also a forest province. More than half of Alberta is covered with trees. Its woodlands rank fourth in size after those of British Columbia, Ontario, and Quebec, but only in the past thirty years have Albertans paid much attention to a renewable resource it can count on after such "wasting resources" as oil and coal are exhausted.

There had been small-scale logging in Alberta for almost a century, supplying railway ties and lumber but never enough to do much harm to the 130,000 square miles of forest, which includes excellent spruce and lodge-pole pine. Preoccupied with ranching, farming, coal mining, and eventually oil, far from seaports and eastern American markets, Alberta had not attracted any pulp and paper mills, though its western foothills were the scene of some of the first forest management in Canada in the early 1900s.

Clifford Sifton, when he was minister of the interior, had begun to worry about the future of the eastern slopes of the Rockies, which provide ninety per cent of the water going into the Saskatchewan River system. This system is of critical importance to the Prairie provinces, watering half the grain-growing and cattle-ranching areas as far east as Manitoba, as well as supplying water to Edmonton, Calgary, Saskatoon, and Prince Albert. Sifton's concern that the foothills always provide a supply of fresh water to the prairies was shared by Elihu Stewart, chief inspector of timber and forestry in the Dominion forestry service. A trip to Europe, in which he saw the devastation caused by erosion and floods when trees were needlessly cut and burned, convinced Stewart of the need to establish reserves free of settlement and indiscriminate logging.

"The future of our fertile prairie country, and that of southern Alberta and Assiniboia [Saskatchewan], will be sadly disappointing if the timber covering the east slope of the Rocky Mountains should be destroyed," Stewart wrote. "Numerous tributaries flowing into the South Saskatchewan are dependent on the precipitation of that watershed for their supply, and equally dependent on the forest with which it is covered to prevent a tumultuous run-off in the spring and early summer. Disastrous as have been some of the floods along these streams in recent years, they will be ten-fold more destructive and frequent if the forest covering along the foothills is destroyed."

In 1910 the federal Ministry of the Interior, which was then responsible for the natural resources of the prairies, took the first step towards protecting the foothills watershed. For 350 miles north from the American border it surveyed and classified land to be kept free of settlement because of soil and other conditions. Fires illustrated the need for concern. A fire north of Crowsnest Pass extended seventy-five miles; a total of 568 square miles was burned over.

Under the Forest Reserve and Parks Act twelve million acres was to be kept free of settlement. Elsewhere in Alberta, which had gained provincial autonomy in 1905, 2,000 square miles of land was under licence to lumber operators on the Athabasca River, the North Saskatchewan, and the Peace River. But the industry remained undeveloped. Most of the 100 mills supplying lumber to Edmonton and Calgary, pit props to the coal mines, and ties to the railways were small and portable. Provincial revenue from the forest was $30,000 a year, a fraction of the value annually destroyed by fire.

In 1930 Alberta, which like Saskatchewan and Manitoba had been trying for decades to wrest control of its natural resources from Ottawa, became free to manage its forests, under the Natural Resources Transfer Act. This could not have come at a more difficult time, for with the Depression there were no funds to continue the programs started by the federal government. Fires cost the province $1 million every year in lost timber. Some were set deliberately. "Everyone was hungry and there was no way to make a dollar," said a provincial ranger. "So people started setting fires. They got fifteen cents an hour and free grub to fight them."

It was only in the years following World War II that Alberta began to lay groundwork for one of the more progressive forestry programs in Canada. Protection of the watershed was the main priority. Saskatchewan was urging that this be a federal matter, but in a compromise in 1947 a joint federal-Alberta Eastern Rockies Conservation Board was established, under the chairmanship of Major-General Howard Kennedy, who had concluded his Royal Commission into Ontario Forests. A $4-million road system was built to give access to 15,000 square miles of forest in need of protection, and a network of fire towers was set up, the one at Ram Lookout perched on a 7,000-foot mountain with a view of 400 square miles.

In 1948 Alberta reorganized its forestry activities into the Alberta Forest Service under Eric S. Huestis, a former forest ranger with an interest in sustained yield. There had been an attempt at sustained yield in 1927 when a coal company in the central foothills had tried to assure a long-term supply of timber for its operations. Forty square miles had been set aside in the Clearwater Forest, but like most of the forestry in Canada it had foundered in the Depression. Now with both of Alberta's neighbours, British Columbia and Saskatchewan, passing legislation to encourage sustained yield, Alberta was ready to try again. Its lack of industrial development was actually a help, since Alberta had not had time to suffer from mistakes committed by the older provinces.

First it created a "Green Area," which separated the forest from regions better suited to farming. Some 150,000 square miles were set aside by the Alberta Forest Act of 1949, in the foothills and the north, to be managed to produce sustained yield. As yet, not one major forest industry had been attracted to the province.

"It consisted mostly of small operations and there was no particular control over them," said Desmond Crossley, who was then working for the Dominion Forestry Service near Calgary. "They were high-grading, taking out the biggest trees on the false assumption that that was good forestry. They took the oldest, biggest trees and left the smallest to grow a second crop, ignoring the fundamental fact that the small trees were smaller not because they were younger but because they were inferior. That was one thing we had to fight."

Another task was to organize an inventory. Questions had been coming in from pulp companies who wanted to know the amount of merchantable timber in the province, but no one knew the answers. Hiring Reginald D. Loomis, who had helped develop the science of aerial photography while working for the Dominion Forestry Service, Alberta began a major survey. In Reg Loomis the province had acquired more than a survey expert, for he and Crossley together were to lay the groundwork for sustained yield in the province.

As the government had hoped, the inventory survey, which took six years, opened the door to the pulp and paper industry, though as it happened none of the companies that had been making inquiries was interested at the time. Then Frank Ruben, a California entrepreneur, visited his ailing Bryan Mountain coal mine in the foothills west of Edmonton in 1949. The railways had switched from steam to diesel, and he had been unable to get preferential freight rates to develop markets farther afield. So, being a pragmatic man, he took advantage of the wealth of water and timber in the foothills to establish the Northwestern Pulp and Power Company and went into partnership with one of the biggest forest products firms in the United States, the St. Regis Paper Company of New York. It then remained to choose a chief forester.

After offering the job to Loomis, who turned it down, they approached Des Crossley, who had been doing silvicultural surveys for the new company in his spare time. After graduating from the University of Toronto school of forestry in 1935, Crossley, who came from Lloydminster, on the Alberta–Saskatchewan border, took a job with the federal Forestry Service, teaching farmers to plant windbreaks around their homesteads. At the end of the war, which he spent in the air force as a navigator and commander of training schools, he rejoined the Forestry Service as a senior researcher at the Kananaskis Forest Experiment Station in Alberta.

"Bob Ruben, Frank's son, was the man in charge of North-western Pulp and Power," Crossley recalled, "but coal and oil were his fields and he had no knowledge of forestry. He was working closely with Pete Hart, the woodlands manager for St. Regis in Maine and the lake states.

"I said, 'I'm very interested, but with one consideration, which is very important to me. You've got to assure me that you are going to carry out meaningful forest management.' Pete Hart looked at me and said, 'Why shouldn't we?' I said, 'Well, nobody else in Canada does.' Obligations to sustain the yield were generally being ignored without reprisal in other provinces.

"Hart said, 'Well, the government insists on it, under the agreement.' So I told them, 'OK, under those circumstances I will be happy to join you.' Several people had expressed surprise and concern that I would leave the shelter of a good position as a civil servant to enter a hazardous employment in a province with no track record for enlightened forestry. But from my point of view this was an opportunity to satisfy my obsession to demonstrate that our forests should and could be managed as a renewable resource without pillaging the land. The fact this could be undertaken on the finest piece of timberland in Alberta was an obvious plus."

Crossley, at the age of forty-five, had spent fifteen years in forest research. "It was becoming increasingly evident that our published research was attracting no more than cursory attention from forest operators and provincial bureaucratic managers," he said. "At the same time disenchantment was setting in over the lack of research leadership from Ottawa. I had put out feelers among the forest companies in British Columbia for employment as a silviculturist, but I was never convinced they considered silviculture anything but window dressing. The silvicultural programs, I felt, would be the first to be axed in the event of any financial setbacks. So my future changed dramatically when I became chief forester of Northwest Pulp and Power, with the assurance that sustained yield was a sincere goal and that the responsibility would be mine."

Hinton, where the mill was to be built, was a CNR whistle stop with a population of 200, an area with only sixty growing days a year where farming had never taken hold, but trees grew

18. *As chief forester for the major North American pulp and paper company St.Regis, at Hinton, Alberta, Desmond I. Crossley, in cooperation with the provincial government, helped to establish one of the best industrial woodlands policies in Canada during the 1950s.*

well. Crossley, whose first job was to build up a team of foresters, had difficulty finding men with experience in intensive forestry. Many were hired right out of university and assigned field work so they could learn Crossley's brand of forestry. "We wanted the staff to be involved from the start in the planning stages so they'd be firmly committed to objectives," he said. "We encouraged initiative but used the team approach. It soon became obvious I was not easily satisfied."

At the ministry, Loomis was to play a major role in Alberta's first forest management agreement. A graduate of the University of New Brunswick forestry school, Loomis had developed a deep concern over the failure of provincial administrators to commit government and industry to sustained yield management in the east, where he had worked in several provinces. This concern was apparent in his contributions to the Northwestern Forest Management Agreement.

"Des and I worked together," Loomis said. "The drafting of the first document had been done by Ruben and a government official who was not a forester and did not know about sustained yield. Then it was turned over to the Alberta Forest Service and to me. There was nothing in it about regenerating

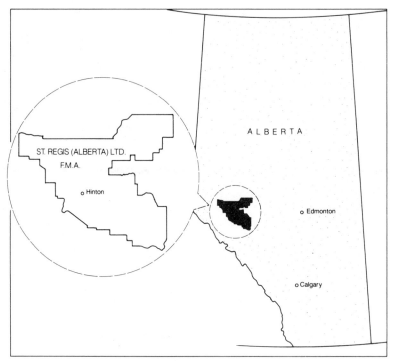

*As the first pulp and paper company to benefit from the Alberta
government's enlightened forest management policy in the 1950s, St.
Regis (Alberta) Ltd., leasing 3,000 square miles of foothills forest
adjacent to Jasper National Park, is something of a showplace for
Canadian forestry.*

the forest, so I managed to get in a clause about sustained yield.
That opened the door to good forest management. Des took
over and did a damn good job."

To feed the pulp mill on the banks of the Athabasca, 130
miles west of Edmonton, the company leased 3,000 square
miles of white spruce and lodge-pole pine in the rolling foothill
country. Tenure was for twenty years, renewable for another
twenty upon satisfactory performance. "I cannot overem-
phasize the importance of that provision," Crossley said. "It
was the cornerstone to success that no other province could at
the time bring itself to accommodate." The government oblig-
ingly set aside an equal area of adjoining forest in case the
company should need it later, but since the original lease was
managed so that it sustained the mill, the option was never
taken up.

"Reg and I were reaching back into our university training," Crossley said. "They had taught sustained yield and this sort of thing in university, although they had down-played it and said, 'It won't be any good to you.' Most of it was theory. We knew what foresters were trained to do, but most of them were not using that knowledge. Here was an opportunity. Here it was all new, with no past policies for the government to protect. At the Alberta Forest Service, Huestis accepted what Reg wanted to do and sold the idea to the government. Our success has come out of the initial co-operation, and hard-headed give and take."

There were conflicts, the first over the question of clear-cutting. Crossley had done research on clear-cutting and believed the only way to deal with an aging timber stand was to clear-cut and start a new crop, because the old timber stopped growing and became a home for insect epidemics and fire. A third of the company's forest was old growth, some of it 400 years old, that had escaped the big fires of the 1880s; those fires had regenerated, in the other two-thirds of the limits, clean stands of healthy, maturing trees.

"I argued that the over-mature timber had to be clear-cut," said Crossley. "That's what it lends itself to. It was all more or less the same age. We felt we should follow the example of nature—cutting it, however, rather than burning it as nature does. We had quite a fight over that at first, even with Reg Loomis, but then he came around and said, 'OK, you make sense. But we want you to do other types of cutting, too, selective cutting.' But we never did, and no one pressed the issue. We introduced regular clear-cutting into Alberta where in the past it had mostly been done to clean up areas that had suffered blow-down from high winds." At first, clear-cut blocks, or strips, were limited to thirty-five acres in spruce or 100 acres in the faster-growing pine. In time regulations were revised to allow cuts of 300 acres.

In 1956, just as the $55-million mill at Hinton was about to open, Northwestern experienced its first setback. "We got four huge fires through our lease, burning two and a half per cent of our forest in one summer. It was a dry year and the fires just kept going, started by carelessness for the most part, two of them by oil explorers. Those fires scared the pants off everybody, for such losses were far beyond what any forest management program could live with."

Government and company set out to solve the problem together. Aerial patrols were stepped up and more fire towers built. Since some fire loss is inevitable, no matter how efficient the protection program, it was decided that the average annual acceptable loss would be 2,000 acres, a tenth of one per cent. Fire suppression programs were developed that held it to less than that. The provincial forest service now boasts one of Canada's most efficient fire control systems. As part of its training program at the provincial Forest Technology School, it set up the first forest-fire simulator in Canada, which presents realistically the sort of conditions trainee rangers can expect to encounter in the woods.

The work of Crossley, for industry, and that of Loomis, on behalf of government, were not the only factors, of course, in the development of Alberta forest management. Their work was adapted and refined into new forest management agreements, for other companies operating farther north around Grande Prairie and Whitecourt, by government foresters like Robert Steele and F.W. McDougall, both deputy ministers of renewable resources.

The introduction of the quota system has been particularly promising. Under this system each licensee of Crown timber receives permission to harvest a specific quota of spruce or lodge-pole pine, which he must cut to government standards and regenerate, whereupon he becomes eligible for a permit to cut a second block. To assist in the regeneration of the forests, the government has established the Pine Ridge Forest Nursery at Smoky Lake, which is capable of producing forty million seedlings a year. The government also adopted "sequential use" of forest land; under this policy, while the new forests are growing towards the age when they can be harvested again, they can also be enjoyed by the public for outdoor recreation.

On a bright June morning, the white peaks of the Rockies rimming the western edges of the foothills, valleys, and plateaus of the St. Regis timberlands, Des Crossley put on his bush clothes and hard hat, packed a lunch, and together with Jack Wright, his successor as chief forester at what is now known as St. Regis (Alberta), drove out with a visitor to view the work of twenty-eight years. "One of the advantages of practising forestry in the same place," Crossley observed, "is the opportunity to become thoroughly familiar with every nook and cranny." In the days when the Hudson's Bay Company owned the Prairie provinces, this territory high up the Athabasca River was the richest in Canada for furs.

The first stop was at one of the two areas where Crossley had encountered difficulty in coaxing the forest to grow. On the

19. At Hinton, foresters have long been cutting timber carefully in patterns that conform to the lie of the land and encourage natural as well as artificial regeneration. Here one can see large stands of original timber interspersed with fresh cut-overs and new growth.

highway west into Jasper National Park, Camp One had been established in 1956, with 100 men clear-cutting old spruce. "It was a big operation and we didn't want to diddle it with one system in one stand of timber and another somewhere else," said Crossley. "We weren't European foresters. We didn't have the staff for that. We wanted one overall system that would work, and so we chose to clear-cut.

"That didn't help our public relations. People had never seen this type of cutting before. 'Why are you doing it?' they asked. 'We don't like it. Look at the mess you are leaving.' There were prairie farmers driving through who had summer-fallowed their land and left everything clean after the harvest and they thought this junk lying on the ground after the logging was just terrible.

"But we said, 'No, it's not terrible. It's exactly what we want, starting a new crop all the same age. Leaving the stumps and the terrain rough like that means seedlings can get a start in some sort of shelter among the hollows and crannies. It stops erosion. If water starts to move it will hit this junk left there and won't carry a silt load very far.'"

Now, a quarter of a century later, young trees were coming up amid the shrubs, grass, and weathered chunks of wood.

Stumps the size of manhole covers showed there had once been a fair number of large trees here, the biggest a 270-year-old white spruce 141 feet high and thirty-six inches in diameter at breast height.

The company got into planting in 1961, filling in gaps left in the natural regeneration. It had tried seeding, but rodents ate the seeds. As well as getting seedlings from government nurseries it established its own nursery, stealing pine cones from squirrel caches. In time it was planting three million seedlings a year.

Even when it was relying almost exclusively on natural regeneration, the company had ploughed or scarified the cut-over with anchor chains and patent ploughs hauled by tractors, to give seedlings a better purchase. "Without scarification there is no crop," Crossley said. But in one case scarification did not work, a cut-over north of Hinton where humus, duff, and debris had been too thick, covering the mineral soil to such a depth seeds could not germinate. This problem was solved by "prescribed burning," a controlled fire that burned down to the soil. Now lodge-pole pine, planted where slower-growing spruce once stood, was growing into a new forest.

Crossley recalled that when he started forest management at Hinton few people understood its meaning or intent. "We were haunted by the historical image of the ruthless timber exploiter who was allowed to tie up too much land, pollute the water, erode the soil, and fail to regenerate the forest he logged. We could have done without this burden. Public suspicion eventually goaded the Ministry of Lands and Forests to commission a study. We managed to satisfy this critical review and proved we could sustain the yield."

To facilitate management the 3,000-square-mile lease was divided into five "working circles," each regarded as a separate forest and in turn subdivided into "cutting compartments" of 25,000 acres. The company pursued a policy of harvesting half a given area at a time, leaving the rest to harvest later, which aids natural regeneration from standing seed sources and assures there is always enough standing timber to protect the land. This system left alternating blocks of sixty to eighty acres of cut-over and a similar amount of standing timber, like a patchwork quilt, sculpted to fit the contours of the hills. "Cutting cycles" assured there was new forest coming back up.

From the beginning, Crossley insisted that forest management be included in operational costs rather than capitalized, as was usual, over a long term. "The failure to conduct effective management could be traced not only to lack of tenure—the lack of assurance a company could reap what it sowed—but to the spectre of prohibitively expensive capital costs for forest renewal. We were not about to accept this widely held misconception. On the contrary, we reasoned that the existing stands ready for harvesting should fund the cost of forest renewal.

"Forest management in other parts of Canada usually foundered on fluctuating budgets, so I felt it important to establish a fixed forestry budget at Hinton. This was set at about ten per cent of the cost of providing harvested wood to the mill. It was no munificent sum. We had to use our imaginations to cut expenses without sacrificing quality."

We were travelling, as Crossley spoke, along the fifty-seven-mile Forest Management Trail established to show the public what forest management is all about. There were signs along the road describing when an area had been logged, whether it had been planted or left to regenerate naturally, and what silviculture practices had been applied. Illustrating what happens in a forest allowed to die of old age, the company had left a large stand of 400-year-old white spruce and fir that had escaped the fires of the 1880s. Choked with underbrush and disintegrating trees susceptible to insects, fire, and windthrow, these old woods seemed devoid of animal life. In other areas there had been occasional sighting of game, and once a whole herd of caribou. Here there was nothing.

"In my book, clear-cutting has been the best thing for wildlife management," said Crossley. "But we still get screams from fish and wildlife people who think we can improve on things. We accommodate them as best we can, but by and large game animals love these cut-over areas because the forage has increased tremendously in the new growth. What's bothering the wildlife people is that the game census shows no increase, but the reason for that is there is so much poaching going on."

Here and there along the Forest Management Trail were some of the 3,000 sample plots, each a fifth of an acre, the company established in 1957 to provide a continuous inventory. Every tree on a sample plot bore an aluminum tag and was inspected every five or ten years. "We put a lot of work into doing it carefully," said Crossley. "We needed an ongoing record of growth, volume, and yield, basic information on which to work out our allowable cut. I think the lack of good information has been the curse of forest inventories across Canada."

The eastern foothills are not as good for growth as the wetter regions of the B.C. coast or the Atlantic provinces, and while lodge-pole pine may reach a height of eight feet in a decade, white spruce takes twice as long. Crossley had planted a lot of lodge-pole pine.

"I was interested in it when nobody else was," he said. "Everybody thought spruce was the big thing. The main attribute of lodge-pole pine is that it is straight. The Indians used to come into the foothills and cut it for lodge poles. They are not big trees, but they are good for pulp and are the easiest to manage."

There had been a time when Crossley had agreed with the West Coast American proponents of "agro-forestry," in which woodlands are domesticated so that they are more like corn fields than natural wild forestland. Over the years he had changed his mind. His approach at Hinton was to optimize yields while producing man-made forests that look like wilderness. "I no longer feel we can always entertain the luxury of maximum wood production," he said. "Our wild forests encompass too many other resources and public amenities to allow me to remain comfortable in the atmosphere of completely domesticating the forest."

The idea of multiple use of forest lands, nowadays a major concern to foresters trying to manage timber limits, was only emerging in Canada when Crossley went to work at Hinton. It had been the theme of the Canadian Institute of Forestry Convention in Banff in 1951 and the World Forestry Congress in Seattle in 1960. Multiple use encompasses timber, water, fish, and wildlife and, in some areas, grazing; but so long as timber had priority, Crossley, for one, had no serious objection to it. Since those days, competition for land had come from unexpected quarters.

Though the Alberta oil boom had started in the late 1940s with discovery of the Leduc reserve due south of Edmonton, there had been no anticipation of the wealth of oil that might lie under the Alberta foothills when the company commenced operations. Then the oil explorers appeared, bulldozing seismic lines through the forest so they could test the land for oil and gas, destroying more timber than was harvested. A seismic line twenty feet wide might run for twenty miles, and so many have been run through the forest that, when they are combined with well sites, roads, pipelines, and power right-of-ways, a timber licence holder can find himself in a quasi-industrial landscape.

A more recent, and potentially more serious, conflict between renewable-resource forest management and non-renewable exploitation was the decision to open the forest to strip mining for coal. There had been coal mines operating in the foothills but they were of the conventional type, tunnelling underground. Most had closed in the early 1950s with the loss of markets, but in the 1970s oil companies, seeking to diversify, had begun to explore for open-pit mines to obtain thermal coal for electricity. More than a quarter of the St. Regis timber lease lay in areas designated as coal reserves.

In an effort to rationalize conflicting needs, the government appointed a Forestry Panel of the Environment Council of Alberta, chaired by Professor Bruce Dancik of the forestry faculty of the University of Alberta. "The serious and widespread effects of the oil and gas exploration and production industries in the Green Area must receive more attention and control," the panel said. "The great value of the extracted resource does not justify substantial impairment of other resources. Many of the problems appear to relate to practices instituted when it was necessary to attract these industries to Alberta. That situation no longer exists. It is time for the petroleum industry to accept its responsibility as a user, along with others, of the Green Area."

The committee suggested a system of portable seismic operations instead of bulldozing the forest. Coal mining, it said, should be approached cautiously. "Unless it can be established that mined lands can be reclaimed at least to their present productivity, approval of coal mining should be deferred."

Some 9,000 acres in the Obed area near Hinton, lands St. Regis had replanted after logging, had already been earmarked for strip mining. The coal company was committed to filling in the pit and reforesting, but foresters feared a whole generation of trees would be lost. Nor did they feel it had been amply demonstrated that adequate reforestation after strip mining was possible. Other land provided by the government to replace the land lost to coal mining would be too far from the mill. The company had prided itself on being one of the few in Canada that had maintained a constant timber-hauling distance of forty or fifty miles, thus assuring its wood costs remained competitive.

The future of the forests worried Crossley just as it had years earlier when, as newly elected president of the Canadian Institute of Forestry, he said: "The picture of the ugly waste that past mismanagement practices have left in the public's mind will not be easy to eradicate. . . . A polluted forest is no more appealing than a polluted river and examples of the attractiveness of a managed forest are seldom available to overcome the accepted public conception that forest land pollution is inevitable."

"I was always interested in forestry during my travels across the country," Crossley said on our visit to the St. Regis timberlands, "and just couldn't believe what they were doing in the east in those days. It didn't make sense. A province like Ontario, the wealthiest in Canada, had agreements then that were supposed to operate the forest on sustained yield and to regenerate cut-over land, but people were signing the agreements and then ignoring them."

Crossley was given the Achievement Award of the Province of Alberta "in recognition of outstanding service in the field of forestry." The Canadian Institute of Forestry awarded him its Forestry Achievement medal and his Alma Mater, the Forestry School at the University of Toronto, granted him an honorary degree. He had joined that small band that had advanced the cause of forestry, and now, in his seventies and retired, he was leaving to others the battle to maintain a foothills forest that had stood as a model. "This is damn good timber," he said, as he looked out over Barbara Valley, where the dark green trees spread out to the skyline. "It's one of the best timber limits in the country. Nothing down east can compare with this."

▲ ▲ ▲ ▲ ▲ ▲ ▲ 9 ▲ ▲ ▲ ▲ ▲ ▲ ▲

Spreading the bad news

"THERE IS A CONSENSUS ACROSS THE COUNTRY from forestry people—whether they be from governments, industry or other forestry groups or associations —that inadequate forest renewal is indeed a serious and fundamental forestry problem. This concern is not yet felt by the general public or by politicians and there is real need...to 'spread the bad news.'" Statement by the National Forest Regeneration Conference, Quebec City, October 1977.

FOR KENNETH HEARNDEN OF THUNDER BAY, good forestry is not only a science but also a matter of Christian ethics. A religious man dedicated in his spare time to church affairs, Hearnden has been known to take forestry to church. Addressing a gathering of Wesley United Church one morning, he recalled the many references to trees and forests in the Bible.

"The threat of destruction of the forest by fire as an important part of the action taken by the Lord to punish an unfaithful people is recorded in Jeremiah 21 (verse 14)," he said, and recalled how the lands of the Bible have since lost their lifegiving forests.

"We have had developing for a very long time in Canada

what I have termed a silent, invisible crisis," he told the congregation. "We have been living richly by the liquidation of our forest capital, like a prodigal son, and are beginning to experience, here and there across the country, the consequences. . . .effective Christian stewardship of our forests will call upon all of us for the sacrifice, in some measure, of the gratification of our material desires. It will require the practice of rather more moderation and careful conservation than we have considered heretofore. These, I suggest, are not unreasonable conditions for Christians who are dedicated not only to personal, spiritual salvation, but are concerned also for the well-being of future generations."

Ken Hearnden is much the same breed of forester as the late Ellwood Wilson, with the courage to speak out at the risk of unpopularity. He is known in Toronto, in company boardrooms and Queen's Park forestry offices, as a gadfly or, as he laughingly remembers, the "Ogre of the North." A tall, slow-spoken man, whose serious demeanour is frequently brightened by wry humour, Hearnden was a prize scholar. After graduation he worked for the Canadian Forestry Service before joining the Abitibi Power and Paper Company at Sault Ste. Marie in 1946.

"Back in the 1940s when I got out of the University of Toronto, nobody dreamed there would be a problem of pulpwood supplies to run the mills," Hearnden recalled. "The inventories were saying we might have wood for 300 years. So why would anyone be interested in sustained yield? The usual response when a mill needed more was simply to exploit more and more untouched forest."

Hearnden's concern for the forest owes a lot to the influence of several foresters he met at Abitibi. "The first of these was A.J. 'Jack' Auden, who was my boss at one time and who gave me some knowledge of the historical background of forestry in northwest Ontario," Hearnden says. "Jack was an idealist and a man whose perspective extended well beyond immediate pressures of getting wood out to the mill. He believed in sustained yield forest management and encouraged an independent viewpoint."

Auden was noted for a laudable, if unsuccessful, effort to encourage "forest communities," to assure the continuity and integrity of places where forest work was the "only game in town." The idea was a return to the simple life of earlier times, but with mechanization such a community had become anach-

20. As an industrial forester and later as chairman at the forestry school at Lakehead University in Thunder Bay, Kenneth W. Hearnden has been a persistent critic of both government and industry policies in the Boreal forest.

ronistic. It had been tried by the Forestry Commission in the United Kingdom; it developed a number of such villages, which all failed. It had been tried at the Ontario-Minnesota Paper Company's Camp Robinson, which flourished briefly and disappeared. Auden proposed the plan to the Kennedy

Royal Commission in the 1940s, to which he was an adviser, but despite its promise of stability for forest management in remote areas, it came to nothing, and the only monument to his work is the name of the community of Auden in northern Ontario.

"Auden's successor in 1954, Max MacLaggan, gave me support to initiate some modest pilot-plant silvicultural projects, but he left the division after differences on a number of issues with head office people." Hearnden remembers discussing the mysteries of logging operations with a veteran camp foreman some thirty years ago. He asked the old lumberjack how he determined the effective life of a pulpwood camp. "His response was simple and direct. 'We start from the outhouse and then cut outwards. When the cutters can't walk any farther, we move the camp.' In that forthright, unadorned, unequivocal statement can be found, in large measure, the story of Ontario forestry for the past 150 years. Substitute 'ride' for 'walk' and it is equally valid today."

One of Hearnden's duties as divisional forester for Abitibi, responsible for management planning over 7,400 square miles of Crown and freehold land in northwestern Ontario, was to record the extent of areas cut and the volumes of timber extracted. There he met Leopold Vidlak, employed by Abitibi to study ways to renew the forest. "By 1959, after many field trips together, Vidlak and I concluded there would be timber supply problems within twenty to twenty-five years. Such predictions were derided, of course, by many."

Hearnden made himself unpopular with his employers when he gave an outspoken speech to the Ontario Professional Foresters Association, a new organization that brought industry and government foresters together to compare notes and generally enhance the cause of forestry. Hearnden told them that with few exceptions an industrial forester had "neither the authority, nor the responsibility, for the management of the forest areas with which he is directly concerned." He said he was using the word "management" in the literal sense, rather than "the indiscriminate, figurative uses to which it is often put in the realm of public relations to describe the operations of the forest industries. The industrial forester is not only unable to practise his profession; he does not feel free to express his views on it and seldom does. This is equally true of foresters in government employ."

There was still only one professional forester in Canada for every 1.1 million acres of accessible forest, a much smaller ratio than considered necessary in Europe where there was one forester for every 34,000 acres. Moreover, most industrial foresters were hired not to practise forest renewal but for one of the jobs described as "the big three"—timber cruiser, logging superintendent, or fire fighter.

The practice of forestry had been rare. "The guys who did the logging were the ones who got the promotions," Hearnden said. "I was chairing a panel on introducing silviculture into logging camps in 1957 when a company forester stood up and said, 'We have no right to deviate from established practice because we don't know enough.' Another, a chief forester, said, 'We are already practising silviculture. What's all this talk about anyway?' But if you look now at the limits for which he was responsible you'll find an inferior forest, with badly stocked cut-over areas and a thick growth of balsam fir."

Like the clouds that dot a tranquil sky, storm warnings were building. The Montebello conference of 1966 had begun to spread the bad news. At an annual meeting of the Canadian Institute of Forestry, New Brunswick forestry consultant E.S. Fellows declared that governments should be alerted to the consequences of "a gradual shift into a shortage of timber." Translating this into a resolution, the CIF asked each province "to give serious thought and study to economic incentives designed to encourage improvements in yield from managed forests."

The Science Council of Canada joined the chorus. There would be a wood shortage, it predicted, though adding it would be regional and local and only at the turn of the century. The Ontario Economic Council, on the other hand, believed local shortages were already apparent, otherwise why were mills trucking logs over such costly distances? "Producers who cut within thirty miles of their mills forty-five years ago," it said in 1970, "have had to extend their operations until now they haul distances of 135 to 150 miles."

Apart from attempts to control fire and—notably in New Brunswick—to hold the budworm at bay by aerial spraying first with DDT and, later, when that proved environmentally harmful, with more sophisticated pesticides, forest management was in its infancy. It was still predicated, as Hearnden put it, "on the orderly liquidation of virgin stands to provide for the levying of stumpage assessments, taxes, rentals, and penalties." The industry was placing its bets on continually improving milling techniques to solve problems of diminishing timber. More progress had been made in milling since the war than had been made in silviculture in a century. Four species, spruce, balsam fir, jack pine, and western hemlock, provided most of the Canadian pulpwood, but there was reason to believe that with proper technology almost any species might be used for pulp, including hardwoods such as aspen, alder, and maple. Some mills were already utilizing chips left over from sawmills and veneer plants.

By this time, in fact, improved technology in both the mill and the woods enabled the industry to operate on a progressively poorer forest resource base. The average tree felled in eastern Canada in the 1850s, for example, was estimated to have contained more than 400 board feet of lumber. By 1970 the average was more like seventy board feet, and the industry was having to haul and process six times as many trees to produce the same amount of lumber.

"Industry has tended to maintain over the years that it doesn't matter what grows on cut-over areas," argued Hearnden. "They said mills could use it, whatever it was, as technology advanced. But foresters believe that if Canada is to keep its position in the world market, it will have to grow a quality forest in which black spruce, especially, is assisted to grow and hold its primary position as the most important pulpwood species."

With no national guidelines, and each province going its own way, the forestry situation across Canada by the early 1970s was, in Des Crossley's words, "chaotic." He deplored "Ottawa's proclivity to hide behind the skirts of its constitutional responsibilities, its retreat into the area of research, its general reluctance to consider new ideas and solutions to meet large-demand projects for wood, and its lack of a national forest policy."

The Newfoundland Forest Service, aided by money provided by the Department of Regional Economic Expansion (DREE), was attempting some forestry work, but the two companies controlling the forest had been under no obligation to practise sustained yield, and their ninety-nine-year leases would run well into the twenty-first century. In this pulpwood province, with dense stands of spruce and balsam fir, the forest provided more employment than any industry except fisheries. Since its high point in the 1950s, the harvest had been declining, even though a government commission had said that with proper forestry the yield could be increased by twenty per cent.

In Nova Scotia the fact that three-quarters of the forest was privately owned had hampered efforts to obtain federal funding. Management policy was lacking on Crown land. Over-cutting had persisted from the time Fernow had surveyed the woods in 1912. Since about half of New Brunswick's forests were on Crown land, the authorities theoretically had more leeway to plan than in Nova Scotia, but in fact little reforestation had been done except by Irving Forest Products.

In Quebec forestry was practised on a limited scale by a few companies. As in Ontario, timber limits were so large there had been no incentive to sustain the yield, and the harvesting of only sixty per cent of the allowable cut contributed to a false sense of security. Since licences ran from year to year—readily renewed so long as token management was shown—the companies complained of insecurity of tenure.

In Ontario results of a regeneration survey had startled those who thought the trees were "forever." It seemed that two thirds of the annual cut-over was failing to regenerate naturally; efforts at artificial regeneration were inadequate. Since 1962 when the government assumed responsibility for renewing the forest, foresters had been fighting an uphill battle, for in the first year of the program, funding had been cut in half, with a promise the difference would be made up "next year." By the time the second year came, priorities were changing and the budget was cut again. By the third year the program had been seriously reduced.

On the prairies Manitoba had been talking sustained yield since it had become a catch phrase in the 1940s, but licence holders were under no obligation to practise it. Hardly a third of the cut-overs were getting attention. There had been lumbering in Manitoba's northern forests, which occupy about half the province, since the 1880s for lumber for regional use. The Pas Lumber Company, which operated from 1910 to 1958 before packing up and moving to greener fields in British Columbia, was by far the biggest producer, though in fact most of its lumber originated in neighbouring areas of Saskatchewan and was floated down the Carrot and Saskatchewan rivers. Manitoba had got into the pulp business with construction of a mill at Pine Falls in the 1920s and shipped large amounts of spruce pulpwood to the United States as late as the 1940s. By the late 1960s The Pas, like Pine Falls, had become a pulp complex, but run by a Crown corporation, Manfor. By the 1970s the industry was beginning to assume more responsibility for forest renewal and a Manitoba forest management policy was emerging.

Saskatchewan had acquired a pulp complex in the late 1960s.

Established by an American group, the Prince Albert Pulp Company has since become a provincial government enterprise turning out bleached kraft and lumber. Committed officially to "a yield on a continuous production basis in perpetuity," Saskatchewan required licensees to take responsibility for reforestation and silviculture, though with government assistance.

In Alberta the progress that began with Des Crossley's work at St. Regis had spread in similar patterns to other pulp companies starting up. The government insisted that the companies reforest at their own expense within ten years after cutting, receiving in return the right to pay reduced stumpage or royalty rates. More than ninety per cent of all cut-overs were being successfully stocked seven years after cutting and the Alberta government was attempting to plant the backlog of unsatisfactorily restocked land that had built up before 1960.

British Columbia's unregenerated backlog was estimated at twenty million acres, with only 100,000 acres being planted every year. The forest industry had assumed responsibility for reforestation on tree farm licences, and the forest policy and tenure system was enlightened, even if good forest management was not being practised on a wide enough basis to sustain the yield.

"When I joined the Reforestation Division of the Forest Service in 1957 there was very little emphasis on tree planting," recalled Bruce Devitt, now chief forester with Pacific Forest Products in Victoria, where he runs that company's reforestation program. "In fact some people believed that all the planting that had to be done in B.C. was nearly completed. That of course was nonsense. Later we went through every conceivable way of trying to attain natural regeneration but finally it dawned on us that we couldn't achieve natural regeneration in the time frame we wanted. Now we know that natural regeneration is not necessarily the cheapest and best way.

"So then we went through a terrific expansion in artificial regeneration—from producing eight million seedlings for planting every year to seventy-five million. The five-year program of the Ministry of Forests today has a target of growing 150 million seedlings annually, but I can remember thinking years ago that we should be planting somewhere around 300 million a year."

If proper regeneration had commenced in Canada in the 1920s, when so many of the major timber licences were handed out, it should have been possible by the 1970s to begin harvesting a second crop. There was still enough mature forest left to aid in establishing new forests, however, and the Ontario Economic Council urged that action be taken right away so that an industry that should be self-supporting would not become a drain on the public purse. It said the principle, adopted in Alberta, that "he who logs also reforests" should be made general across Canada; that profits from a current crop should, as in farming, contribute towards growing a second crop as good as, or better than, the first.

The argument over who should pay, government or industry, had been going on since enlightened foresters had begun to point out that nature was going to need help in renewing the forest. R.D. Craig, a forester with vast experience across Canada and head of the Economics Division of the Dominion Forestry Service before World War II, had believed the answer was simple. "On the licensed lands the state and the licensee should share the responsibility for the perpetuation of the forests," he said. "At present the licensees are inclined to shirk their responsibility. The excuse offered is that their tenure being insecure, they are not justified in making investments for which they may never secure returns. As a matter of fact, their licences are for the most part renewable in perpetuity though considerations of royalty, rental and regulations are subject to change."

A quarter of a century later, however, industry was still insisting that government was solely responsible for forest renewal, causing Hearnden to comment, "I think the argument is basically a smoke-screen to hide the desire not to commit any funds to forestry. It seems to me that no government would ever deny a mill employing hundreds or thousands of people the right to continue to exist by depriving the mill of its wood supply."

There had been cases when government had reclaimed Crown land, but never a company's whole concession. In the 1930s the Hepburn government in Ontario, seeking timberland to attract new mills and boost employment, took back a sizeable chunk of the limits controlled by Great Lakes Forest Products. The Quebec government had reclaimed, for a wildlife park, Crown land that Consolidated Bathurst had reforested in the St. Maurice Valley. Whether in Ontario or British Columbia, where leases ran for a renewable twenty-one years, or in New Brunswick, where they ran for thirty to fifty years, uncertain tenure was the reason given when a company was asked why it did not renew and manage its cut-over lands.

"Tenure can be a major factor," acknowledged Professor Dan MacArthur of the forestry department of Macdonald Agricultural College, McGill University, outside Montreal. "If the government should say to Company X, 'Here is a tract capable of supplying one and a half times your current needs of raw material. You may either buy it or lease it but this is your limit; you get no more,' then management would become a live issue for the company. I guess that a few companies might buy but more would not. Companies have grown into the habit either of having much more land than they really need or being sure that new limits can be found. There probably has never been any real pressure for practical management."

By the 1970s, however, governments were beginning to change their old passive supervisory role into a "hands-on" involvement that was making industry uneasy. New Brunswick led the way. After two centuries of high-grading, the pressure on the New Brunswick forest—that is, the harvest per acre of productive land—was the heaviest in Canada. The number of sawmills had declined, in part because of the depletion of sawlog-quality timber. The number of pulp and paper mills had climbed to eleven, and wood accounted for half of all manufacturing. In 1972 an Industrial Inquiry Commission on Pulp and Paper expressed concern over the industry's ability to provide stable employment. The rate of harvest was overtaking the allowable cut.

A report on forest resources recommended controls on clear-cutting, better utilization of the harvest, and investment in forest renewal. "There is now no available surplus of spruce, fir or pine to be had for the taking. Whatever more is needed must be cultivated and once we start cultivating more wood we should also cultivate better quality wood." To the consterna-tion of industry, it called for a revolutionary change in the allocation of New Brunswick's Crown land. Instead of the traditional "area agreements" in which companies rented des-ignated areas from which to supply their mills, industry would be guaranteed timber under "volume" agreements. The gov-ernment would gradually assume responsibility for forest man-agement, and in some cases for logging, under a Provincial Forest Authority. Critics saw this as tantamount to taking away timber limits and replacing them with a "woodpile."

The Forest Authority set up a pilot project on a million acres of Crown land held by Consolidated Bathurst in the northeast corner of the province to co-ordinate the harvest, assuring a stable supply of sawlogs to lumber mills that had been experiencing shortages. This government attempt to take on the functions of private enterprise was costly and cumbersome and finally ran into market problems, but it did set the stage for a dynamic new policy in the late 1970s.

Saskatchewan, too, opted for more government intervention. In 1973 the NDP government in Regina declared that no company would be allowed "exclusive control over the timber in any geographic area" and began renegotiating Crown licences. The government's Saskatchewan Forest Products Corporation was given more power.

But it was in Quebec that reforms were to be most dramatic. There had been pressure for change, for apart from piecemeal alterations, legislation had been on the books for a century and a quarter. The companies had been paying rent and royalties, carrying out inventories, and practising fire suppression, and some were submitting harvesting plans. In exchange they had exclusive rights to the wood on their limits. Government regulations prohibited cutting trees less than sixty years old; otherwise companies were free to practise forest management or not.

Public demand for reform had been rising with the growth of *maîtres chez nous* nationalism. The pulp industry had always been dominated by anglophones. There was a growing dislike of the colonial aspects of the industry, a dislike even of phrases like "concession" and "timber limits" and of the practice of putting up barriers on logging roads to isolate leased public land. Lumber mills, which unlike pulp mills were frequently owned by local people, had been complaining of the need for better sawlog supplies. To accommodate them, the government had created Domanial forests, which differed from the old Crown limits in that cutting could only be done by special arrangement.

Public hearings began in 1965, and seven years later a Liberal government White Paper, *Exposé sur la politique forestière*, recommended fundamental changes. It had found a confusing mélange of management strategies, almost as many as there were concession holders. For generations the forest had been carved up in a haphazard way, sometimes not even in accord with the wishes of the companies involved. The forest had become older, but because they had so much, companies often failed to log off the more mature timber while it still had value, so it lingered on into useless old age.

21. Once blessed with thick forests of tall trees, large areas of the Eastern Townships of Quebec have been reduced to unproductive scrub by generations of over-cutting and lack of forest management. Many smaller mills have had to close down over the years, and the surviving mills have often had to import the wood they need from the United States.

As in most of Canada, wasteful logging methods and questionable management decisions were gobbling up younger timber that would have continued to appreciate in value with a few more years of growth. Wood costs were increasing, outstripping those of the southern United States. The Gaspé, the St. Maurice Valley, and the Abitibi region reported local shortages, as did the area north of Montreal. There was a shortage of hardwood in the Eastern Townships, where furniture factories were having to import wood from the United States, as did factories in southern Ontario.

Quebec and Ontario have always been Canada's major hardwood lumber producers and until the 1960s ran a thriving export trade to the United States. Because of diminishing supplies this had changed and Canada had become a net importer of hardwood, buying from the United States twice as much as it exported, the most important imports being white oak, ash, mahogany, and walnut. (Canada has been able to avoid, however, importing large quantities of its national tree, the maple.) In the Eastern Townships of Quebec, where the old hardwood stands of thirty or fifty years ago have largely disappeared, one large company at Cowansville, Vilas Furniture Company, has to import three-quarters of its wood. Hardwood for veneer and plywood has been very hard to secure, and in some areas mills have had to close.

But shortage of hardwoods was only one of the concerns that led to the revolution in the industry in Quebec. At the urging of Kevin Drummond, minister of lands and forests and an anglophone from Westmount with a belief in the principles of *maîtres chez nous*, the Liberal government in 1973 overturned the old licensing system. During the next decade, control of Crown land was to be gradually withdrawn from eighty companies, including the Big Nine pulp and paper corporations. With government assuming responsibility for management, including planting and silviculture, each mill would be guaranteed an adequate supply under ten- to twenty-year "volume agreements." The government made provision to pay industry $70 million for roads and other infrastructure. The wood was to be cut by the companies under government supervision. Some companies at first welcomed this "retrocession," as it was called, as a simpler way of obtaining wood without the cost and trouble of managing the forest, but problems began to emerge—including the separation of cutting from regeneration.

"With retrocession, a lot of interest in forestry was lost by the companies," said Louis-Jean Lussier of Quebec City. Frequently a consultant to government and industry, Lussier was to serve, between 1975 and 1977, as director of the government's Groupe de Conseiller en Gestion des forêts (COGEF), charged with developing an overall management plan.

"On paper it looked OK; in practice it was very difficult," said Lussier. "The problem is that you need agreements covering the area being logged as well as agreements guaranteeing a certain volume of wood to the mill. Under retrocession the companies were not responsible for managing the areas they were logging. If the company knows that right after logging it also has to reforest and manage the land and put it back into production in five years or so, I'm sure it will make an effort to prepare the site. Otherwise it will try to minimize costs, take out only the best trees, leave the slash, and so on."

One way the government had planned to implement retrocession was by creating the Société de Gestion forestière to co-ordinate management, but this proposal met opposition and was shelved. Quebec had also planned to beef up its forestry staff by hiring professionals no longer needed by industry, but this too had to be curtailed because of constraints on the growth of the civil service. As time went on the government began to back away from retrocession; the policy had not been successful.

It did, however, strengthen its Crown corporation, Société de récupération, d'exploration et de développement forestière du Québec (Rexfor). Rexfor's role, when it was established in the 1960s, was to salvage and sell timber from the vast region to be flooded by Hydro Quebec's Manic V dam on the north shore of the St. Lawrence. It was typical of the lack of thought given to the forest that no one had considered salvaging the timber, and when it was decided to do so, pulp and paper companies were approached but showed no interest. Rexfor's mandate was extended to logging, reforestation, and the milling and selling of wood products. It began to work with private companies and developed into a unique organization, with 3,000 employees in twenty-eight localities from the Gaspé to Ville Marie on the northwestern border. Required to pay its own way, it was well suited to develop industrial forestry in regions that might have been bypassed by private companies.

In Ontario progress had been more pragmatic but the problems were often similar. Nine pulp companies occupied eighty

per cent, or 80,000 square miles, of the productive timberlands. Smaller outfits occupied another 7,000 square miles,
but as in Quebec they were finding difficulty in getting suitable
sawlogs. The large size of pulpwood limits meant that "allowable cut" had little meaning.

Since 1929 Ontario had been struggling with sustained
yield, but efforts to reforest 1,000 acres every year for sixty
years had been wrecked by the Depression. The Crown Timber
Act of 1954, which aimed to saddle industry with responsibility for regeneration, was taken seriously by two or three companies, given lip service by a few more, and ignored by the rest.
When the government, tired of arguing over tenure, standards
of regeneration, and reimbursement, regained responsibility in
1962, it ran up against the problem of separating logging from
regeneration.

In 1972, with world markets expanding, Ontario committed
itself to a major regeneration program, which it called a Forest
Production Policy. To increase yield per acre by fifty per cent, it
promised "to allocate funds, staff, equipment and nursery
expansions to regenerate sufficient cut-over areas in need of
artificial regeneration to sustain an annual cut of 9.1 million
cunits [a cunit is 100 cubic feet of solid wood] by the year
2020." Expenditures were tripled. By the mid-1970s the government was spending most of its direct forest revenue, $50
million, on the forests.

Despite these developments, Canada was losing its economic advantage as forests and milling techniques were
improved in Europe and the United States. Canadian wood
costs had almost doubled without any compensating increase
in productivity. Pulp mills designed to use softwoods were
finding themselves stranded in areas where there were only
hardwood and inferior softwood stands. Mills were aging,
failing to keep pace with technology. There had been little new
construction since the 1950s in eastern Canada, but thirty-
seven pulp and paper mills and fifty-two plywood plants had
been built in the American south, which was producing sixty-
three per cent of all U.S. pulp.

From Texas to North Carolina, where original forests had
long given way to cotton and tobacco fields, land had now
been reforested to fast-growing southern pine. The southern
states were planting 300 million trees a year, at a time when
Ontario, with Canada's largest provincial program, was only
planting 37 million. With careful seed selection and other

means the southern states were trying to double their allowable cut and boasted a survival rate thirty per cent higher than Canada's. They were successfully meeting the challenge of a growing market in a way that Canada was not.

British Columbia had tackled this problem by expanding its pulp industry into the interior, where before 1960 there had been only sawmills, but the lure of the American south was strong. MacMillan Bloedel cancelled plans to build an $86-million mill at Kitimat on the northern mainland, complaining of inadequate wood supply, and turned instead to Alabama to build a complex.

As for eastern Canada, there were few large forested areas left that could support new pulp mills. Timber cutting had been moving steadily north, and in Ontario ten per cent of the harvest was being cut north of the fiftieth parallel, particularly in the northwest, where neither the soil nor the climate gave the best tree growth. During the hearings of the Ontario Royal Commission on the Northern Environment, Justice E.P. Hartt concluded: "It is only in the West Patricia area of the northwest that major renewable timber resources remain. Even these resources are likely to be needed to supply the demands of existing mills, rather than to feed an expanding industry, and it will only be through vigorous steps to improve forest management that long-term shortages will be averted."

In one of those vast areas, south of Red Lake and seventy-five miles northeast of Kenora, the British-owned Reed Paper Ltd. made a controversial and unsuccessful bid in the late 1970s to establish a $400-million forest products complex for which it hoped to draw wood from a 19,000-square-mile area. Among those opposing it was Jim Foulds, NDP member of the legislature for Port Arthur, who maintained that "no single company should have the sole rights to the last remaining timber stands in Ontario." Other groups, including Indian bands, protested the Reed proposal. At the Lakehead University forestry school, Ken Hearnden said that the western section of the proposed timber concession was covered by a thin layer of mineral-poor soil on which regeneration of black spruce was difficult. In this confrontation, the environmentalists and other opponents won, but the Red Lake district lost 2,000 jobs when the company proposal was turned down.

In 1972 the Canadian pulp and paper industry, which was supplying two-thirds of the international trade in newsprint, requested the federal Department of Industry, Trade and Commerce to make yet another in the long series of investigations

22. F.L.C. "Les" Reed, forest economist, assistant deputy minister in the Department of Environment, Ottawa (1980-83), professor of forest policy, University of British Columbia. Reed's analysis of regional short-falls in timber supply in the 1970s was a major contribution to the movement to take better care of our woodlands.

that, like milestones, have measured the history of the woods industry. At the beginning, markets were the focal point and the question of wood supply was overlooked. Eventually the Vancouver consulting firm of F.L.C. Reed & Associates was hired to answer four critical questions: How much wood is there? Where is it? How suitable is it? What does it cost to deliver?

"I went in to see them in Ottawa," Les Reed recalled, "and said, 'You fellows have done a lot of work on wood industry transportation costs, taxes and so on, but you have done nothing about timber supply.' They admitted there was a vacuum in that area, a sort of no man's land. They said it was not their job to look at timber supply, it was something the federal Forestry Service should be looking into. At the Forestry Service there had been a Forest Economics Research Institute, but it had been gutted.

"At the Montebello conference in 1966 I had focused my paper on timber consumption, not on supply. In my presentation there I had merely put in a reference that it was clear we had already begun to erode our sawlog stands. However, what I discovered made me begin to worry about the total supply situation, including pulpwood.

"In my report to Industry, Trade and Commerce I was able to go farther. I hadn't yet put my finger on the details, but it was clear we were in trouble, and not only in sawlogs. As economists, of course, we were interested in the allocation of the resource. And what we did was to travel across the country, which to my knowledge was the first time that had been done, and add it all up and make some comparisons."

Convinced that planning had always foundered on a superficial understanding of supply, Reed set out to translate all the inventory data he could find into economic terms for a better understanding of Canada's forest potential. He had begun to develop a theme that was to change the forestry of the 1980s: "It might well be that the most economic additions to our harvest would come through intensive management of the presently occupied forest land, rather than from northern forests," he said.

Reed's report, published in 1974, rang few alarm bells. Some people missed the point and considered it not a warning but rather an assurance there would be ample supplies, since Reed did say that there was an overall national surplus, which he defined as the difference between the allowable cut and the actual harvest. He also said that in national terms only half the annual allowable cut was being logged. But then he began to zero in on the heart of the matter: as in Nova Scotia and New Brunswick, a growing number of regions had reached, or were soon to reach, the end of merchantable timber reserves. The difference between random trees and merchantable timber was crucial—one a forest economist was equipped to point out.

"It is clear that some provinces and regions have already occupied those timber stands which can be harvested and sold at a profit," Reed said, "leaving unattractive surpluses which may not be exploited for decades. This demonstrates the necessity of dividing national and provincial data into smaller zones in order to present a realistic picture of the surplus."

Too much of the surplus was inaccessible, in Boreal swamps, on precipitous mountainsides near the 11,000-foot timberline, or too distant, beyond the reach of transport. Inventories usually failed to take such factors into account.

Reed's findings were supported by Canadian Forestry Service predictions that regional timber deficits would become severe within thirty years. In British Columbia, tens of thousands of acres where Douglas fir and western hemlock once flourished had been reduced to useless brush and weed trees. In Quebec, reforestation and silviculture had not been practised with consistency and determination. In Ontario, one government forester, Steve Brodie, had written Des Crossley: "How can we even talk about allowable cuts when we know from experience, statistics and all other sources of information that a minimum of one-third of cut-over lands will not produce a second cut. All this in the face of world demands for forest products which within thirty-five years, one-half of a rotation period for tree harvesting, will strain the full productive capacity of our forests. These are important facts. What can be gained in trying to escape them by endless argument or trivialities of no consequence?"

Attitudes towards forestry were still divided, as the silviculturist George Marek remarked when addressing a graduating class at the Lakehead. "Nowadays, some foresters say there are no serious forestry problems in this country, and that everything will be fine if we maintain the *status quo*," he said. "Others, mostly field foresters, say we are slowly but surely accumulating problems and that the future will present serious consequences. Therefore, if they are right, it will be you who will have to face them. The abundance of wood and the vastness of our country are continuing to give many people a false sense of security. Your predecessors may have rightly or wrongly justified or ignored many mistakes, but you will be challenged. You should have no trouble in finding mistakes from the past to learn from."

The Lakehead school under Hearnden's direction had been producing foresters who were questioning both the old methods and the *status quo*. Writing in the February 1973 edition of the *Forestry Chronicle*, Michael Folkema, a fourth-year student, took government and industry to task. In an article entitled "The Use and Misuse of Public Forests in Ontario," Folkema asked: "While the liquidation of timber generates almost $300 million in federal and provincial taxes yearly, can not more than a miserable one or two per cent be plowed back into our province in the form of new trees?

"Unfortunately it would appear that the government is not interested in spending the stumpage revenues on reforestation. Other projects such as Ontario Place or another highway for southern Ontario have much more priority than reforesting the vast, barren clear-cuts produced yearly in northern Ontario."

Citing an article signed by the president of a company, who insisted that "the facts will convince the people of Ontario that their forests *are* well managed—a result of long-standing cooperation between the forest industry and our government," Folkema said: "It should become evident that the Ontario government and the forest industries are both striving to create a sophisticated image of respectability around existing harvesting and regeneration practices instead of creating an effective forest policy."

To which Hearnden added, "My blunt assessment of the situation [is that] industry...has tried to evade having to commit funds to the deliberate growing of the second forest." Lack of forest renewal, he believed, had become more a political than a technical matter, since there was a growing body of evidence of what was really happening under the impact of logging. Abitibi Price had carried out revealing tests. Back in 1925 it had established forty-eight sample plots in cut-over stands near Iroquois Falls. As these were monitored over the years, it became clear that if they were left to natural regeneration, the less desirable balsam fir would replace black spruce on high ground. While doing better down in the swamps, black spruce was having a hard time competing with faster-growing alder. In other words, the new forest was not regenerating naturally to the standards of the original forest. Nor was the practice of clear-cutting huge areas aiding nature to regenerate, since clear-cuts tend to need replanting. "I don't think it is ethical to range across the landscape cutting indiscriminately and creating conditions the consequences of which you cannot solve," said Hearnden. "If it can't be regenerated it should not be logged."

As to how the logging was being done, Eduard Fernow once

23. *While clear-cutting remains the most common method of harvesting timber, smaller "patch clear-cuts" are being encouraged, particularly in the black spruce of northern Canada, which often fails to regenerate by itself after logging.*

said there were no fewer than thirty harvesting methods, none good or bad in itself, whose efficacy depended on the site they were being applied to. There were, however, only three basic ones.

The method known as selection cutting, the logging of mature trees singly or in small groups at intervals, depends on natural regeneration, is easy on the terrain, and looks presentable to the public. It provides a continuously maturing mix of uneven-age timber, ranging from sizeable sawlogs to small pulp-wood. It is complex and costly to administer, and not suitable for shallow-rooted species or species whose regeneration cannot establish itself in heavy shade. It is commonly practised in the hardwood forests of eastern Canada.

The shelterwood system, also amenable to natural regeneration, involves harvesting of softwoods in stages, to leave sufficient standing timber to protect and shade young growth coming up. Like selection cutting, it is costly in that it needs a lot of road building. Unlike selection cutting, it gives rise to an even-age forest, much like clear-cutting or natural fire.

The most common method of harvesting in Canada, however, is the clear-cut, which accounts for more than eighty-five per cent of all logging. Because of their initially ugly appearance, and concern for the environment, clear-cuts have been the most controversial of all forestry practices, except for the spraying of chemical insecticides and herbicides. The aim is to harvest all marketable trees as economically as possible. Since it removes virtually all the trees from a given area, clear-cutting causes the greatest change in environmental conditions, exposing the soil to sun, rain, wind, and extremes of temperature. Clear-cuts may range from a few acres to tens of thousands, and in occasional cases have extended for 50,000 acres, denuding whole watersheds and valleys.

It is widely agreed that clear-cutting is the way to manage forests mutilated by high-grading or those dying from old age, disease, or the budworm, since the other methods would leave stands without protection, vulnerable to wind storms that knock them down to rot on the ground. Clear-cutting, because it needs fewer roads and because machinery, once brought to a site, doesn't have to be moved away and then back again, is also the cheapest of the systems.

The Boreal particularly invites large-scale clear-cutting because the terrain is reasonably level, the trees are even-aged, and timber leases are large, making massive harvesting financially attractive. As a former president of the Ontario Forest Industries Association, George Genge, once said, on the basis of long experience as a forester in northern Ontario: "In my opinion trees should be harvested like a crop of wheat or any other grain. If it isn't harvested it will rot away or burn and be of use to nobody, including the preservationists. It isn't practical to cut trees in strips in many areas of northern Ontario. All the trees are of the same age due to fire kill at one time in the forest's history. Furthermore coniferous softwoods growing in swamps have no tap root to anchor them to the ground. If the forest were cut in strips, the trees at the edge of the clearings would be blown down by high winds which occur every so many years and the end result would be a great waste of timber."

Since the economic efficiency of the method does not necessarily guarantee that it is ecologically sound, clear-cutting became a focal point of debate over timber management during the 1960s and 1970s when concern was growing over the renewability of the resource. Conservationists blamed clear-cutting for upsetting the balance of nature, condemning it in

24. *Though clear-cutting is sometimes blamed by the public for destruction of productive forest land, it is often not logging methods but subsequent fires or faulty road-building that do the most damage. Here forest land has been lost to flooding due to poor road-building in which no culverts were dug.*

general because of problems like soil erosion and stream siltation encountered on particular sites.

There was a tendency to confuse the issue, as when conservationists in Canada cited the findings of Dr. Robert Curry, an environmental geologist at the University of Montana, who said that clear-cuts produced permanent scrub land and arid hills. While this was true enough in dry areas like Montana, it hardly applied to the damp coastal forests of British Columbia, nor indeed to most of Canada.

There are obviously some areas, however, where clear-cutting is not a good idea. On Rennell Sound on the western fringe of the ecologically vulnerable Queen Charlotte Islands there was trouble when a stand of no more than forty acres was cut. The trees in question stood above Riley Creek, a salmon-spawning stream, on terrain subject to seismic activity as well as heavy rain. The federal Department of Fisheries tried to have timber cutting banned in a test case to establish the principle of putting vulnerable areas off limits. What followed was a head-on confrontation between the federal and provincial governments, the latter supported by the International Woodworkers of America, representing the loggers involved. When the loggers appeared on the site, refusing to abide by the federal edict not to cut, many were arrested, but the province ruled that cutting could continue, and the charges against the loggers were dropped. Eight months later came the sequel, which in hindsight seemed inevitable. Autumn rains eroded the cut-over and caused landslides of the sort the fisheries men had tried in the beginning to avoid.

On the east coast of Canada, there was another sort of confrontation. Addressing the Canadian Society of Zoologists, Dr. W.O. Pruitt of Memorial University in St. John's contended that clear-cutting was turning large areas of Newfoundland into "virtual tundra landscape for many years." Not so, said the Newfoundland regional director of the Canadian Forestry Service, Dr. W.J. Carroll. Carroll argued that clear-cutting, when all was said and done, was "a thoroughly respectable forestry practice and the only economically feasible method of conducting pulpwood operations." With economics and ecology now mixed together, Pruitt replied that Carroll was arguing interpretation rather than fact. "Dr. Carroll's touchstone appears to be single-use economic gain," he said. "Mine is long-term ecological stability."

Even in less sensitive regions, there has always been danger that logging pollution will increase water temperatures and hurt aquatic life. Wildlife organizations have opposed large clear-cuts on grounds that they deprive half the bird kingdom

*25. From Newfoundland to British Columbia, there are tracts of
wasteland like this which once supported stands of spruce or balsam fir.
Repeated fires on this section of the Bonavista Peninsula in
Newfoundland have left the soil unable to grow a new crop of trees.*

and about one-seventh of the mammals of food and habitat.
Large clear-cuts can be disruptive to ground-nesting wildfowl
such as mallards and black ducks, and are anathema to wood-
peckers, which favour rotten trunks full of insects; chickadees,
which nest in cavities; and squirrels, which use trees as dens.
Moose refuse to venture into large clear-cuts and prefer to
graze along the edges. Deer, on the other hand, go into clear-
cuts to take advantage of the tender young shrubs and seedlings, and blue grouse feast there, abandoning the area only
when the forest canopy begins to close in again after eight or
ten years.

Nor was the argument confined to conservationists and
academics. Among foresters there was a rainbow of opinion,
shading from George Genge, who recommended clear-cuts for
almost all occasions, to D.M. Trew of Victoria, who felt clear-
cuts should be banished from the land. Trew favoured logging
selectively in patches and strips as in France, where he once
worked, even though there were those who claimed such
methods had harmed the forests of France.

"No forest is homogeneous, but is composed of varying
species and age classes that change with every fold of land,"
Trew argued. "These varied types of stands seldom maintain

uniformity over more than ten or a maximum of 100 acres, and even when the latter exist they may straddle a creek or contain other environmental features which warrant special logging considerations. Thus, to clear-cut an area that stretches up hills and down vales over such heterogeneous conditions is to practise 'forestry' in its most primitive form."

Trew had worked for the British Columbia Forest Service, which tried in the early 1970s to limit clear-cuts to 200 acres. It sought to encourage patch logging, which separates small cut-overs with blocks of standing timber so as to provide fire breaks, wildlife protection, and natural seed sources, but industry did not like the idea, and the guidelines were relaxed so that the shape of the cut, rather than its size, was the main criterion. At the same time, efforts at reforestation were stepped up, though Trew for one was not appeased.

"When the public does not keep a watchful eye on politicians," said Trew, "governments tend to advocate policies that reap maximum revenues from resources without reinvesting for proper management. The reliance on reforestation alone, even if it were fully implemented, is mere band-aid forestry in comparison to management planning based on a variety of selective logging options. . . ."

At Dryden, northwest of Thunder Bay, John Cary, a provincial field forester, reported that "uncontrolled clear-cutting in Boreal softwoods and partial-cut high-grade practices in the Boreal mixed-wood stands occur not only in Dryden but across northern Ontario. Both these methods of cutting are not part of any forest management system to my knowledge. From my experiences, and conversations with foresters in the Boreal region, my situation is unfortunately far from unique." At that time, 1975, hardly a third of the cut-over in the Dryden region was growing back to quality matching that of the original forest. "If Dryden is a representative microcosm of Ontario's coniferous forests," said Cary, "the awesome spectacle of huge acreages going out of production annually must alarm all foresters."

Such persistent warnings were percolating through to the government administrators in Toronto, who had begun to express fears, at least among themselves, that clear-cutting in the Boreal had been getting out of control.

In the wet, unstable soil of the Clay Belt, which stretches more than 300 miles from Hearst to Cochrane and then on east across the border to Amos, Quebec, mechanical skidders were gouging deep ruts that disrupted natural drainage and turned into water holes; the mud then dried out in sun and wind, creating barren hard pans where nothing would grow for years. West of Hearst, where the soil was drier, there were regions where it lay so thin that regeneration was difficult and half the seedlings were dying off. George Marek at Beardmore believed the critical factor was moisture. "When you clear-cut everything in an area, the soil can dry out, or on the other hand it can become quite wet, depending on where you are. Trees that had grown naturally won't grow again, and instead you get poplar, or perhaps moose maple, alder, or raspberry bushes."

A study prepared in 1976 for the Ontario government by two highly regarded foresters, J.F. Flowers and F.C. Robinson, recalling how little on-site research had really gone into clear-cutting in Canada, urged that controls be imposed and clear-cuts be smaller to improve regeneration. Some industry foresters claimed that government concern had been excessive, that scientific documentation was lacking—in other words, that the government people really did not know what they were talking about. Others suggested that it was not the size of clear-cut that mattered but such things as its mix of age classes and configuration in relation to the terrain, and the level of planting and natural regeneration that followed it.

Instead of implementing the Flowers-Robinson recommendations the Ontario government came up with a trial balloon in the form of a "proposed policy" on clear-cutting. As mild as this was—it bore the legend "for discussion purposes only"— the industry wanted none of it. The Ontario Forest Industries Association found the proposals costly and restrictive and mainly an effort to improve "wildlife habitat, aesthetics or recreational values." It said the private sector could not possibly afford to follow it and still remain competitive on world markets. With their trial balloon tattered, ministry planners withdrew to search for other ways of assuring forest management.

After clear-cutting, a planting program is usually required. "Very few fir and spruce actually seed in following a cut-over," says Gordon Baskerville, dean of forestry at the University of New Brunswick. "For the most part, where fir and spruce are flourishing on cut-overs, the seedlings were present as advance growth under the previous stand before it was harvested, and they have survived the cutting operation. Harvesting methods that damage the advance growth reduce the amount of spruce and fir in the stand that develops following cutting. The method of harvesting influences how rapidly softwoods grow up."

New Brunswick, which has been trying, on paper at least, to control clear-cuts for more than thirty years, has suggested guidelines to keep cuts to 500 acres in a patch pattern, with irregular boundaries so that the "edge effect" will accommodate wildlife. Quebec is still struggling with the question.

"We always used to believe that after clear-cutting we got good regeneration," said Louis-Jean Lussier. "But that was based on clear-cuts done thirty years ago with horse logging in winter, when snow protected the young trees that had been left. I do not think we have as good natural regeneration now with summer logging and heavy mechanical equipment. Surveys in Quebec show a quarter of the clear-cuts are not properly regenerating. We have a serious problem and I think our clear-cutting system should be revised. We should continue to clear-cut in small areas and on only the best sites of mixed black spruce and balsam fir. I think that medium- and poor-quality black spruce should not be clear-cut. When you do, you have no regeneration for a long time."

Like most things in forestry, clear-cutting is complex, often unpredictable, and to the layman downright confusing. There are certainly wastelands, generally due to fire that has swept through the debris and stumps left in the area after cutting. These can look awful, but in the end it often boils down to how long you are prepared to wait for regeneration. Ontario government forester John Cary remembers clear-cuts north of Dryden and Thunder Bay so big and unpromising he had little hope for them. "I went back there eight years later," he said, "and despite our incredibly gloomy predictions they had reforested to decent standards. It amazed me, but there they were. Nature can be very forgiving."

The controversy can only be resolved with more knowledge, since the problems of growing a new forest are essentially ecological ones. But it is also a matter of economic priorities. People directly dependent on timber for their livelihood believe that clear-cutting, being considerably cheaper than other methods, is the way to go. Canadians in general, chancing across a clear-cut during a vacation trip, find the results offensive. Convinced that nothing can ever grow there again, some will go home to write letters to the editor protesting "the rape of the forest." They lament the sacrifice of handsome trees for the manufacture of the very newsprint, containers, and toilet paper they are not prepared to do without.

The press, until recently, has done little to explain the mysteries of logging, apart from dispatching an occasional feature writer to describe shattered trees hugging the shores of clear blue lakes and decaying stumps marring gentle hills in "the deserts of the north." A press photo of a clear-cut growing back as a thrifty new forest is rare.

By the mid-1970s, the condition of the forest had worsened, if anything, since the Montebello conference. Too much of it had turned into junk or silvicultural slums, skimpy anaemic stands alternating with stands so thick they could not grow, or miles of uncommercial hardwoods and brush that, in summer when the leaves were out, gave the illusion of viable forest. If lumped in one place, this wasteland would equal the size of Great Britain. In addition, 200,000 hectares of junk forest were building up every year.

A Swedish forester, Dr. Borje K. Steenberg of the Royal Institute of Technology in Stockholm, jolted Canadian foresters when he pointed out that although his country had only one-tenth of Canada's forests, it was cutting almost one-half the amount harvested in Canada. The reason was not hard to find. No major forest nation was investing less than Canada, where money allocated to forest renewal was one-eighth of Sweden's investment. "Sweden never had as much standing timber as it has today," Steenberg said. "Canada probably never had so little."

In an attempt to do something about a problem that was obviously not going to solve itself, the Canadian Forestry Association called a National Forest Regeneration Conference in Quebec City in 1977. Attended by 250 representatives of government, industry, the forestry profession, and environmental organizations, the conference agreed that forest renewal was no less than an urgent national need. It was time to "spread the bad news."

"In Canada, forest regeneration is a topic we treat like the weather," said Kenneth Armson, then with the forest faculty at the University of Toronto. "We talk about it, to a degree we judge its suitability by our immediate needs or position, and finally we do little about it, frequently with the assertion that somehow whatever grows fortuitously will be capable of utilization, so why bother."

A dismal picture was sketched by speaker after speaker. "This is Canada's shame," exclaimed the president of the Canadian Forestry Association, Maurice Vézina of Quebec City. "It cannot be allowed to continue." A delegate from Newfoundland, the most recent target of budworm, said, "Canada, as a whole, has been deemed to have a crisis in respect of long-term supplies of suitable timber within economic range of established mills. Newfoundland passed the crisis state a long time ago."

John Walters, a British-born expert on regeneration and a professor at the University of British Columbia, told the conference: "The statistics we can gather, regardless of how conservatively we analyze them, paint an alarming scene. . .a litany of apathetic administration and gross mismanagement. Neither politicians nor the public seem aware of this. Public opinion, brainwashed in the mythical merits of public ownership of forest land, must be changed by conferences such as this. Public ownership of forest land has resulted in the plunder of Canada's forests. Public ownership has provided neither good stewardship in the past nor hope for the future. When we talk of forests we use terms like 'national heritage' and 'sustained yield.' The record shows indisputably that neither provincial nor federal governments can or will provide the investment which forestry so desperately requires." In fact, industry's record on freehold land has been even worse.

Gilbert Paillé, an industrial research forester, later director of the federal Laurentian Forest Research Centre at Ste-Foy, Quebec, said: "The sad fact of the matter is that foresters, of all people, remain unconvinced of the urgency of problem number one." Foresters in industry were used to concerning themselves with physical supplies of local timber, usually for one mill. This approach was sufficient when there was plenty of wood, but shrinking supplies called for more complex analysis. The problem, now nationwide, centred on the need to ascertain the condition, type, and economic accessibility of the reserves of specific commercial species such as firs, spruce, jack pine, and hemlock and their cost at the mill gate. It was a question best tackled by an economist who specialized in renewable resources.

Since the Montebello conference, Les Reed had been wrestling with the question of timber supply, and his speech to the Quebec conference reflected the signs of impending shortage he had detected since his last report to Ottawa in 1974. His message was based on a study, "Forest Management in Canada," that his consulting firm, F.L.C. Reed & Associates, had just completed for the Canadian Forestry Service.

Reed's point was not that Canada's forest lands were in danger of becoming wastelands barren of all vegetation, but that stands of merchantable timber of a size, quality, and accessibility suitable for existing mills were seriously diminished; that in some areas the mills would require more wood than was being grown on a continuous basis. Excess of mill capacity over timber supply threatened to lead to increased prices and to Canada's becoming non-competitive on the world market.

"The fact is that many forest-based communities are in trouble today because their mills cannot secure an economic wood supply," said Reed. "The profile of the remaining mature forest is much less attractive than it was ten or fifteen years ago. In many areas the resource has been high-graded and the mix of species, log sizes and grades has deteriorated measurably."

The reserve of economically accessible softwood across the country in 1977 was only half what Reed had described in his report to government in 1974. Reed reported on each province and found all wanting. "It is an accepted fact that governments and industry alike have generally fallen short of an acceptable performance. In spite of the customary litany about sustained yield, much of the forest is not being managed now at a level which will support existing employment and output indefinitely."

Governments and industry had become victims of their own optimistic slogans. "Forestry legislation and regulations have been on the books in most provinces for years and one might easily conclude that forest management is being practised at acceptable levels," Reed said. "Such is not the case. Annual reports of provincial forest services are frequently deceptive, inasmuch as they do not relate performance on public lands to formal requirements. For example, a shortfall in regeneration can go unnoticed for years. Nor do the private companies report sufficient detail on forest management to enable interested observers to evaluate their achievements.

"Harvesting is generally conducted as though it had no relationship to subsequent silvicultural work. A case in point is the habit of leaving residual hardwood and softwood trees standing in a so-called clear-cut. The result is that mechanical site preparation is thereby prevented, and this in turn leads to inadequate regeneration."

Although the industry was harvesting only three-quarters of

the annual allowable cut, half of the statistical reserve was economically inaccessible. The Maritimes already had less merchantable wood than needed, since budworm and fire were taking ten times more than the annual logging harvest. (In eastern Canada, some eighteen million hectares had been devastated by budworm and another thirty million would likely be lost before the current infestation abated.) The budworm was wrecking the forest on Cape Breton Island, where the Nova Scotia government had banned the sort of chemical spraying that was keeping the industry alive in New Brunswick.

"Allowable cuts are increasingly suspect in these circumstances," Reed said, "setting the stage inevitably for painful adjustments in forest-based communities." The Canadian Forestry Association had said, "Inadequate attention to forest regeneration is responsible for restricting expansion possibilities in some regions, has reduced employment in others, and will result in a continuing decline in future forest-based jobs and revenues." Reed went farther. He estimated that dozens of communities would face economic distress within the next twenty years—perhaps as many as one-third of the 300 communities in Canada that rely solely on wood products for their livelihood.

"I know that they are running out of good sawlogs in the Alberta foothills," he said. "I know that in Ontario the hardwood industry has used up its best stands. In Quebec the southern part of the province has been over-cut. There are no options any more in New Brunswick—eleven pulp mills and a softwood supply for eight. In Cape Breton the Nova Scotia Forest Industries, a Swedish-owned company, had mounted one of the better forest management programs in the country until the spruce budworm came in and made a shambles of things. There is a physical timber reserve in British Columbia but some of the stuff in the allowable cut, in my judgement, is not economic to log. It is too far up the mountainside, or of inferior species, or it is too low in volume per acre, or in remote northern stands of slow wood growth which would cost too much to open up.

"Suddenly you see a pattern emerging," said Reed. "But it's not so much like falling off a cliff as sliding down a slippery slope. It had become apparent that half of the timber reserve, that is, the difference between the annual allowable cut and the actual harvest, was economically inaccessible. Moreover, the accessible half appeared relatively less attractive than that which was being currently harvested."

Reed's report came at the right time. It coincided with a growing awareness of the importance of the forest resource for Canada's economic and social well-being and with rising concern for national productivity. The message was sobering: unless decisive action is taken immediately to advance intensive forest management, there will not be enough wood. There was still a lot of scepticism about industry's desire to practise forestry, but a heartening sign of the times, at least, was the increased awareness of what was beginning to be called a crisis.

Running out of timber

"THE GOOD OLD DAYS WHEN GOD GREW THE TREES and we cut them down practically on our doorsteps have gone. And they won't be coming back. The era of the limitless forest resource is over."

Len Marchand
Minister of Environment, 1977

THE WARNINGS IN THE PAST HAD BEEN FITFUL and fragmentary, either dealing with one species, such as white pine, or muffled in the language of science or big business. Research had not been put to use on any significant national scale and consisted for the most part of academic studies by a handful of federal and university foresters. Despite a lack of reliable statistics, there was need to relate supply and demand right across the country, and this Les Reed had set out to do in 1976.

"I had come to the conclusion Canada should have a nation-wide survey of forest reserves to clarify the sort of problem we were letting ourselves in for," he said. "I believed there was a growing supply problem which sooner or later was going to be massive. I did not believe the companies really understood the problem except in their own backyards, and it was always muted. Anyone wanting to spend money on forestry had to fight like the devil. Industrial foresters were usually submerged under a woodlands manager whose primary aim was to get out wood to the mill as cheaply as possible."

Approaching the Canadian Forestry Service, Reed had secured a contract to make a one-year study. "We set out to paint a national picture of the sort which had never been done," he said. "This stimulated interest, for if you just said that things were bad in, say, northern Ontario, that would not have created much stir, least of all in Ottawa. But if you said things were bad in *every* province, that opportunities were being missed and we were failing to capture world markets, that we were living off our forest capital and degrading the resource—well, that had impact!"

Since forming his consulting firm in 1971, Reed had worked in more than a score of countries where he developed his ideas about proper use of forest land. He had no patience with arguments that sought to justify lack of forest renewal on the grounds that it was a poor investment. Whether reforestation showed a rate of return equal to the bank rate was only part of the picture, and it was high time to combine the economics of stimulating demand with the need to stimulate supply. Reed, a slim, friendly westerner, says his interest in land management derives from his childhood on two quarter-sections near Three Hills in southern Alberta. "My father taught me idle land was a crime."

As one of a dozen children on a subsistence farm, Reed went to work in his teens, skidding logs for the bush mills between Rocky Mountain House and Calgary and working for MacMillan Bloedel at Port Alberni on Vancouver Island. Putting himself through college, he took an MA in economics at the University of Oregon and went to work as an economist in British Columbia for Forest Industry Relations and later for the Council of Forest Industries. He has something of the enthusiasm of an evangelist.

"I came from a devout line of Methodists," he explained. "In the Scriptures there are constant references to land use, and an important passage in Genesis says man was put in the garden to tend and care for it, not to dominate it and use it for selfish purposes. I came to believe that forestry is more than science and technology and economic analysis. I came to believe that forest land is not something we merely inherit. It also is something we borrow from our children and it is wrong to misuse it because our children and their children will need it."

Attempting the first definitive survey of commercial timber reserves, he gained the co-operation of every major industrial association as well as the provincial governments. "I knew I could get into trouble unless I had local people to keep me straight, so I arranged for half a dozen of the top foresters across Canada to help me." These included Gordon Baskerville and Gordon Weetman at the University of New Brunswick, Louis-Jean Lussier in Quebec City, Kenneth Armson at the University of Toronto, Desmond Crossley in Alberta, and Harry Smith at the University of British Columbia.

"I think one reason people had not done nation-wide comparisons of provincial forest resources was that every province had its own inventory system and allowable cut calculations. I suppose it took courage to add all these up and try to come up with a national figure. I know I never had the luxury of working from good statistics, but such as they were, I had to make the figures talk and tell a story as best they could."

In the spring of 1977, with only a couple of months to deadline, Reed began to make last-minute checks on his information, starting in Newfoundland. He had begun to see that the timber reserves on paper did not fit the economic realities. "It was one of those misleading statistical things," he said, "giving a mistaken impression that we had a comfortable cushion—an illustration that a little knowledge is a dangerous thing.

"I'd call on people and say, 'I've got some text I want to check with you.' Sometimes I sent it on ahead and sometimes I just carried it in. If it was a company, I'd say, 'How much are you spending on forestry?' This was often nil, or negligible. They would say, 'Well, it's not our responsibility; it's the responsibility of the provincial government.' Then I'd go to the provincial government and say, 'This is your timber base. This is your allowable cut. Are you meeting the growth rates and forest renewal targets you've set?' Ken Armson had studied the Englehart jack pine management area in northeast Ontario and found they were doing neither. Harvesting had exceeded the calculated annual cut; an inaccurate inventory was causing problems.

"In Fredericton one afternoon I sat down with Gordon Baskerville in his office at the UNB forestry school. He had been my adviser for all the eastern provinces and he began to ask me questions, like 'Have you thought of this?' or 'There's

26. Gordon Baskerville, dean of the forestry school at the University of New Brunswick and one of the architects of the province's new efforts to restore its forests, once a major source of Canada's famous white pine, to healthy productivity.

another little angle to this,' or 'You may have missed something here you might like to consider.' He never came out and said, 'That's lousy,' or 'You've missed the whole point,' but by four o'clock I said, 'Gordon, I concede. I've got the message. I'll throw everything away and start over.' This was in June. We had already done a year's work and I was supposed to have the report finished by mid-July.

"What I had tried to do was to grade the provinces, the federal government, and industry, saying a good job was done in one thing and not in another. Trying to make distinctions. But under Baskerville's prodding I had to take another look. I came to the conclusion that virtually nobody could claim good marks in forestry. With few exceptions there had been negligence. Industry had been very short-sighted. The provinces had milked the resource. The federal government had turned its back on Canada's most important natural asset.

"I came to the conclusion that things were worse than I'd anticipated, and that the only way to make an impact was to lay it out in all its gory detail. I had been trying to coat the pill with a little sugar, but in the process I was obscuring the very thing I wanted to clarify. So I threw away the old text and started over."

Reed flew back to Vancouver and spent ten weeks rewriting his report. He was convinced now that the cost of intensive forestry close to the mills would be far less than the cost of opening up the remote North. In northern British Columbia, for example, there was probably enough wood for three or four new pulp mills, but it would cost a billion dollars to open the region with roads and other infrastructure.

"Places like that were beyond the economic margin," Reed said. "What we did was make a judgement on economic accessibility, including the areas that 'patient money' had bypassed because they were too costly to log. But the report still had a gap. We needed figures that would say, in effect, that if we managed the land intensively it would cost so much per hectare to raise the allowable annual cut the extra notch needed. And if we spent a certain amount more we would be able to sustain the yield."

Of the $448 million being spent by the various governments on the forests every year, most of it by the provinces, only $95 million was earmarked for regeneration and silviculture. Though very little information had been reported on private expenditures on forest management, Reed concluded that forest renewal in the private sector was also seriously inadequate. With that in mind, he worked up tables he believed would give his report definition and focus. In this work he had the help of two professional foresters, John Potter and Bayard Palmer.

Additional funding to maintain current forest yield would cost $80 million, he estimated. To increase the yield substantially would cost nearly $200 million. Though his figures for site preparation, planting or seeding, and silviculture were open to argument, it was the first time anyone had tried to establish just what it would cost to restore Canada's forests. More sophisticated methods have been worked out since that include growth rates and more exact information, but Reed's report had suddenly narrowed down the discussion from words into hard figures.

"In the final analysis," he said, "forest management must be recognized as a necessary condition of staying in the forest business. . . . Our forests have not been well managed, and we've forgone a lot of opportunities, but that does not mean we are out of the ball game. What it does mean is that the time has come when we can no longer afford the luxury of neglect. We have to begin to manage our forests like grown-up people."

By the end of the century many areas in Canada would be coming to the end of their accessible softwoods. Canada's share of world markets, which had already slipped from thirty-one to nineteen per cent, would decrease still further. In an industry that accounted for one-fifth of all exports and was the largest dollar earner, this was a cause for national concern. It was a sombre picture for an industry that, directly or indirectly, accounts for one in every ten Canadian jobs. Reed proceeded to describe three possible options.

One was to make better use of available wood, including those parts of the tree that had usually been wasted. There was evidence that many operators were using less than two-thirds of harvested wood. He suggested that technology be perfected to use less desirable species such as poplar, which in some areas grew in abundance with only small quantities being utilized in existing pulp mills.

The second, less palatable option was to push farther into remote woodlands on the northern fringes of the Boreal or high up mountain slopes, even harvesting with helicopters or captive balloons. Both of these methods were costly and most of the trees harvested would be too small for lumber, although usable as fibre for pulp or chipboard.

The third option, and the one Reed favoured, entailed more intensive management of land already under licence, on the most productive land, closest to the mills. He looked forward to the day when the concept of sustained yield would be supplanted by "augmented yield," wherein planting and tending would not only maintain but enhance the forest and reduce the cost of fibre. In the beginning this would call for commitment and funding far beyond what had ever been invested, but on grounds of public revenue alone it would be a paying proposition. Failure to manage the forests, he argued, would show up sooner or later in the form of abandoned mills, decaying towns, rural unemployment, and a greater deficit in Canada's balance of payments. Neglect would have to be paid for out of reduced tax revenues.

The public coffers were receiving $3 billion a year from the forests, evenly split between Ottawa and the provinces. But only five and a half cents of every dollar was going back into forest renewal. Nor was industry filling the gap. Of the $68 million the companies spent on the forests, less than a third went to forest renewal, a large portion of that in British Columbia and Alberta.

27. *"The land of little sticks," stunted trees that peter out in the tundra that borders the Boreal forest in a jagged line from coast to coast. These conifers, disfigured by the wind, are near Churchill, Manitoba.*

The Reed report, bearing on its paper cover a desolate scene of a clear-cut that looked like a battlefield, was published early in 1978, a few months after the Quebec regeneration conference. Blunt, comprehensive, remarkably free of the jargon of economics or forestry, the two-volume document became a rallying point and was to have an impressive effect in popularizing the issue among civil servants, politicians, and the industry, if not among the public at large, though Reed tried to get his message across to the public as well.

"If you work in the industry and are under forty years of age," he said, "the chances are very good that you will face a crisis before you retire and be forced to move out of your community and find work in another industry. Canada has been supplying one fourth of world exports of manufactured forest products. The opportunities are enormous, but they will not be realized if we settle for snail-pace forestry."

Like most efforts to speed the tide of change, the Reed report had detractors who felt it overstated the problem and oversimplified the solution, but by and large it was received in the crusading spirit in which it had been attempted. "What I did could only have been done within the framework of what others had been doing, both fifty years back and more recently by men like Ken Hearnden and Des Crossley," said Reed. "No one would have listened to me if those men had not paved the way. I was one of those people who happen to come along at a particular time. Maybe an economist was needed to bring it all together."

The most important thing was that he was being *listened* to and within months became the most sought-after speaker in the industry. He was invited by the Canadian Pulp and Paper Association to commence further studies to flesh out the conclusions reached in his report. In Toronto A.J. Herridge, a forester and assistant deputy minister of natural resources, said, "Though some may dispute the accuracy of individual figures, it is doubtful if further study and refinement would alter the conclusions. . . . Within Ontario, these conclusions cannot be disputed."

If that was the case, the future of the public forests was much different from the reassuring forecasts the public had been used to hearing in the past. Evidence was piling up that a third of the forest land base was going out of commercial use. John Jeglum, a black spruce expert from the federal Great Lakes Forest Research Centre in Sault Ste. Marie, urged that black spruce be cut in narrow strips, rather than big clear-cuts, so it could regenerate itself. "It is a tragedy," he said, "that so much of Ontario's forest land is going out of production because of inadequate regeneration of cut-overs."

Fred Haavisto, another black spruce researcher, said: "Prior to mechanization there were few problems in renewing black spruce cut-overs as the surrounding stands afforded sufficient seed for natural regeneration. Forest harvesting machinery and present forest management have changed everything. Advanced growth has been damaged, and the cut-overs are unlimited in size, precluding natural regeneration." Haavisto believes that in some areas as much as forty per cent is not regenerating as it should.

In northwestern Ontario, more than half of one logged-off area under study had to be written off for early regeneration, because of poor soil, difficult topography, or logging practice that had left too many weed trees to strangle the advance growth of spruce. In some regions there had been over-cutting. In others there was under-cutting, so that over-mature trees were rotting and going to waste before they could be cut.

Critics of government policy were more numerous. Jack Stokes, the NDP member of the Ontario legislature for Lake

Nipigon, went so far as to say black spruce was "an endangered species" and that "clear-cutting of black spruce in the Boreal forest is rarely followed by a healthy and vibrant new growth." Like Jeglum and George Marek, he urged that the spruce be cut in narrow strips, rather than in patches and clear-cuts, though there are industrial foresters who do not agree.

At Thunder Bay, Tulio Mior of the Lumber and Sawmill Workers Union said that unless forests were managed, 11,000 jobs would be at stake. He predicted " real dogfights" if some mills ran out of wood while others had more than they needed because of the size of their pulpwood limits. As few as five companies controlled 2.4 million acres.

An example of the problem could be found a dozen miles south of Hearst, where the Algoma Central Railway to Sault Ste. Marie cuts through the beautiful mixed forest made popular by painters of the Group of Seven. There the Newaygo Timber Company ran a sawmill, cutting two-thirds of its wood from lands it had owned for sixty years. At its current rate of consumption, the company might have had wood sufficient only for another ten years or so, because of lack of regeneration in the past, though this particular problem became academic when, following a recent strike, the mill closed down. "It is already getting very thin in places like Hearst," Reed agreed. "It's the only game in town, and when the sawlogs run out it is going to be tough." Half a dozen lumber mills support a population of 5,500 in Hearst. There is some question whether the remaining wood supply can sustain existing production, let alone any expansion to meet the future market which is expected to double by the year 2000. But it is not only Hearst. In northern Ontario many communities will feel the pinch— from Kirkland Lake and Chapleau in the east to Thunder Bay, which supports four pulp mills.

Around the mill communities, large areas of scrub and junk forest have grown where there was once productive forest, and the business of getting rid of it and replanting will be costly. As for areas farther from the mills, there are fears that they will yield twenty per cent less wood than needed, unless ways can be found to bridge the gap before a new crop is available. Since trees take so long to grow, planting alone is not the answer. The shortfall will have to be reduced by better fire protection, by silvicultural methods such as thinning, weeding, and fertilizing, and by insect control.

How tight the supply was becoming in the Lakehead area became apparent when George Marek of Beardmore found himself in one final battle, before his early retirement from government service, to uphold the banner of sustained yield. "Sustained yield?" he scoffs. "It will be a myth until there is a true, analytical, practical concept of what we have growing out there, until we have good inventories and growth rates."

In essence the argument was over inventory figures. As wood had receded from the mills, and truck hauls had extended farther into the distant reserves in the late 1970s, lumbermen had begun to look hungrily at what seemed a likely tract of unallocated timber on Black Bay Peninsula, which juts into Lake Superior between Nipigon and Thunder Bay. The smaller logging outfits in the area assumed that when it was opened up the timber would all be theirs; it would be the thing to keep them going. They were upset when it became clear that the government was intent on leasing the limits to an "outsider," an up-and-coming Montreal-born lumberman named Ken Buchanan. Buchanan Forest Products Ltd. was after Black Bay timber to supply a mill that was not in the Nipigon district at all, but 180 miles to the west at the little community of Sapawe, which had wood supply problems.

When the government instructed the young forester in charge of Black Bay to draw up a ten-year operating plan and put the deal through there was trouble. Don MacAlpine, a graduate of the Lakehead school, where good forest management is an article of faith, believed that Black Bay was one of the areas where reserves had been seriously over-estimated by aerial surveys. He had been in to look at it himself and felt there just was not enough wood for the harvest required by the Buchanan company and to supply the local needs as well. To harvest on such a scale would make nonsense of sustained yield, he believed. As he told the press later, "The field samples had revealed discrepancies I could not accept." Marek, his senior colleague, knew the peninsula well and supported MacAlpine fully.

MacAlpine found that his arguments against granting cutting rights to Buchanan were being ignored by the ministry, and he was under pressure to give "top priority" to the company wanting access to Black Bay. In frustration, he took his case, along with internal government documents he felt would support it, to his local member of the legislature, who happened to be NDP member Jack Stokes, one of the most persistent critics of government forest policy. The story appeared in the press and was debated in the legislature.

Whatever was going on at Black Bay Peninsula, MacAlpine

considered it "professionaly unacceptable." He soon found himself without a job, fired because he had broken his pledge, as a government employee, not to disclose inside information without authorization. The issue of good forestry had become sidetracked into one of civil service regulations.

Backed by the Ontario Public Service Employees Union, MacAlpine appealed on the grounds that the public, as owners of the forest, had a right to know what was happening. Marek testified on his behalf, as did another of his colleagues, who declared that MacAlpine was doing the profession a service. Local lumbermen who felt MacAlpine was championing their own right to cut on Black Bay gathered 1,500 signatures in support of the young forester. The case went to a tribunal, which ruled that the penalty, firing, had been too severe. Later a government appeal against that ruling was dismissed and MacAlpine found himself working again as a unit forester in Nipigon. But rights to cut have been given out for Black Bay Peninsula, which include rights to Buchanan and to local logging companies.

In Canada's forest history as a whole, the MacAlpine case does not loom large, perhaps, but it serves to illustrate the argument that public servants should have no secrets and that professional foresters should be granted more authority and professional status.

"If a forester has status and backing he can say, 'Hold your horses, boys, this is no good; there are other commitments,'" said Marek. "There has to be compromise between making a buck now and the future." The MacAlpine case pointed up the question of inventories, which Reed had found at the root of the nation's forest problems. But Reed had barely submitted his report to the government in 1978 when federal funding for inventory surveys was cut, along with much else that was good in the forestry program, in the name of fiscal restraint. The timing was particularly unfortunate, since it was a period when the provinces and industry were stepping up their efforts and clearly needed all the leadership and support they could get. What made it more ironic was that within a few months Ottawa was to offer $235 million in grants to modernize and expand old mills, a lopsided combination of austerity and generosity, since expanded mill capacity would be pointless without adequate wood supply.

Ottawa had been cutting back its Forestry Service since the 1960s, causing the Canadian Council of Resource and Environment Ministers (CCREM), made up mostly of representatives from the provinces, to complain that the federal government was discriminating against forestry. It almost seemed the Liberal administration wanted to hand all forest responsibility, including that for research, over to the provinces since its commitments to fisheries and agriculture were so much stronger, despite the $1.5 billion Ottawa received annually from the forest and its products.

What was particularly upsetting was the federal proposal to close the Petawawa Forest Experiment Station, which had been operating for sixty years; it had a staff of seventy-eight and covered thirty-eight square miles of laboratories, nurseries, and research forest containing experiments that were unique and irreplaceable. Opposition house leader Walter Baker called the proposal "mindless and ill considered," since the forest contributed one dollar in every five earned abroad, our largest source of foreign exchange. The service had already been cut back forty per cent in ten years, and the minister, Len Marchand, had promised there would be no more erosion.

According to Reed, who later found himself with the job of restoring morale and momentum as assistant deputy minister in charge of forestry in Ottawa, "within a week they knew they had made an embarrassing governmental decision. We had Liberal members of Parliament, mayors of towns in the area, employees of forest products companies and of the federal government raising a ruckus."

In the end Petawawa, which luckily was in a Liberal constituency, was saved, at the expense of the Canadian Forestry Service in Ottawa, where fifty jobs were cut. In the confusion there was loss of morale and many researchers quit. The Fire Research Institute and the Forest Management Institute were dismembered and their remnants moved to distant Petawawa, though the latter needed contact in Ottawa with industry and all the other government agencies, perhaps twenty, involved in forestry. But the uproar, at whatever expense, did have some positive effect in publicizing the need for better forestry.

In the aftermath of the cuts in the Canadian Forestry Service, the director general, R.J. Bourchier, became convinced that yet another statement on the federal government's policy on forestry was badly needed to stem further cutbacks and build a base for future expansion. He believed the federal government had an important role to play that went far beyond research. Bourchier and other senior men in the CFS, I.C.M. Place and

H.M. Babcock, prepared a cabinet document and discussion paper that would define the federal role in forestry and, when approved by cabinet, form the basis for the required rebuilding job. Bourchier argued that a higher profile was required for the CFS; the minister, Len Marchand, agreed and announced his intention to have the service headed by an assistant deputy minister.

A change of government delayed the process but John Fraser, the minister responsible in the new Progressive Conservative administration, was convinced of the need for action and took the reworked proposals to cabinet, where they were approved in late 1979. It was a beginning. Although the assistant deputy minister question was now clarified, Fraser was thinking of even bigger things for forestry. A comprehensive federal role was defined and a Forestry Sector Strategy Committee was set up to co-ordinate federal programs, but the 1980 election was called before Fraser could do much with his forestry mandate. The new minister, John Roberts, did, however, implement Marchand's decision, and the CFS was raised to full-service status with an assistant deputy minister at its head.

Whatever the problems on the federal scene, the provinces had generally been making progress. Nova Scotia, with no firm forest policy up to the 1970s, had assumed responsibility for Crown land renewal. Quebec had increased its forestry budget five-fold in ten years and the 100-man task force, COGEF, was working on plans to improve and rationalize the harvest. Newfoundland, burdened with a colonial system that had exacted no stumpage charges from the two big licensees, finally put a price tag on its resource and introduced taxation systems to get the companies to improve their timber limits.

During the previous thirty years Newfoundland had mounted several royal commissions and task forces. The first of these, handicapped by lack of forest inventory and inability to get the major companies to provide the intensive management needed, did not achieve much except a greater appreciation of the problem. There were warnings that timber demand would surpass supply unless measures were taken to improve protection, wood utilization, and forest management.

The task force established in 1973 was more effective and certainly the best study yet made of the Newfoundland forest. By this time an inventory had been completed, and there was factual evidence that costly intensive forest management was going to be needed. Damage from insects was increasing. The hemlock looper had defoliated large areas of balsam fir and the spruce budworm, not previously recognized as a serious pest in the province, was in epidemic. In the face of this, plus the fact the industry wanted to expand by setting up a new plant to produce linerboard from pulp, the provincial government set about correcting some longstanding forest abuses. It passed legislation requiring licensees and forest owners to provide some meaningful forest management plans—something most provinces had done many decades earlier, though with indifferent success.

By 1980 the spruce budworm attack had become so bad that another royal commission was convened. One of the main recommendations was insecticide spraying, without which the fir forest would be completely destroyed, as was happening on Cape Breton. (Fir and spruce made up seventy-five per cent of the merchantable wood in Newfoundland.) The commission warned that if chemical spray was not used, the timber supply would deteriorate to fifty per cent of requirement by the year 2025. A spray campaign was mounted in 1981 (though not before a million acres had been defoliated) that cut back the epidemic and saved Newfoundland's fir from complete destruction. Meanwhile, with federal help Newfoundland had started a modest planting and silvicultural program.

The most successful steps, however, were taken in New Brunswick and to a lesser extent in British Columbia and Ontario. These had much in common, pursuing sustained yield by placing responsibility for forest management on industry, while providing financial assistance and keeping an eye on company progress. With government and industry pulling together, it was easier to unite harvesting with forest renewal. To accommodate industry's demand for sufficient security of tenure to make forest management economically worthwhile, all three provinces introduced "evergreen" licences. So long as a company lived up to government standards and passed review every five years, a licence would be extended. While companies got the sort of tenure they felt they needed, the principle of retaining the forests under public ownership was preserved. An interesting sidelight was that in all three provinces the reforms were introduced largely by academics from the forestry schools.

The "green revolution," as it was called, began in British Columbia in 1975 with yet another Royal Commission on Forest Resources, this one headed by Peter Pearse of the University of British Columbia. Despite tremendous growth and change, there had been no overall review since the second Sloan commission in the 1950s. In the southeast interior, where lumbering had been going on since early in the century, problems were developing around Fernie, Creston, Cranbrook, Vernon, and Kelowna. In the Okanagan Valley, there had been a rapid expansion in the forest industry during the 1960s, with pressure on the land from other sources, such as tourism and urban expansion. There was reason to believe that the Vancouver forest district, which includes Vancouver Island and half the mainland coast almost to Prince Rupert, was being over-cut by ten per cent. At the current rate of depletion foresters believed that within thirty-five or forty years lack of suitable timber could be serious indeed.

The various forms of timber allocation and management evolving out of the two Sloan reports had brought inevitable problems. "I was concerned that allocation of timber was getting out of hand," said Pearse. "There were a lot of *ad hoc* arrangements not firmly grounded in law, and the whole situation had been evolving very quickly." Pearse expressed concern about company consolidations, which were robbing the industry of its competitiveness. The NDP government had been under pressure to change the timber quota system, but since that would have snatched established rights away from major companies, Lands and Forests Minister Bob Williams felt it wiser to investigate the industry again in a rational way. In hearings in half a dozen centres during the course of a year, Pearse looked into everything from taxation to recreation.

He found evidence that the Forest Service was often pressed to support theories not in the interests of sound management —one example being pressure to limit all clear-cuts to 200 acres. He felt that merely limiting the size of clear-cuts was not the answer, since instead of easing the impact of logging on the environment, it was having the opposite effect. Nothing in logging disturbs soil and water more than road building, and since several small clear-cuts must necessarily be spread over a much larger area than one big one, two or three times more roads were being built. One of Pearse's recommendations was that logging be brought into line with the needs of the environment, rather than reduced to arbitrary clear-cut sizes.

The Forest Act of 1978 that followed Pearse's report resulted in the renegotiation of the tree farm licences that Sloan had put in place three decades earlier. The new agreements were to run twenty-five years with reviews every ten years. Cut-over land was to be reforested by the licence holders, who, with the help of government funding, were expected "to use it and manage it or lose it."

The most important change, apart from a government promise to increase the amount of forest revenue it had been reinvesting in forestry, was provision for long-term planning and budgeting to recognize the length of time it takes a forest crop to grow. But even this did not answer the question of whether successive governments would continue to give forestry the continuous funding it requires—and in fact within five years the recession of the early 1980s was to negate the government's intent. It is indicative of public response to forestry matters, even in British Columbia, that the new act, one of the most important pieces of legislation in twenty years, failed to elicit much public interest.

Though Pearse in British Columbia found no reason to change Sloan's policy of allocating timber limits, changes were occurring in New Brunswick that were reallocating timber in a way reminiscent of land reform. This naturally caused concern in the industry, but there was no question that drastic measures were needed, for New Brunswick had become the first of the forest provinces to find its back against the wall.

Though it was probably over-dramatic to say, as the *Daily Gleaner* of Fredericton did, that "New Brunswick can no longer produce enough trees of the size needed for its own hydro and telephone poles," the industry was certainly in trouble. Years of harvesting and poor management had reduced large areas to trees of small diameter, robbing the lumber mills of sawlogs. Budworm was killing off trees before they could be harvested and, despite a costly and controversial program of chemical spraying, had been reducing the forest at an annual rate of nearly ten per cent for three decades. A twenty-per-cent shortfall of spruce and fir within twenty years was predicted. If New Brunswick was to have enough wood to sustain industry, intensive management would have to be extended to practically every productive acre.

New Brunswick's problem was not unlike that in other parts of Canada. If there were to be enough mature forest to last until the next crop was old enough to cut, in thirty or forty years, it would have to be husbanded. If cut too fast, the supply would run out before the new crop was ready, causing chaos in the industry. If cut too slowly, half of it would be so mature, or over-mature, that it would rot and fall before the loggers got to it.

"We discovered in the late 1970s that we needed every one of our trees," said Gordon Baskerville, who had been hired away from the University of New Brunswick forestry school to mastermind the new program as assistant deputy minister. "Every tree we were going to cut in the next half-century was already out there growing, and every single one had the name of a processing plant on it, so to speak. It was all committed."

In a profession with so many imponderables, Baskerville is a forester whose grasp and insight encourage confidence. Soft-spoken, of middle age, he seems more the academic than the outdoors man, and teaching is his main occupation, but he is the sort of person others turn to when things go wrong. Sitting in his small office on the UNB campus overlooking Frederic-ton, Baskerville explained how things had gone *so* wrong and what was being done to correct them.

"We had changed the pattern of the forest in the last twenty or thirty years," he said. "There were no more great big areas of forest any more. Even in the 1950s you could have started at Edmundston and flown fifty miles over continuous forest. Now, instead of 400,000 acres you might find 100,000 and all in little blocks."

There were almost 300 separate chunks of Crown land under licence, varying in size from one square mile to 1,700 square miles. For generations there had been little change in policy and usually the sole requirement of the licensee had been that timber dues be paid on time. In some cases licensees had no mills of their own but merely acted as brokers of Crown timber. "It was something of a dog's breakfast," said Baskerville.

The policy that began to emerge in 1978 was aimed at simplification. A measure of how badly the resource was ailing could be found in the strength of government intervention in an industry founded and fostered on private enterprise. The strongest medicine was to be cancellation of all timber licences, so they could be reallocated on a more rational and, it was hoped, more productive basis.

The leased areas were to be reduced from 300 to ten, each occupied by one of the major pulp and paper companies, which would in turn play host to smaller outfits that were its subtenants. The big company would be responsible for managing, harvesting, and replanting the area under government supervision. It would hold an "evergreen" twenty-five-year forest management agreement, renewable every five years, a practice borrowed from British Columbia. Since there was a self-regulating provision in the lease, it was not likely a licence would have to be revoked because of poor performance. A licensee practising silviculture could count on government assistance.

Each of the ten primary licensees might have up to twenty sub-licensees holding five-year tenures, renewable annually upon government review. Each was assured an adequate volume of wood, usually sawlogs. The idea was to ensure, for the first time, a stable supply to all mills, big and small, pulp or lumber.

In a province where forty per cent of the forest is in private hands, the government ruled that Crown land was not to be the first source of supply, but rather the "residual supply." That is to say, Crown forests could be used to make up the deficit only after the logging of private land and the utilization of residue such as chips. In this way it was hoped to see the industry through the lean years ahead.

"We borrowed ideas from wherever we could find them, from British Columbia, Alberta, and elsewhere," said Baskerville. "In fact, if there is anyone from whom we did not borrow an idea, I apologize. We made use of computers, and perhaps only in a computer age could we have worked out the solution to our problems. But a big factor was the appearance of a new minister who was the right man at the right time."

Without the support of the public, through their elected politicians, forestry in Canada can never succeed. In the person of J.W. "Bud" Bird, minister of natural resources, former mayor of Fredericton and owner of a Maritimes building supply company, forestry got an energetic champion. He is the sort of man who automatically matches a problem with a solution.

Under Bird's buzz-saw enthusiasm, the legislature adopted a Crown Lands and Forest Act that thrust New Brunswick into the forefront. There was remarkably little opposition from industry, which believed that what it lost in control of the land it was gaining in government support and security of timber supply.

"Times are changing," said Bird. "We are no longer living in a world of plentiful resources where there is no real penalty for

inaction. The most exciting thing about forest resource management today in N.B. is that *everyone* from the oldest industrial mossback to the most time-worn civil servant knows we
have to act. We don't argue 'whether or not'; we argue about
'how.' In this atmosphere there is no room in any organization
for people who don't give a damn."

With more direct control than it ever had before over fifteen
million acres of forest, the government of New Brunswick was
able to incorporate at one sweep five vital forest management
functions—planning the harvest, allocating it among various
users, reforestation, silviculture, and fire and pest protection.
Forest management agreements were negotiated with remarkable speed, and New Brunswick entered the Eighties with new
hope.

Ontario, meanwhile, was embarking on a less revolutionary
course, its plight not being as serious as that of New Brunswick.
All the same, Ontario's situation had not improved much since
the government had taken responsibility for forest renewal in
1962. There was no statutory commitment to sustained yield.
While it had managed to increase regeneration from a pitiful
5,000 acres to 180,000 in 1976, the Forest Service was, like
poor Sisyphus, condemned to push the stone up the hill only to
have it continually roll back. It was trying to fill the backlog of
unregenerated land while regenerating what industry was cutting currently. The yearly harvest had increased substantially,
and thousands of square miles of uncommercial forest land
were building up in northern Ontario.

Realizing the folly of dividing harvesting from reforestation,
the government in the late 1960s had tried again to involve
industry by offering regeneration agreements that would reim-
burse a company for out-of-pocket expenses. There were
disagreements over costs and regeneration standards, and what
work was done was generally poor. Forestry was running into
another of its famous log jams when, in 1975, the government
was jolted by a report from one of its own agencies. The Timber
Revenue Task Force declared, "Given continuance of the current level of regeneration there is a distinct potential for timber
shortage in the 1980s."

Ontario took action. Its first step was to borrow Kenneth
Armson, the University of Toronto forestry professor and soil
specialist who had contributed to the Reed report, to investigate the whole question of forest management, or lack of it. No
armchair pedagogue, Armson put on his hard hat and went out

28. *Kenneth A. Armson, while a professor of forestry at the University of Toronto, drafted a report in 1976,* Forest Management in Ontario, *which was to set the province on a new effort to make the most of its timber resource. He was retained by the government as special advisor and then chief forester and in other senior positions to implement many of his recommendations.*

into the woods, confessing he was humbled by the small amount of forestry actually done in relation to what was obviously needed. He identified the various "institutional roadblocks," picked up fresh ideas across the country, particularly in British Columbia, and within a year had drafted a seminal report, "Forest Management in Ontario."

"The fact that the forest is viewed as a resource to be exploited is still the most serious impediment to forest management," Armson said. "It is evident in the view of the public who are concerned with the exploitation of the forest by industry, and with the conservation and protection of it by government—but not with its management. It is evident in the views of those who are concerned with the preservation of forests for recreational or aesthetic purposes which is merely another form of exploitation—the locking up or 'consuming' of large areas for single uses—but without management. It is evident from the views of industry who are concerned with the allocation of wood from the present forest to supply their mills —today, tomorrow and a few years ahead—but not with forest management. It is evident in the attitudes and views of civil servants and politicians who view the forest as suitable for regulation and administration—but not management."

Borrowing freely from British Columbia and Alberta, Armson devised "evergreen" licences that were to consist of twenty-year agreements that can be extended for five years at the end of each five-year period. The government would pay for site preparation, planting or seeding, tending, and part of the road building. A company was free to undertake additional silvicultural treatment at its own expense if it wished, with the assurance that any increase this brought in timber growth would be reflected in reduced royalty charges. On the other hand a licensee would have to replant at his own expense if he over-cut. At the end of each five-year term the company was obliged to report on how much harvesting there had been in relation to growth, so that a balance could be maintained between the two in the interests of sustained yield.

The path that Armson was suggesting would avoid the pitfalls of the 1960s by making it legally binding on companies to practise forest renewal. The crucial breakthrough, after a mixed reaction, came when the Ontario Forest Industries Association, representing the major companies, responded favourably if cautiously, urging "an amendment to the present legislation, transferring responsibilities for forest management of certain Crown lands to industry at the option of the licensees." This meant, however, that from now on it would be a slow process, negotiating new forest management agreements, one by one.

Hiring Armson to see the project through, Natural Resources Minister Frank Miller, who acknowledged that Ontario had failed to close the gap between harvesting and regeneration, said: "I have accepted the philosophy of Ken Armson that harvesting and regeneration are one function and the person who cuts the trees should be the one who plants them. The way people cut timber affects the ability to regenerate the land. Up to this point we have simply given the companies licences to cut timber, not to regenerate it. They have cut it in the manner which is advantageous to themselves, but not necessarily good for reforestation." In the end, about three-quarters of Armson's recommendations were adopted by the government.

In 1980 the first of the Ontario forest management agreements, named after their forerunners in Alberta, were signed; companies took over management planning, road construction, regeneration, and silviculture on behalf of the real owner, the Ministry of Natural Resources. The target was to be thirty-five FMAs by 1987, covering seventy per cent of the Crown land under licence. Except for details, the agreements were basically the same, all aimed at ensuring sustained yield. It seemed that timber supplies would be tight by the year 2000, but the ministry believed that, like New Brunswick, Ontario was finally on the road to bridging the regeneration gap.

There was, however, one concern outstanding: the lack of understanding by the public, and its politicians, of the continuing need for public funding. There was still no legal obligation that required the government to continue the funding if other priorities interfered, as they had so often in the past.

"The new agreements are an attempt to allocate some public funds to a renewable resource that has been the mainstay of the economy," commented that perennial gadfly of the industry, Ken Hearnden. "But whether enthusiasm for sustaining the forests can be kept up into the future through the lives of successive governments is the question. But since all of us have benefited from the exploitation of the forest, we should be prepared to allocate tax dollars to its renewal. Perhaps a forest renewal surtax on all forest products would serve as a public reminder and ensure an independent source of funds."

*T*he battle for the trees

LEFT TO THEMSELVES WITH NO INTERFERENCE from mankind, forests will see to their own renewal century after century, slowly creating new wood and enhancing the quality of air, soil, and water. So slow is this process that unless a forest is attacked by fire or bugs or blown down by a gale, it hardly seems to change at all. But change, in fact, is constant in the dynamic ecosystem of plants, microbes, worms, insects, mammals, and birds, in which the most visible components are trees, fascinating subjects for study in themselves. No machine devised by man can equal the efficiency of the meanest tree.

Powered by the sun, a tree feeds, heals, and re-creates itself every spring and summer. Through a system of filters and valves more efficacious than a patent suction pump, a tree can suck up fifty gallons of water laced with minerals every day to the foliage forty or fifty feet above the roots that anchor and feed it. Through the green chlorophyll of the foliage, which absorbs solar energy, the nourishing broth, mixed with carbon dioxide from the air, is converted by photosynthesis into several pounds of carbohydrates, or starch, sugar, and glucose. The oxygen manufactured in this process is let off into the air through valves called stomata, which siphon in the carbon dioxide, thus freshening the atmosphere. Excess water escapes into the air through transpiration. A forest creates a mini-climate all its own, while in the ground the roots, soil, and forest debris form a sponge that controls the flow of water and protects the land from flood and erosion.

The carbohydrates are carried back down into the tree in the form of sap through the filter called phloem, and in towards the tree's core through those hairline cracks that can be seen on stumps. So with nourishment flowing up through the sapwood and back into the tree, the layer under the protective bark, called cambium, adds another annual ring to the inert heart-wood—solidified sunshine, it has been called—from which lumber and pulp are fashioned. The life-blood of a tree contains oxygen, hydrogen, and carbon, as well as traces of a dozen minerals such as calcium, potassium, and copper, which contribute strength and up to one per cent of a tree's dry weight. Minerals compose most of the ash that is left when wood is completely burned.

While West Coast trees, Douglas fir or cedar, can live a thousand years or more, and eastern white and red pine three or four centuries, the average tree life in the east is closer to 100 years—then the trees topple over to make way for a younger generation. In a vivid description of the virgin mixed forest of coniferous and deciduous trees that flourished in southeastern Canada a hundred years ago, Francis Parkman in *The Old Regime in Canada* found it "dim and silent as a cavern, columned with innumerable trunks...gnarled and knotted with wens and goitres, roots intertwined beneath like serpents petrified in an agony of contorted strife; green and glistening mosses carpeting the rough ground, mantling the rocks, turning pulpy stumps to mounds of verdure, and swathing fallen trunks as, bent in the impotence of rottenness, they lie outstretched over knoll and hollow like mouldering reptiles of the primeval world, while around, and on and through them, springs the young growth that battens on their decay—the forest devouring its own dead."

This funereal shade is in great contrast to the light and life of the open woodlands, where trees have a chance to flourish and grow. Although such over-mature woods are valued by naturalists and artists, to foresters they are decadent silvicultural slums, and the sooner they are cleared away the better, either by the clean-sweep logging method known as clear-cutting or by fire.

Fire has always been nature's method of replacing a decadent old forest with a healthy new one. It cleans out dead wood and debris, exposing the mineral soil that acts as a warm incubator for growth; unless a second fire occurs, it frequently only scorches lightly the vigorous living trees. Trees that have difficulty growing in shade, such as spruce, jack pine, and Douglas fir, do particularly well after fire, and modern foresters, particularly in B.C., emulate nature by starting controlled fires to clean out an area.

Two or three years after a fire, there follows a more or less predictable series of natural successions. Grasses, pink and green fireweed, and blueberry bushes appear. If the original forest was largely made up of black spruce, infant trees begin to appear, followed in five or six years by such pioneer species as birch, poplar, and balsam fir, all of which compete with the spruce. If the spruce gets a proper lease on life and is not choked out, the other trees, which have a shorter life span, will fade out of the picture within five decades, leaving a spruce forest similar to the one that was there before the fire.

Given a temperate climate in the growing season and moist, stable soil, which is usual in much of Canada, the land will clothe itself with trees after a forest is destroyed. Eventually, with enough time, it will even get around to producing the same sort of mature "climax" forest that was there in the beginning. But time is precisely the problem we are up against. World demand for wood fibre has grown too urgent to leave forest renewal solely to nature, which requires 150 years to work through the usual succession of more or less uncommercial species to produce the spruce, Douglas fir, and other trees we need.

Logging has changed dramatically in the past twenty years. Articulated, hydraulic skidders, equipped with huge rubber tires and resembling a cross between a tractor and an armoured vehicle, are now the work-horses of the woods. Lumbering through the forests like metallic dinosaurs are ingenious machines like the multi-ton Beloit Harvester, which can shear off a tree near the ground and cut off its top and branches in what is called the "tree length system," which accounts for sixty per cent of the timber harvest in eastern Canada.

Like the "shortwood system," in which trees are cut into lengths right at the stump, then hauled to the road by machines, the tree length system leaves unsightly slash and debris that can fuel fire and otherwise make regeneration difficult and costly. A third method, the "full tree system," avoids that by lugging the complete tree out to the road. But it too has drawbacks, since it can be destructive to advance regeneration and removes leaves and branches that the other systems leave to decompose, thus enriching the soil.

Unless great care is taken, such methods increase the danger Eduard Fernow warned about early in the century when he wrote, "No proprietor has the right to injure the fertility of the soil, lest as it is written in the Scripture, 'The lands cry out against them and the forests thereof complain.'"

Removal of natural vegetation traditionally left on the site is likely to increase because a new forest product, industrial energy, has caught the imagination of scientists. The oil shortage arising out of the Arab embargo of the mid-1970s encouraged consideration of "forest biomass," which is everything in the forest ecosystem that is combustible, including needles, leaves, branches, even stumps and roots, which together contain thirty per cent of the biomass of a tree. Though bulky and not as good a source of energy as fossil fuel, forest biomass has advantages over coal and oil—less air pollution because of a low sulphur content, renewability, and possibly a lower price in the future. Whether it will be developed on a large scale remains to be seen, but if it is, and large areas of forest are cleaned out, literally root and branch, on "fibre farms" where efforts are made to grow trees ever faster so they can be harvested on shorter rotations, foresters will have new problems to contend with.

"It will make forestry much more similar to agriculture, and we may expect a number of problems that are common to agriculture but that have been traditionally regarded as insignificant in forestry," says forest ecologist K.P. Kimmins at the University of British Columbia. "Unfortunately, many forests grow on very infertile soils, and in these situations, the nutrients available for tree growth are in the tree themselves. If we take away the entire tree there may be insufficient nutrients left for the next crop. Fertilize, you say? Unfortunately fertilizers do not work equally well on all soils and many of the poor soils on which this problem can occur are not capable of utilizing fertilizer additions very efficiently. The only solution is to harvest in a way that does not result in excessive depletion of nutrients."

In Germany and Switzerland, where forests have been repeatedly logged for centuries, soil productivity has long been under study. Australia developed a system of classifying forests according to soil, climate, and vegetation. These methods were brought to Canada by the Canadian Forestry Service some time ago, but in British Columbia Kimmins especially credits Vladimir Krajina, a Czech who came to the University of British Columbia after World War II to teach botany and forestry. "He taught that the forest should not be exploited without regard to ecology," said Kimmins. "It was essentially due to his work that B.C. was able to launch intensive forestry on a sound ecological basis." Krajina prevailed on the government to establish ecological reserves so that foresters could be assured of places to study how nature might function if left to itself, undisturbed by man.

Another promising addition to forestry is the computer, used in programs such as Kimmins's own at UBC, which he calls FORCYTE (forest cycling trend evaluator). It predicts long-term effects on the soil by logging and intensive management. Since history contains so many examples of failures to anticipate the long-term consequences of human actions, the new science of computer simulation holds particular promise for a profession that must plan in advance for as much as 100 years.

Computers, satellites, and infra-red scanners are all in use to protect the forest. Using past records and the latest weather information, a computer can predict fire outbreaks while infrared scanners can reveal hot spots indicating latent fires that cannot be detected by eye because of lack of flame and smoke. Satellite images are used to note changes in foliage for the early detection of insect epidemics and disease. The $5-million fire hazard forecasting system developed by the Canadian Forestry Service is saving the provinces millions of dollars a year in suppression costs. Even so, the various governments have to spend $250 million a year. Although fire control was our first attempt at forest management more than a century ago, more than 5,000 fires begin every year, three-quarters of them caused by man and most of the rest by lightning. In the bad fire season of 1980-81 fire destroyed six times more timber than was harvested by loggers. It is estimated that improved control would increase forest productivity by as much as one-fourth.

Like everything else in forestry, the fire issue is complex. We owe most of our best forests to fires that swept through and removed decadent timber some time in the past. Species like jack pine have needed fire to regenerate. Foresters, particularly on the West Coast, use controlled fires to clean out old areas for a new crop. Ken Armson, now chief of forestry for the Ontario government, recalls a survey in the 1960s in which he found that fire, in fact, had not hampered regeneration in a huge area stretching from the Manitoba border to the Albany River near Hudson Bay, except where it had occurred twice or more in a period of ten years. But in some areas fires can knock out timber production for a long, long time. An example is the Paul fire, which swept 50,000 acres northwest of Burns Lake in northern British Columbia one summer day in 1961. About thirty-one square miles of lodge-pole pine and white spruce stands were so badly scorched that only a salvage logging program would have saved them before the trees rotted out, dried, and eventually collapsed into a dismal landscape of bleached and barkless snags. But the area was too remote and nothing was done, until finally twenty years later the provincial forestry service began a costly rehabilitation program.

The woods most vulnerable to fire are those attacked by insects after the natural controls that normally resist an explosion of the insect population have failed to function. The tremendous Miramichi fire in 1825 has been attributed to a budworm epidemic, which caused the balsam fir and spruce to sicken and dry out.

The timber lost annually to forest pests and decay has not been measured precisely but is estimated to rival the amount harvested by industry. Some pests, like the balsam woolly aphid, have been unwelcome immigrants from other countries. In the 1950s the European spruce sawfly threatened to become as serious a menace as the budworm until the Forest Biology Division in Ottawa brought it under control by introducing a virus to fight it—probably the most successful application of biological control in the annals of world forestry.

Of the native pests, and there are many, the mountain pine beetle has killed or maimed many times as much timber as is destroyed by fire in the interior of British Columbia and Alberta. Since it bores under the bark it cannot be controlled by chemical sprays. No plan of control has had any lasting effect. On the B.C. coast a serious problem is the ambrosia beetle, which bores into green logs, infecting them with a black fungus that shows up in lumber and veneer as black holes and causes considerable loss in otherwise good-quality lumber.

In eastern Canada the most destructive pest by far is the spruce budworm, which has been part of the ecosystem since the last ice age 10,000 years ago. Nor has it always been a bad thing. Like fire, it has helped to create fresh new stands by speeding up the death of over-mature forests. It has only been since man has begun competing with these natural forest scavengers for wood that the budworm has been seen as intrinsically evil. As revealed by growth rings in old tree trunks, the first recorded outbreak occurred in 1704, and there have been half a dozen in the last 180 years, lasting up to ten years and subsiding after the larvae, which are the infants of small brown moths, eat themselves out of house and home.

Since the worst damage is caused to balsam fir, outbreaks were not regarded as serious in the days before fir became commercially important. In New Brunswick, which has traditionally suffered most from the budworm and whose forests contain forty per cent balsam fir, this attitude began to change in the 1920s with development of the pulp industry, which relied on fir as well as spruce. The epidemic was so bad along the Miramichi that companies were forced into bankruptcy and the area was passed by as the pulp industry expanded in other parts of the province. In the mid-1920s the Dominion Royal Commission on Pulpwood blamed the outbreak on faulty lumbering practices, something of an over-simplification since there had been outbreaks long before lumbermen ever appeared.

"Perhaps there is no better illustration than the budworm epidemic, as to what may happen when, through continued exigent utilization of the more valuable species, and the leaving of others which apparently have no value, the natural balance of forest conditions developed by nature is seriously disturbed," the commission said. "Although forest insects may be found operating in any healthy stand of timber growing under natural conditions, it is to a great extent due to the upsetting of, or interference with, such natural conditions that outbreaks of this character occur. In other words the methods of utilization adopted in the country have been such as to disturb the natural balance. Our methods have predisposed the forest to attacks of such insects."

In the last eighty-five years the budworm has attacked the equivalent of one-third of our present crop of standing timber. It can be found as far west as British Columbia, but it is a really serious menace only east of the Manitoba border. In fact, though Ontario has quantities of balsam fir, the tree has not been as commercially important as it is farther east, so the main provinces to suffer have been Quebec and the Atlantic provinces, where the bug seems to have become more destructive in the last forty years.

Usually held in check by cool spring weather and by birds and other predators, the budworm population explodes every few decades, usually after several dry summers. The epidemic is heralded by great clouds of moths, flights so big and compact they have been traced by radar and may be what people have sometimes identified as UFOs, as they have a metallic sheen when reflecting moonlight or the rays of the sun.

Blown into stands of aging conifers, they do their damage after mating and laying masses of green eggs on the undersides of fir and spruce needles. In the spring greyish larvae spin loose webs and feed on buds and shoots, defoliating the trees and disrupting the photosynthetic process. After feeding for several months, they turn into moths and the cycle is repeated. The oldest stands suffer most. In heavy infestations the budworm can strip a tree of all its new foliage; moderate attacks cause only partial loss, mostly in the top foliage. So long as a small amount of foliage is left, a tree may be able to recover, but usually, its vigour sapped, it succumbs to disease or beetles and other insects, and dies. Unless a salvage logging operation is mounted, the timber becomes dried out, fuel for forest fires.

The best way of dealing with budworm is through forest management, reducing large concentrations of elderly fir, but this takes fifty years and more. The easier, more common method, though relatively crude and bringing with it problems of its own, is to spray with toxic chemicals. Spraying began on a large scale in the early 1950s in New Brunswick and Quebec when a major outbreak, which had been predicted by foresters thirty years earlier, began to defoliate two-thirds of New Brunswick's woodlands. DDT, still regarded as a wonder substance, was the only chemical available and in the Gaspé and other regions of the lower St. Lawrence in Quebec it was sprayed on the forest from aircraft until the epidemic collapsed. New Brunswick mounted the biggest spray program in the world.

Though the initial aim was to eradicate the budworm entirely, this proved impossible, and government and industry decided to compromise by keeping the budworm population at a level where the timber crop could at least be kept alive. Abating in 1959, the only year in the last three decades when New Brunswick has not sprayed, the problem flared up a year later with the arrival of moths from Maine and Quebec. By this

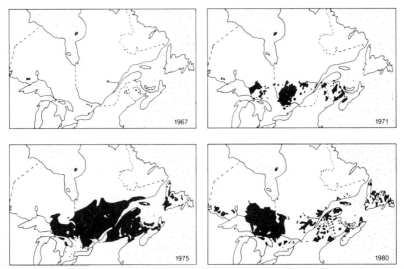

Waxing and waning every quarter-century or so, spruce budworm infestations have been a part of the ecology of the Canadian forest since the last Ice Age. Only when man began to harvest the trees the budworm feeds off, balsam fir and spruce, did the budworm become a real problem. The latest epidemic, which began some fifteen years ago, has attacked great areas of valuable timber in Quebec, New Brunswick, Nova Scotia, and Newfoundland.

time the hazards of DDT had become evident, particularly its propensity to recycle itself instead of breaking down and disappearing from the environment. Before Rachel Carson had warned of the dangers in her book *Silent Spring* in 1962, it was known in New Brunswick that DDT was killing aquatic insects and affecting the salmon population, even if it seemed then to have no discernible effects on birds or mammals. By the end of the decade, DDT had been banned in Canada and replaced by insecticides considered less harmful. These included aminocarb and the organophosphate fenitrothion, which, whatever their relative merits, were not specific to the budworm and killed such useful insects as bees.

The most recent outbreak began in the late 1960s in northwestern Ontario, western Quebec, and central New Brunswick. Some seventy-five million acres, an area a dozen times the size of Nova Scotia, suffered varying degrees of defoliation. Newfoundland was hard hit and fought the invasion with Matacil, an aminocarb that the government declared posed only "a minimum threat to the environment." Nova Scotia, whose eastern regions were badly affected, decided to maintain a ban on chemical sprays and to fall back on a strategy of salvage logging and replanting. As a result, the softwood forest of Cape Breton Island, which runs mostly to balsam fir, was lost, and along with it years of promising silvicultural work carried out by the licence holder, the Swedish-owned Nova Scotia Forest Industries. Later, in an effort to cut the losses on Cape Breton Island and on the eastern mainland, the government began to spray the safer (biological rather than chemical) insecticide *Bacillus thuringiensis* (BT).

BT, though more expensive and less effective than chemicals, attacks only moths and butterflies with no apparent effect on other living things. A natural bacterium first isolated by a German in Thuringia in 1905, it looks promising but more research and development are needed. Research is continuing into the potential of natural predators, and such things as a synthetic scent simulating that given off by the female moth trying to attract a male, which is released gradually into the air in an effort to confuse male moths and prevent breeding.

During the past ten years enormous areas have been sprayed with fenitrothion and aminocarb. Where they have been used the forest has been kept alive, and foresters point out that less than five per cent of the chemical insecticides used in agriculture have been sprayed on the woods. The controversy over budworm spraying has centred on New Brunswick and reached its height when an organization called the Concerned Parents Group said the spray was linked with the deaths of several children who had contracted Reye's Syndrome, which breaks down natural immunities to other diseases. Since there was no direct evidence that spraying was the cause, the government continued spraying, though limiting it now to areas at a distance from habitations. Subsequently, studies conducted by members of the National Research Council and an epidemiologist at McGill University have indicated no discernible connection between the spray and the syndrome.

All the same, while requirements for registering pesticides in Canada have usually been more rigorous than in any other country and government agencies claim to provide reasonable safety for both people and environment, pesticides are poisons and thus can never been regarded as completely safe. There is agreement among foresters, as well as other concerned groups, that more sophisticated methods of control, such as BT, must be further developed.

As for the various tree diseases, it is indicative of the narrow public interest in forestry that the best-known malaise is Dutch elm disease, because it has attacked the decorative trees around urban centres. Since its discovery in Richelieu County, Quebec, in 1944 this European disease has spread its deadly fungus over hundreds of square miles from Manitoba to Nova Scotia and has caused considerable commercial as well as aesthetic loss. But other diseases have been more commercially destructive, including white pine blister rust, which originated in Asia and arrived at the turn of the century to help give the *coup de grâce* to what was left of the white pine industry.

The latest threat to the forest, however, is not disease but acid rain (or snow or fog), which quietly drips a pollution of sulphuric acid from industrial plants burning fossil fuel. Its most apparent effect has been in robbing lakes of life. As for its effects on the forest, it has long been known what happens to woods downwind of smelters at places like Wawa or Sudbury or Bathurst. Acid rain, whose source and presence are not so clearly apparent, is more insidious, and much of the air pollution threatening the forests and lakes of eastern Canada comes from smokestacks in the United States, travelling hundreds of miles and several days.

The degree to which acid rain attacks our forests is just beginning to be understood. Damage to foliage may disrupt the vital photosynthetic process, and its effect on soil may include excessive acidity. Both could result in loss of growth and, in extreme cases, death of trees. While evidence has been accumulating that acid rain has been causing damage to the forests of northeastern Europe, particularly in Germany where pollution levels are high, the extent of the threat to Canada has not been clear. But whatever the complexities and uncertainties, acid rain has been developing into one of the serious environmental issues of the 1980s. A more immediate problem, however, has been the aerial spraying of woodlands with chemical herbicides, which foresters insist are vital to control brush and hardwoods that crowd out valuable young conifers and produce junk forests.

Compared with other pesticides, most plant poisons have been considered relatively harmless in the past, and one kind or another has been in use, mostly in agriculture, since the late nineteenth century. The discovery of the phenoxy herbicides 2,4-D and 2,4,5-T during World War II gave herbicides a new importance in agriculture and eventually in forestry (and also notoriety in Viet Nam many years later, when they were sloshed on the jungle in immense quantities as Agent Orange, with a lethal potency unknown here). It was found that 2,4-D, while effective against the birch, pin cherry, and alder that overwhelm new conifer growth, was of less use against maple and aspen and no use at all against the raspberry bushes that choke young seedlings. The 2,4,5-T, however, was useful against the latter and the two were often used together, though they were still not effective against grasses and ferns.

For many years these were the only herbicides available to forestry, though there had been a wider range available under government regulations to farmers for crops and home owners for weeding and feeding their lawns. Like all pesticides in use, they were registered under the Pest Control Act by Agriculture Canada and their application was reviewed by other federal departments, including Health and Welfare, Fisheries, and the Canadian Wildlife Service. In forestry they were employed to control weeds in tree nurseries and to relieve natural conifer regeneration and young plantations from the effects of competing vegetation.

Both were in general use in the 1980s—though mostly in agriculture and for clearing power-line rights of way and the like, with only a small amount used in forestry—when traces of an unwanted by-product, the dangerously toxic dioxin (TCDD), were discovered in 2,4,5-T. (Following this discovery methods of manufacture were adopted that reduced dioxin content to a minute fraction of the level found in Agent Orange.) Scientific proof of dioxin's effects on humans has been elusive, since obviously experiments cannot be carried out on people, but some of its effects on animals were known and some scientists suspected it of being teratogenic (fetus-deforming). Amid much controversy Agriculture Canada took steps to assure itself that any contamination was eliminated from commercial 2,4,5-T products, and the health officials allowed it to remain registered—though several provinces decided either to place severe restrictions on its use or to ban it entirely. British Columbia, where vegetation grows fast and thick in the coastal climate, was one of the provinces to virtually ban 2,4,5-T, which left foresters with only 2,4-D.

"Vegetation management is probably our number one problem," says Gary Lloyd, provincial silvicultural officer for a forest of spruce, pine, and cedar that stretches from the northwest interior to the Queen Charlotte Islands. "We are losing millions of dollars' worth of plantations because valuable young conifers are being choked out by aspen, alder, cottonwood, willow, and salmonberry."

An example of what he means can be found along the valley highway between Terrace and Kitimat, which was logged ten years ago and planted to Sitka spruce. Now for nearly twenty miles all one can see is thirty-foot thickets of alder and willow; the few spruces to survive are only a foot or two high and in poor condition. "Everyone now accepts the fact we have to plant trees, but there is a tremendous need to follow up, through weeding and brush removal," said Lloyd. "Some of this can be done manually, but most will have to be done chemically."

Theoretically there are alternatives to aerial spraying. One consists of backpacking cylinders of chemicals into the woods and hosing a mist of herbicide on the trees. Another is the "hack and squirt" system, where a small amount of herbicide is applied to a cut made in a tree. Then there is mechanical or manual weeding, which, though it may get rid of a weed tree, does not eliminate roots that produce suckers that grow into so many new alders or willows that the problem is exacerbated. Stumps can sprout up into ten-foot trees in a year, but restrictions are so tight that even 2,4-D, considered relatively low in toxic danger, cannot be daubed on a stump with a paint brush without a permit.

"I believe there is a misconception about the use of herbicides among environmental groups and the general public," said Lloyd. "People want us to apply herbicides from the ground rather from the air, but unfortunately once the brush grows three metres high this is not possible. We really need a public awareness program so people know what we are doing and why. We are not talking about large spray projects with total dispersion, but rather very specific areas where there is a brush problem. For this we need a complete range of herbicides because if you have three brush species and only the means of killing off two of them, then the third merely spreads and becomes 100 per cent of the problem. We have been using 2,4-D but we need others, like the glyphosate Roundup, for use against grasses."

The B.C. Council of Forest Industries has stated that judicious use of chemicals could increase timber production generally by ten per cent. Since 450,000 acres of potentially productive forest land are occupied by useless brush the increase could be much more than that in certain areas.

Given the high cost and dubious results of weeding by hand, most foresters agree with Lloyd that the solution must lie in careful spraying. Those who have been using herbicides now for twenty years, though they have some reservations, do not believe them to be a serious hazard. "The impacts on the environment and especially on non-target species may be significant in the short term, but they are no more serious ecologically than many natural impacts such as fire, wind-throw, or insect epidemic," said the Association of British Columbia Professional Foresters.

In the spring of 1983 there was intense interest on the part of foresters and environmentalists across Canada in a test case being fought in Nova Scotia, the first time the herbicide issue had been fully tried in a court of law. The Nova Scotia government, which had banned the use of chemical insecticides in the battle against budworm, had made no move against the use of herbicides, and the provincial epidemiologist at the Department of Health had, in fact, found no reason to ban the chemicals.

"The alleged adverse health effects due to exposure to phenoxy herbicides appear to have been exaggerated," he reported in March 1983. "The herbicides 2,4-D and 2,4,5-T are not a significant health hazard to the bystander and the degree of risk is no greater than that from an extremely large range of other industrial, agricultural and domestic products that are in common use....The health hazards, to the bystander, due to aerial application of herbicides, although often perceived to be significant, are negligible and the risk is probably no greater than application from the ground, when appropriate control measures are adopted."

But a group of small landowners in Cape Breton, advised and supported by Elizabeth May, a young law graduate and environmentalist whose family lived near the area to be sprayed, considered herbicides a sufficient threat to seek a ban through the courts. The defendant was Nova Scotia Forest Industries, the licensee of the Crown woodlands that had also been decimated by budworm. The hearings were held in Sydney before Justice D. Merlin Nunn of the Nova Scotia Supreme Court.

During twenty-three days in the spring of 1983, fifty witnesses from Canada, the United States, and other countries testified as to the nature of the controversial 2,4-D, sometimes known as Esteron 600, of 2,4,5-T and its dioxin contaminant TCDD, and of Esteron 3-3E, which is a mixture of 2,4-D and

2,4,5-T. Testimony filled seventeen volumes. Three months later Justice Nunn delivered his decision in the form of a 182-page statement, whose length he found justified by the nature of the case, the publicity it had received, and the very volume of evidence presented.

"Based on this evidence, fully weighed and considered, this court is of the opinion that these spraying operations can be carried out in safety and without risk to the health of the citizens of this province," Justice Nunn ruled.

In theory, since it was the first important test case, the Nova Scotia decision cleared the way for more general use of herbicides. Quebec, however, was moving in the opposite direction. Having heard evidence from environmental groups, the Bureau d'audiences publiques sur l'environnement (BAPE) declared that chemical herbicides were an unacceptable risk. Instead, the government began to hire workers to weed by hand. Though easing unemployment, hand weeding is both expensive and frequently ineffective. It is well known that the best way to get a raspberry bush to grow is to clip it; thus it is usually necessary to come back and weed as many as three or four times, whereas one or, at the most, two applications of aerial spray would suffice. Having mounted the biggest planting program in Canada, Quebec was now facing the problem of protecting it.

Clearly there is a credibility gap. Mistakes have been made with pesticides in the past, DDT being the best-known example, though Rachel Carson, we now see in the light of twenty years of hindsight, seems to have overstated the case. At any event she did not set out to ban all chemical spraying completely. This is not to say that challenges to the use of sprays should not be made and efforts increased to find efficient alternatives. In the meantime, however, there is evidence that blanket condemnation is no more reasonable than blanket recommendation if we are to have a viable industry. Without spray operations, the industrial forest in New Brunswick would be about one-third what it is today.

Pieces of the puzzle

"IT IS SO IMPORTANT THAT THE POTENTIAL WOOD supply from private land be increased, that the governments, or industry, or both should be able to approach a landowner and obtain permission to plant trees on his land. . . . If this procedure were followed, in due time the wood received year by year, by any mill, could be very substantially increased and the possibility of a Canadian wood shortage lessened."

M.R. Wilson,
Quebec woodlot owner and
retired industrial forester

ONE DAY NOT LONG AGO BRUCE DEVITT, CHIEF forester for Pacific Forest Products, a branch of Canadian Pacific, stood with some friends in a little hollow at Goldstream Park, ten miles northwest of the city of Victoria, and contemplated two ancient cedars. Somehow the trees had escaped the logger's axe and were 500 years old, museum pieces pensioned off to die of old age. They were scruffy, probably infected with rot, and someone had been scalping strips of bark from them, but the striking thing was their great size.

215

*29. Cathedral Grove in MacMillan Park west of Parksville on
Vancouver Island is one of the last preserves of majestic, centuries-old
Douglas firs, once the mainstay of the West Coast lumber industry. The
twelve-hectare preserve is endangered now not only because of age and
disease but because the cutting around the fringes of the park could
expose the stands to wind damage and blow-down.*

Trees like this, tall as a steeple and thick as an elephant's
torso, are the last of the giants that made British Columbia
forests famous around the world. There are still a few here and
there, even in Stanley Park in Vancouver, one of the great
urban forests of the world. There are some in Cathedral Grove,
part of the park H.R. MacMillan bequeathed to the province
on the road to Port Alberni, that were sizeable trees when
Columbus was a boy. At Nimpkish River there is a tract of
forty-five acres that was owned by a logging company but that
fortunately has not been harvested. But they are very scarce,
dying off, and in years to come will be found only in ecological
reserves.

"We'll never see the likes of these trees again," said Devitt,
whose enthusiasm for forestry is contagious after a few minutes
of conversation. "People are just not going to wait. In the time
it takes to grow trees this old we can maybe have eight crops of
timber, harvesting twice the volume of fibre we see right here in
front of us."

British Columbia has been growing trees for industry since 1925, but not on any large scale until the massive Campbell River fire of 1938 prompted a disaster-area program at what is now the Sayward Forest. By the mid-1960s industry had begun to plant on a worthwhile scale, both on private land and on the tree farm licence land created to bring about sustained yield forestry, a phrase Devitt did not like.

"Sustained yield is an unfortunate term," Devitt maintained. "To me, the old sustained yield calculations were strictly a rationing process for the old-growth forests. The allowable cut, or rate of harvest, should be a dynamic thing subject to economics, politics, the pressure of society, and management input. It's not fixed. You have to decide what you are sustaining to."

A few miles on we came upon an illustration of Devitt's new-style forestry. Spreading over hundreds of acres of what had once been a clear-cut of ugly stumps and slash, there was a new crop of tender green that would be ready for harvesting within half a century. "We've learned by now how to produce the same volume of wood in fifty years that it takes nature unaided 150 years to grow," Devitt said. "We've got great opportunities for job creation in this industry, because we could increase forest capacity by three or four times if we went about it the right way."

On Vancouver Island, which boasts the largest intensively managed forests in Canada, Devitt's company is unsurpassed, though not alone, in its forest renewal, with the largest tree fertilization program in Canada, active silviculture, and its own seed orchard. It is spending twice as much per acre on reforestation as the provincial government. As an industrial forester, Devitt believes there are four good reasons for renewing the forest: for profit, for maintaining an allowable cut, for compliance with laws and contracts, and for public relations.

As Ellwood Wilson had preached seventy-five years earlier, Devitt is working to bring the forest back to the mills, where it would provide the best return on investment. C.D. Orchard had tried it, though with no success, in the 1940s when he sought to rehabilitate depleted woodlands in the Fraser Valley by employing jobless war veterans. The same idea had been tried with good effect in the southern United States, Scandinavia, and New Zealand. Had it been used in Canada there would now be supplies of maturing timber within an hour of the mills instead of hundreds of miles away. As the centrepiece of his project, Devitt has established a seed orchard on a large plot of land at Saanich, just outside Victoria. This is headquarters for a renewal and management program for 300,000 acres of private forest on Vancouver Island.

Most of CP's land lies on what remains of the two million acres the government gave the entrepreneurs who built the Esquimalt & Nanaimo Railway up the east coast of Vancouver Island at the turn of the century. This land, along with the E & N itself, was inherited by the CPR, which for a long time sold off portions to H.R. MacMillan and others, until it decided it would be better business to log the property. Much of its land had been logged more than sixty years ago by such pioneer outfits as the Shawnigan Lake Lumber Company in the days before anyone thought of forest management.

"What's wrong here," said Devitt, stopping in one of the old stands where the land had not reproduced a commercial forest, "is not the way they cut it but the fact they walked away from it. Cut and run! They didn't space or thin the forest or look after it, and as a result we lost a whole generation, a whole crop rotation. We are trying to ensure that won't be what the people find who come along in the next generation behind us."

Large chunks of this logged-over land had grown up into junk forest such as alder, which Pacific was converting into Douglas fir stands. Such rehabilitation projects can be expensive, but these woods were close to the market and Pacific had managed to make the project self-supporting, selling the alder for firewood.

"There's no magic green wand," said Devitt, as we rode on up into the rainy highlands of the island, deep into the company's private land, where he has an unusual opportunity to practise silviculture without government supervision, but also with no assistance. "But we're trying to generate enough wood to plug the twenty-year regeneration gap between the harvesting of old growth and harvesting the new, tended growth coming up."

Though there has been logging on Vancouver Island for a century, the bulk has been done only since World War II, which means most of the second crop is less than thirty-five years old and not half grown. Nearly half the trees on Pacific's land are immature; of the remainder, two-thirds are mature enough for cutting and the final third are in the new plantations, superior trees grown from the company seed orchard and expected to produce a marketable crop ten to fifteen per cent sooner than a plantation originating from unimproved seedlings.

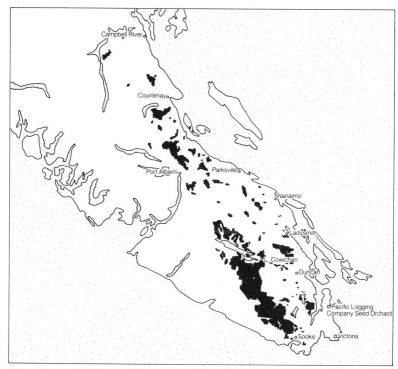

The private holdings on Vancouver Island of Pacific Forest Products Limited. With 300,000 acres of its own in a province where ninety-five per cent of the forest land is owned by the Crown, the company has been a leader in West Coast reforestation.

Since most of the land on which Devitt farms trees is privately owned, he is inclined to believe that Canadian forests would be better off if there were more private holdings. If they were managed like Devitt's, this might well be true, but the sad fact is that most private forests in Canada remain unmanaged, over-cut, under-cut, or neglected entirely.

Apart from a number of large corporate freeholds, many of them remnants of the early railway grants, most of Canada's private land is scattered in small parcels in a patchwork quilt. Mostly they are concentrated between eastern Ontario and the Maritimes. There are almost half a million, and the owners could be almost anyone: truck drivers, school teachers, churches. Half the owners are farmers, whose woodlots are what used to be known as "the back forty."

Though less than ten per cent of the national total, they produce a disproportionately large amount of Canada's pulpwood and sawlogs—in Quebec as much as twenty-five per cent. They offer real potential in efforts to stave off a national timber famine. Most of their 227,000 square kilometres lie south of the Canadian Shield, on the fringes of the farm lands, which means they enjoy better soil and a longer growing season than the Boreal, and as a consequence produce more fibre. Close to roads, labour, and mills, they are ideally suited to the movement to bring the forest back to the mill. In 1980 the various governments were spending $46 million on private-land forests and forestry.

The drawback of the woodlots is that most are too small, too uneconomic to attract good management, which is costly and calls for experts. Taking a lead from Europe and Japan, Nova Scotia, New Brunswick, and Quebec have been trying to solve that problem through owners' associations. By far the largest aggregation of private woodlots—a total of 72,000 square kilometres and 120,000 different owners—is in Quebec. Even in their present largely unmanaged state, they provide one-quarter of Quebec's commercial timber supply, plus millions of gallons of maple syrup and about a million Christmas trees every December, most of which are sold in the United States. Together they command a yearly income of more than $100 million.

Though it has barely scratched the surface, Quebec boasts the largest and most comprehensive woodlots program, and assistance administered by the Ministère de l' Energie et des ressources is channelled mainly through two organizations. The Fédération des Producteurs de Bois du Québec, an association of wood producers founded in 1968, concerns itself mainly with marketing and legal matters, but also inventories and management plans. Groupements forestiers, founded four years later and patterned after an owners' organization in France, permit pooling of small properties into larger units for management purposes.

The Groupements contain 8,000 members in nearly fifty management units that range from 300 to 1,000 square miles; those at the upper end of the range are in the class of small-sized corporate woodland operators. Owners receive technical advice, are paid to work their own woods, and receive one-third of the selling price of timber produced on their property. The Groupements log, market, plant trees, and carry out silvicultural work. One of the most successful, the Société d'exploitation des ressources de la Vallée, in the Matapédia Valley, has been rehabilitating old marginal Gaspé farm land, where balsam fir was attacked by budworm, by planting black and white spruce. Nursery stock is supplied free by the government.

After a dozen years of effort, only five per cent of all owners are actively involved, and considering the expense and work the scheme has been rather disappointing. However, it seems to be effort well spent, for even if just one-third of Quebec's private woodlots were properly managed, they could produce more wood than was harvested in all the province in the 1970s.

Ontario has been managing woodlots since it began its Agreement Forests Program in 1922, under which it managed land owned by various southwest counties in order to halt erosion caused by deforestation. More recently it has been signing agreements with private owners at the rate of 800 a year, under a Woodlands Improvement Act that provides tax incentives. Though fewer than Quebec's woodlots, these lots produce considerable quantities of pulpwood and sawlogs, perhaps thirty per cent of the total, if fuel wood is included.

In the Maritimes, woodlot development is particularly important, given the large amount of private land. The forest is all private in Prince Edward Island, except for parks; the three-foot-thick white pine and large spruce that once sustained whole towns are long gone. In more recent times the island has produced sawlogs for local mills and pulpwood has been exported, since there are no pulp mills. More recently still, the government has been looking into production of fuel wood since it possesses no coal or oil. Through tree improvement, planting, and a heavily subsidized silvicultural program, the province is re-creating part of that old Acadian mixed-wood forest that once graced the island. As Prince Edward Island enjoys good soil and rainfall, and is careful with its harvesting methods, its regeneration record is better than most. Of the 3,000 acres cut yearly, one-third is planted and most of the rest regenerates naturally to the desired species. Care for the land has even extended to the revival of horse logging so machinery will not chew up the ground. Like most things in Prince Edward Island, this is forestry in miniature.

In Nova Scotia things are more complicated. Pulpwood company land makes up half the private holdings and woodlots make up the balance. Ten years ago woodlots were contributing sixty per cent of the total harvest, but this has dropped off to forty per cent; in proportion to their share of the forest base, the woodlots are not contributing as much as they could, or

30. *Once richly covered with big white pine and spruce, by the 1970s Prince Edward Island had lost virtually all of its original forest. The provincial government has recently mounted a comprehensive forest management policy, including tree breeding and silviculture and the acquisition of marginal farm land for reforestation.*

should. An average acre produces a third of the fibre it could grow under better forest management. This, in turn, has put correspondingly heavy pressure on the one-third of the forest that is public land, compounded by the budworm attack that devastated the balsam fir forests of Cape Breton.

Elmer MacKay, the Progressive Conservative cabinet minister from Pictou County, has been one of the few federal politicians working for a better forest and, like his father, Gordon, a veteran lumberman, and his grandfather before him, he has carried on a tradition of tree planting and silviculture.

"It has been only in the last twenty-five years," he said, "that any significant amount of reforestation has been undertaken....Some of the large forest companies in Nova Scotia have come to a belated realization that they have to put something back in, that they have to take part in reforestation and make certain that the kinds of trees that are planted are of good quality....Various diseases affecting both hard and soft woods have caused great losses to Nova Scotia. Our beech, birch, and now elm have been affected. Logging practices in recent years have been abominable. Heavy equipment has been taken in and the land has been scarred. New growth has been destroyed, which has led to erosion and very severe damage to the environment."

MacKay noted there had been a change from a sawlog economy to a pulpwood economy. Throughout the province the old sawmills were closing down. "I wouldn't be a bit surprised that inside of twenty years there will be Scandinavian lumber coming into Nova Scotia," said his father, Gordon.

One way or another, it has taken a long time for Nova Scotia's forests to get into such serious condition. It will take perhaps fifty years for recovery. Those trying to deal with the problem at the ministry in Halifax are optimistic. If nothing else, the fate of the Cape Breton forest has forced re-evaluation of the entire industry through a royal commission, and management on private woodlots is being upgraded through a recent shared-cost agreement with Ottawa.

Teams of government foresters have been assigned to help such outfits as the North Nova Scotia Forest Owners Cooperative at Pugwash, which boasts twenty-five members whose lots range from Arnold MacEwan's thirty acres to Stan Moore's 1,500 acres. "Pugwash has exported pulpwood for years," said the manager, Ralph Thompson, "and most of the better-quality forest has been over-exploited. There'll be a lot more planting here than in other areas because the forest has been high-graded for so long that there's almost no breeding stock left."

In New Brunswick almost one-third of the forest is controlled by 35,000 woodlot owners. Some of these, like Bayard Hoyt not far from Fredericton, have made a good living. Starting in the 1920s with thirty-five acres of mixed woods across the road from his home in a small settlement, also called Hoyt, he and his son increased their holding to 2,000 acres. He sells pulpwood, poles, sawlogs, and Christmas trees and cuts two cords per acre, considerably more than the provincial average. Hoyt has lived to regret the disappearance of the horse and the advent of mechanical logging. "The woods lost its best friend when we lost the horse," he said. He does not approve of clear-cutting and attributes success to "good judgement and a love of the woods."

It is too late to bring the horse back into the woods, but since the best logging system is that which disturbs ecology as little as possible, there is a need for small logging equipment rather than big unwieldy skidders and the even bigger harvesters. There is also a case to be made, on many woodlots, for the cultivation of poplar, known also as aspen, which has historically been regarded as a useless weed tree. Some pulp mills are already making use of it, but the market has been limited. It grows so thick in its wild state in the northern reaches of the Prairie provinces that industry has been trying to find ways to make it pay.

Hybrid poplar looks particularly promising, since it can attain a height of forty feet in ten years rather than the thirty or more required by wild poplar, and after twenty years a hybrid can produce big logs for veneer mills. Though it has long been cultivated in Italy, the first major Canadian breakthrough in growing hybrid poplar was made a few years ago at Cornwall, in southeastern Ontario, where Domtar is growing it to bring its wood supply closer to the mill. This came about because Domtar found itself having to reach out too far—150 miles and into the state of New York—for its wood. Within a scant twenty-five miles of the mill, however, there was plenty of abandoned farm land, marginal for agriculture but fine for growing trees. Domtar began to buy it up or lease it, signed a joint agreement with the federal and Ontario governments, the first of its kind, and with subsidization began a hybrid poplar tree farm. Domtar hopes to begin using hybrid poplar in its mill by the late 1980s, assuring an economic fibre supply while making use of otherwise wasted land. In the efforts to fill in the holes in the jigsaw puzzle that typifies Canadian forestry today, it is at last becoming accepted that forest renewal must begin at home—or as close to the mills as possible.

Today's crisis: Tomorrow's forests

"OAK AND ASH ARE NEARLY ALL GONE, AND OUR pine, spruce, birch and tamarack are following so fast that we will soon have nothing of commercial value." James Little at the Montreal Forestry Congress, 1882

"What we are here to say and prove is that we are at the limit of the bounty of the present forest. That being the case, new initiatives are imperative." Adam H. Zimmerman, Canadian Forest Congress, Toronto, 1980

BY 1980 THE FOREST INDUSTRY HAD NAVIGATED ITS WAY through a century of dire predictions, boom and bust, bureaucratic dithering, scattered attempts at woodlands management, and a profound reluctance to spend money on a God-given resource that had always grown wild for the taking. Ninety-eight years after the Montreal congress had focused attention on forestry, Canada was still living off its natural forests, somewhat as our prehistoric ancestors had lived off wild plants before they learned to cultivate them. Unlike our ancestors, however, Canadians could hardly claim the excuse of lack of technical knowledge.

Despite advances in silvicultural techniques, a chart of forestry progress, had anyone cared to draw one, would show more valleys of neglect than peaks of enlightenment, and in hindsight it was clear that opportunities had been missed, again and again, to ensure a sustained yield of merchantable timber.

On the other hand, a chart of timber production or a graph depicting financial gain would show a fairly steady ascent since the early 1800s when governments began to regard the woods as a prime source of revenue. This makes the current crisis somewhat difficult to understand: it has not, after all, developed in some obscure and minor sector of the economy but in what qualifies in many ways as the nation's most important industry, contributing more to Canada's international balance of payments than agriculture, mining, petroleum, and fisheries combined. Compared with a yearly output of $23 billion worth of lumber, pulp and paper, and other wood products—most of it shipped to 100 countries, chiefly the United States—grains fetch only about $4 billion and fish $1 billion.

The forest industry accounts for a fifth of all investment in manufacturing and provides employment, directly in the woods and mills and indirectly in support services, for one million Canadians. One railway carload in every five consists of goods going to or from the wood products companies, whose activities are by now generating $2 billion annually in direct government revenue and half as much again in indirect revenue. Somehow the importance of all this has got lost in the woods, so far as the public and its politicians are concerned. Rarely has forestry emerged as an important political issue, in part because of the almost atavistic belief that Canada will always enjoy unlimited timber.

It is a belief that, fuelled by ignorance, does not die easily. As recently as 1980 a panel of foresters advising the president of the United States on the future of resources reckoned, in "Global Report 2000," that the United States could always count on Canadian lumber. The report was based on outdated information released by the Canadian Forestry Service several years earlier, and failed to grasp the fact that Canada has the worst forest inventory in the northern hemisphere.

One indicator of impending crisis is the lowering in many regions of the annual allowable cut. The AAC is a rough estimate imposed by provincial governments to indicate how much timber can be harvested without jeopardizing a second harvest within a reasonable period of time. The information going to make up the AAC, including estimates of the areas logged and how much is regenerating, has usually been vague —a lot of imprecise figures amassed to provide a supposedly precise total. But by now what has seemed a comfortable margin between the AAC and the yearly depletion of timber is proving more apparent than real.

Meanwhile, there is every indication that the world demand for wood could increase by at least fifty per cent by the year 2000. To meet that challenge, and to avoid further slippage in Canada's traditional position as chief wood exporter to the world, the Canadian Council of Resource and Environment Ministers (CCREM) decided in 1980 that Canada must increase its harvest by forty per cent over the next thirty years.

The council, the closest thing in Canada to a national policy-making body, proposed that tree planting be doubled to 500,000 hectares a year and silvicultural treatments increased four-fold to 400,000 hectares. Loss from fire, disease, and insects would have to be reduced and large areas of junk forest rehabilitated and returned to commercial production.

It suggested a price tag of $400 million a year for five years for this massive project, though considering the size of the backlog needing attention, a more realistic figure might have been $500 million and the time span ten years rather than five. Though this seems a formidable figure—$5 billion, mostly in government funding—it is less than three per cent of the yearly sale of wood products and only a quarter of the yearly tax exacted from the industry. In 1980 only five and a half cents of every revenue dollar was being spent on forest renewal, most of that by the provinces.

One indicator of the seriousness of the situation was the concern expressed by industry. Up to now, the infrequent conferences held over the years had been arranged by governments or by groups, such as the Canadian Forestry Association, not directly affected by profit and loss. The two-day conference held in the glittering Ontario Science Centre in Toronto in

September 1980 was organized, however, by the industry's biggest umbrella group, the Canadian Pulp and Paper Association. Its importance was reflected in the large number of company chief executives, bank presidents, and union leaders who sat down with the usual contingent of foresters and academics.

The co-chairmen were Jack Munro, the leader in Canada of the International Woodworkers of America, which saw the crisis in terms of lost jobs, and Adam H. Zimmerman, chief executive in the Noranda Group, which had diversified from mining into one of the most important forest products outfits in the country.

Setting the tone, Zimmerman, an accountant by profession, said: "Our concern these two days will be first, education, and second, some definition of the road ahead. It is probably fair to say that this room holds the bulk, if not all, of the forest knowledge in Canada. It may also be fair to say that we, recognizing the beginning of the era of the managed forest, know what has to be done. We are a lot less clear on who is to do it."

Not unexpectedly, spokesmen for industry held to the line that the governments, as owners of the resource, should provide the funding. The union leaders, new to such conferences, insisted the governments and industry should share the burden, while expecting no contribution from the unions. Though stalled once more on that essential point, the conference took on the aspect of a revival meeting with speaker after speaker painting a gloomy picture of what would happen if we failed to look after our greatest renewable resource. While in itself planting no trees, the meeting achieved a new crest in what was becoming a nationwide surge of forest awareness. "We have now reached a point where we either maintain our coniferous forests or accept a major decline in our economy," said F.W. McDougall, deputy minister of renewable resources for Alberta.

"We are talking about an industry that over the next two decades could create 300,000 new jobs, direct and indirect, and an industry that could double the contribution it makes to the economy," said the president of the Royal Bank of Canada, Rowland C. Frazee. "The future should be bright indeed. Instead it is clouded. And the stakes are high. Not only may we jeopardize the extraordinary opportunities for growth; worse, we may not even hold on to what we have today."

Les Reed, who saw the Toronto meeting as a culmination of the work he and others had been doing since the Montebello Forestry Conference sixteen years earlier, told the delegates: "The question is whether Canadian timber supplies can be stretched sufficiently to maintain our share of world markets. Given present levels of forest management and utilization the answer is no. Forgone opportunities are already in prospect on a grand scale."

Largely because of his eye-opening report of 1978, Reed had been appointed assistant deputy minister in charge of forestry at the federal environment ministry, where a move to upgrade forestry had begun in 1979 during the brief period when the Progressive Conservatives held office.

Having once worked for the Prices and Incomes Commission, Reed was no stranger to Ottawa, though his outspoken, crusading style was hardly typical of the usual civil servant. Convinced that forestry now enjoyed more cabinet support than at any time in twenty years, he sold his Vancouver consulting firm and arrived with a briefcase full of proposals. Normally not a centralist, he was convinced that the necessary leadership could only come from Ottawa. Millions would be needed to revive the Canadian Forestry Service's research and development initiatives; forestry schools would need subsidies to get foresters out into the woods; the provinces would require large sums for forest renewal. Forestry would have to compete for funding alongside more popular candidates such as education, agriculture, highways, and fisheries. But Reed was prepared to make a strong case for investment, since he believed 25,000 new jobs could be created in forest renewal alone, plus three times as many through the increased manufacture of wood products resulting from bigger and better harvests.

"The whole picture had changed," Reed recalled. "There was a sense of urgency. I was told to go out and negotiate forestry agreements with all the provinces as quickly as I could. There was a new sense of commitment in industry as well."

The change was reflected in institutional advertising. Twenty years earlier industry had been running ads with the carefree message that "growth exceeds the cut." Now the ads were more realistic, seeking to enlist public understanding and support and admitting frankly that reforestation was an urgent need. Outspoken woods managers like H.J. "Joe" O'Neill of the Acadian Forest Products Company in New Brunswick preached a disturbing gospel: "In New Brunswick our spruce and fir forest is sick," said O'Neill, with Miramichi Valley candour. "It is a slum, mostly old, run-down, low-quality, and in many cases, on private woodlots, a dead, budworm-killed fire trap."

Paradoxically, for twenty years New Brunswick would have what appeared to be an over-supply of timber, O'Neill said, but it was budworm-damaged and aging, and logging it would amount to a salvage operation. Some mills might have to close, but if the province could struggle through for forty years, until the new crop came up, all might still be well.

"Our plantations will be ready, and in addition our treated and untreated natural regeneration from clear-cuts made between 1960 and 1980 will be ready. . .assuming we can stay alive for the next forty years," said O'Neill.

Quebec, with enough mature timber to last thirty-five or forty years, was only better off by comparison. Though the budworm had attacked 85,000 square kilometres, public reaction had hampered the chemical spray campaign. The harvest had increased thirty per cent in ten years, while the resource base grew smaller. Though surpluses on the North Shore were masking shortages on the South Shore and in the northwest, there were sawmills not far from Quebec City already importing half their softwood from the United States.

The government had adopted a strategy of harvesting mature timber where it could, while renewing the depleted southern forests as quickly as possible. Having lagged behind Ontario and British Columbia in reforestation, it had been planting sixty-five million seedlings a year, and Premier René Lévesque promised this would be stepped up to 300 million, though the promise was blunted when the government announced that chemical herbicides would be banned from the important task of protecting young plantations from weed trees.

Since passage of the retrocession law in 1974, under which the Quebec government had begun to regain control of Crown land held by the big companies for generations, industry had lost interest in the practice of silviculture. The task of forest renewal was undertaken by government, which had neither the funds nor the manpower. Moreover, the retrocession program had almost ground to a halt, only a third completed. On the more positive side, COGEF, the team set up to draft a plan for developing and reallocating Crown forests, had completed work that resulted in the old timber limits being divided into forty-four sustained yield management units, which at least laid the groundwork for future developments. Industrial foresters were beginning to urge that the province adopt the modern forest management agreements of Ontario, or perhaps even the revolutionary system adopted by New Brunswick. Quebec found itself at a crossroads.

The Toronto conference having been inspirational rather than practical, a smaller, more business-like sequel was held a year later, in September 1981, at the Banff Centre School of Management. It was expected to provide answers to what should be done, and, more importantly, by whom. But having agreed the price of forest renewal should be $600 million a year, considerably more than the amount suggested by the CCREM and almost triple what was then being spent, the delegates meeting among the forests and mountains of Banff National Park had no more success than earlier conferences in getting to grips with just how this was to be funded. "I am told," said one, "that senior civil servants and politicians were amazed at the magnitude of the problem." They felt that industry, in expecting government to shoulder the financial burden, was ignoring political realities, including forestry's traditional lack of political sex appeal.

Marcel Lortie, a forestry professor at Laval University and a former regional director general of Environment Canada in Quebec, who was reported to have been offered the job of assistant deputy minister but turned it down for personal reasons, saw the problem as political. After stating that "the wood supply situation is almost desperate in some parts of Canada," Lortie said: "Most provincial government foresters are sincere in their desire to be good natural resource managers. Politicians, however, are faced with the dilemma of managing a resource that takes thirty, fifty, sixty years (and sometimes longer) to be ready for harvesting while their immediate concern is their own re-election. Consequently it is difficult for them to take seriously a wood deficit which will occur in twenty or thirty years....It is too tempting to leave to future governments the problem of coming up with solutions after the resource is depleted."

Most delegates agreed that the money would largely have to come out of the public purse, since the public owned the forests. With the help of figures and recommendations put together by Canadian Forestry Service officers the conference defined the magnitude of the task ahead. Reed, who had organized the Banff conference and assumed the mantle of activist-in-chief for good forestry, was trying to make the CFS once more the cutting edge of forestry development. Like a latter-day Johnny Appleseed, he seemed to be everywhere, giving media interviews, addressing meetings, popping up in Vancouver, Regina, Edmonton, Toronto, Montreal, and even the United States, to plug forestry.

A few weeks after the Banff meeting the Canadian Forestry Service published "A Forest Sector Strategy for Canada," signed by the Minister, John Roberts, but bearing Reed's unmistakable hand. It was refreshingly blunt and detailed. Apart from a poor inventory, the country was lagging behind competing nations in research and practically everything else: silviculture, forest protection, capacity of seed orchards and tree nurseries, and the ability to plant trees with an acceptable survival rate. To increase the harvest by the modest forty per cent recommended by the Council of Resource and Environment Ministers, the federal government said it was prepared to collaborate closely with the provinces, industry, and woodlot owners.

Ottawa had involved itself to some extent in reforestation between 1952 and 1966 under the federal-provincial agreements, and again between 1974 and 1981 under DREE agreements that accounted for most of the forest management programs in Atlantic Canada and large portions of those in Quebec, Ontario, and British Columbia. But by and large, since 1867 when the British North America Act had handed responsibility for the forests to the provinces, and since 1930 when the Prairie provinces assumed responsibility for their forest lands, the federal government had concentrated on research.

Now, a year after the meeting in Banff, the government unveiled a new policy entitled "A Framework for Forest Renewal," which involved it in massive forest renewal for the first time. It also raised the ante to $650 million a year by 1987, at a time when $300 million was being spent by government and industry combined. The new figure was to include $50 million a year to restore some of the idle, neglected backlog of junk forest. Ottawa promised to increase its contribution by fifteen per cent to $130 million a year on condition that the provinces, for the most part, but also industry, increase their financial commitments. The provinces, or more precisely the

31. Strip mining for coal at Hinton, Alberta. When added together the areas of productive forest land alienated each year for highways, power and pipe lines, and strip mining, and simply for urban sprawl continually reduce the size of our most important renewable resource. The Canadian Institute of Forestry recommends that the forest land base be maintained at its present 200 million hectares in order to meet Canada's needs in coming generations.

people who live in them and pay taxes, would be responsible for almost eighty per cent of the funding, as usual, but industry too was beginning to regard reforestation as the cost of staying in business. A survey by the Canadian Pulp and Paper Association indicated that spending by various companies on forest renewal had doubled in five years. A notable change had occurred, for example, in Newfoundland, where the two companies occupying the productive forest land, Abitibi-Price Inc. and Bowaters Newfoundland Ltd., had taken on half the cost of reforestation.

Attitudes were generally changing for the better. Though it was still under-staffed, the Canadian Forestry Service had been slightly beefed up (by ten per cent) from its low point of 1979. A newly overhauled Forestry Statistics Branch at Petawawa put computers to work in an effort to produce a decent national inventory. It showed that while forty-four per cent, or 4.4 million square kilometres, of Canada is forest land, only half of that is able to grow merchantable wood. Moreover, at least ten per cent of that half is classed as NSR, or "not sufficiently restocked."

Belief in the effectiveness of natural regeneration having waned due to the disappointments over the years, the popularity of such things as genetic selection, seed orchards, nurseries, and artificial regeneration had been growing. Though some stands can regenerate by themselves after logging, the benefits of improved genetic stock and shorter crop rotations had become obvious, holding a potential for yields of more than fifty per cent higher than natural regeneration. One of the centres of tree breeding is the Intensive Forest Management Program at Petawawa, Ontario. "If one assumes Canada is to enter an era of man-made forests," said the program director, Robert Ackerman, "then developing genetically improved stock is one of the best investments we can make. There are approximately 300 million trees planted each year in Canada. That figure will probably go up to 600 million a year by the end of the decade. I think there is no question in anyone's mind that a significant part of the forest in the future will be man-made, largely because of mismanagement in the past."

Given the slow growth of Canadian trees it will take at least fifty years to get much benefit from man-made forests now being planted. In the meantime, the current crop of mature timber must be eked out by decreasing the waste that robs the industry of a third of its harvest. By utilizing tree tops, limbs, and chips, more fibre can be obtained, and mills could be adapted to the thermomechanical process, which uses less fibre than the old groundwood pulp system. Mills may also be adapted to use species such as alder and larch that grow in profusion but have always been regarded as weed trees.

With forestry awareness at a new plateau in 1983, there was reason to hope that Canadian forestry had finally come of age, but among foresters with long memories the optimism was distinctly muted. "Expect no miracles," said Ken Hearnden at Thunder Bay. "It's still a matter of speculation whether the current, apparent level of concern and commitment will be sustained through the long decades ahead." And indeed as industry lost money and governments found themselves with reduced revenues in the new recession, the good intentions were already beginning to fade.

Since nothing happens quickly in forestry it took a while for the bad news to reach the forest. Early in 1983 a government spokesman assured the House of Commons that new agreements would be signed with all ten provinces before the end of the year, and the government promised to allocate $22 million for research and $15 million to subsidize the forestry schools. But already the new federal policy was crumbling. Only two of the Forestry Development Agreements, promised with much fanfare the previous year, were signed, one with Nova Scotia and the other with Prince Edward Island. Fiscal drought was making it difficult for Ontario and British Columbia to come up with the lion's share of funding as required by Ottawa.

Reed said things began to change for the worse that summer. "We had crafted a good policy," he said, "but I had come to realize then that forestry was going to be given a lower priority in the federal structure and that with the possibility of an election in the air, decisions would begin to be based on politics rather than the long-term needs of the forest."

At a meeting of the Canadian Institute of Forestry that autumn at Sault Ste. Marie, one of the many communities that had seen its timber resource seriously eroded over the years, Reed publicly expressed his frustrations. "The signs of retrenchment are quite evident, apart from the growth we had hoped for," he said. "The targets identified in the Banff Agenda for Action in 1981 begin to look like empty promises."

Having arrived in Ottawa under the government's executive exchange program with industry, Reed had experienced the usual advantages of a new broom—and disadvantages in lack of acceptance and bureaucratic experience. Though he had come to the end of his original term, he had more or less decided to stay on for one more year to see various projects through when the disappointments surfacing in 1983 caused him second thoughts. Amid signs of funding restraint and other changes, including John Roberts' departure to another ministry, the new minister, Charles Caccia, though trained as a forester in Europe, seemed to Reed to lack the commitment to chemical spraying Reed felt was necessary. Within a few weeks after his speech in Sault Ste. Marie, Reed handed in his resignation and returned to Vancouver to teach forest policy at the University of British Columbia. "A bureaucrat quits in despair," said the *Toronto Star*.

Reed had brought to Ottawa the commitment, energy, even emotion that forestry needed. Now he was gone and the Liberal administration, with an election on the horizon, evidently saw no point in replacing him with another outsider to carry on gingering things up. Federal-provincial negotiations were breaking down over the question of funding. Good intentions and real progress in forestry again parted company as they had so often in the past. This was particularly evident in British Columbia, where half of every dollar comes from wood and where many tens of thousands of jobs are always at stake. Since the 1950s British Columbia had taken the lead in forestry, though its lead had been challenged by Alberta and, more recently, New Brunswick. Now deprived of the anticipated federal funding, the provincial government announced it would not increase its own spending. It would fulfil its tree-planting commitments, which have a high political profile, while neglecting the less visible but equally important silvicultural follow-up to ensure growth.

Meanwhile the cost of forest renewal is mounting. The Canadian Institute of Forestry says that within the next ten years it will rise to $750 million, which triples what is currently being spent. When the cost of protection, research, administration, and road building is added to that of planting and husbandry, the national expense of forest management could easily reach $2 billion a year by 1994.

Since most of this will come out of taxes, nothing troubles foresters more than their failure to communicate to the public the consequences of the loss of the nation's forest heritage. Continued deterioration means a lower standard of living, not only for those in the industry but for everyone. It raises the serious question of whether our grandchildren are going to enjoy the same forest bounty we have taken for granted.

So far as the shortage of commercial wood is concerned, it boils down to how much the public is prepared to pay to replace the spruce, Douglas fir, jack pine, and a few other species. The costs are fairly well known by now, as are the remedies.

We obviously need to cut down waste due to fires and other causes in the industrial process, logging, and milling. In an era when self-propelled "tree-eating machines" can fell a tree and chew it into pulp chips in the time it took an old axeman to cut his first notch, there is a need for care and moderation. Clear-cuts will have to be limited on vulnerable soil or in black spruce forests where regeneration is a problem, and elsewhere they must conform to the lay of the land and accommodate wildlife and satisfy a public that understandably does not want its forest to be an eyesore. Cut-overs must be promptly regenerated and then cared for and protected from insects and diseases, and from fire, which over the past ten years has scorched enough timber to supply seventy-eight pulp mills for one year. With only half as many foresters as a country like Sweden, which has a much smaller forest area, we will have to train more professionals, and that will involve more public money for the schools. Only by doubling our corps of foresters can we deal with regeneration, something of course will grow, tories. If they are not out there, something of course will grow, but neither the species nor the volume that we require.

There is a clear need for a long-term federal-provincial strategy reflecting the value of the forest to the nation. A Canadian Council of Forest Ministers to co-ordinate provincial policies and keep the issue before the public would certainly be useful, but leadership and support from Ottawa are also needed. Nothing short of a full-fledged ministry of forestry, or at least a strong forestry department within a ministry of renewable resources, is likely to maintain decision-making at a proper cabinet level. Since forestry has so often withered over the question of funding, and particularly federal funding, there is a need for long-term federal commitment in the form of the transfer payments guaranteed for such things as pensions and medicare.

With so much productive forest land lost to single-purpose industrial or recreational use, it is now vital to stabilize the present base of commercial forest land at 200 million hectares, with well-defined and carefully policed guidelines. At the same time a "wise-use ethic" will have to replace the old confrontations between loggers, who see the woodlands only in terms of lumber and fibre, and the conservationists, who insist that wilderness, even if it is junk forest left by poor logging practices, be preserved everywhere and at any cost like something in a museum.

Since we do not live by wood alone, and the forest is an important part of the environment in which we live, we are fortunate that this country is big enough to permit the necessary trade-offs: preservation versus utilization, a healthy natural environment and magnificent scenery versus economics.

Nor is it too late to develop mosaic forest management. Since multiple use of forest land does not necessarily mean simultaneous use by a variety of exploiters, the idea of mosaic management is to keep some areas for intensive logging, some for a compatible mix of recreation and limited harvesting, and others for pure recreation, including enjoyment of whatever untamed wilderness we may have left. Areas can also be reserved for the protection of water, wildlife, and tracts of unspoiled ecosystem that will provide a gene pool and a natural laboratory to generations of foresters still to come.

Something along these lines has been developed in Ontario's Algonquin Park. In the 1960s, with the rise of the conservation movement, there was pressure to get loggers out of the park completely so that it might revert to a real wilderness area. To Les Reed, who was commissioned at that time by the Ontario Department of Lands and Forests to study the problem, it was clear that halting logging completely would deprive communities on the fringe of the park, and dependent on park timber, of at least 3,000 jobs, half of them in logging, sawmills, and other wood-processing activities, and the other half in support services, such as bakers, grocers, and service stations.

"So I simply told the government that if you decide to stop logging completely you will have to find ways to buy out companies whose assets have been destroyed and then you will have to relocate and train the people who will be out of work. The politicians said, 'We simply cannot do that to those communities.' So they put in a Forest Authority to do the logging, and brought about a trade-off between wilderness and semi-wilderness. If only the companies had been sensitive enough to the issue in the first place, not putting their log dumps beside canoe routes and so on, this problem in fact might not have arisen."

Back in the early 1900s Eduard Fernow, the pioneer of forestry in this country, predicted that effective forest management would commence only when Canadians realized they were running out of wood. That time, hopefully, has come, for if the situation is left much longer the degradation of our forests will become irreversible in practical terms and too costly to cope with. It is already clear that through past neglect we have forfeited the opportunity of developing our industry during the next thirty years to the level that it might have reached.

Canadians are fortunate in possessing, after Russia, the

second-largest coniferous forest area in the world. If we merely mine it, as we have for the past century and a half, forest products will contribute less and less to the economy and our place as a prime wood-producing nation will be taken over by other nations.

We need accessible timber to provide the raw material with which we can double forest product exports, increase tax revenues, and create tens of thousands of new jobs. We need healthy forests to provide a setting for the multi-billion-dollar outdoor recreation industry. We need them to provide a safe and beautiful environment. Without enough trees our share of all these good things will diminish, as it has in so many other nations.

Saving and renewing our forest heritage must certainly involve a change of philosophy—from mining the forest to treating it like a renewable heritage—so in the short term the job will prove expensive. Lacking any magic formula, it will take time, money, enlightened self-interest, adaptation, compromise, and trust between governments and between industry and governments. It will also demand commitment from the owners: the people of Canada.

Notes

Introduction

PAGE   LINE

viii   13   Unable to get enough local pine of the special size and quality needed for veneer, a mill at McAdam imported it from Chile. It has since closed down.

xi   1   "Forestry Imperatives for Canada," 1979.

Chapter 1   *The Forest and the Trees*

PAGE   LINE

3   1   By way of contrast, however, not many miles away the author visited 1,800 acres that had been logged in 1975, had been replanted and sprayed with herbicides, and was showing good growth of four to five feet.

3   22   Marek, interview, Beardmore, Ont., 1983.

4   17   Kenneth W. Hearnden, to Ontario Forest Regeneration Conference, Thunder Bay, 1978.

5   24   Estimates vary as to the amount of unproductive brushland or low-value hardwood forest we are creating each year. Taking all factors into consideration, the Canadian Institute of Forestry, in a brief to the Macdonald Royal Commission on the economy in December, 1983, placed the yearly total at one million hectares. Earlier that year the Science Council ("Canada's Threatened Forests") put the total between 200,000 and 400,000 hectares.

| 7 | 29 | Kimmins, interview, Vancouver, 1984. |
| 11 | 21 | "Canada's Threatened Forests," 1983. |

Chapter 2 *Hurling Down the Pine*

PAGE   LINE

15	28	In Bedard, *Forestry in Quebec, Past, Present, and Future*.
19	25	*Quebec Gazette*, Feb.3, 1820.
21	43	Testimony before the Select Committee on the System of Management of Public Lands, Journals of the Legislative Assembly of Canada, 1854-55.
26	28	Gillies' recollection cited by R.D. Craig, *Canadian Forest and Outdoors*, October, 1926.

Chapter 3 *"Woodman, Spare That Tree!"*

PAGE   LINE

32	2	The speeches presented at the American Forestry Congress, both in Cincinnati and in Montreal, appeared in its *Proceedings*, printed in Washington, 1883; also in the *Journal of U.S. Charcoal Iron Workers III*, 1882; in the *Report* of the Fruit Growers' Association of Ontario, 1882; and in the *Montreal Herald*, Aug. 21-26, 1882.
32	23	Phrase coined by Benjamin Gott of Arkona at the 1880 meeting of the Ontario Fruit Growers' Association, in the annual *Report* of the Commission of Agriculture and Arts.
37	3	In R.D. Rodgers' *Bernhard Eduard Fernow*.
44	25	The size of Algonquin Provincial Park was eventually doubled, largely by incorporating land leased to lumber companies. Three-quarters was "multiple-use" for forestry and recreation, the remainder being zoned as a natural wilderness free from logging or hunting.
45	14	In the 1908 *Annual Report* of the Canadian Forestry Association, Senator Edwards also said, "the legitimate lumberman is the very best friend of the forest."
45	31	By 1905 there were, in addition to Algonquin Park, 16,400 square miles of forest reserves in Ontario. Quebec was creating well over 165,000 square miles of reserves which it hoped, unrealistically as it turned out, would be the key to a progressive new forest policy.

| 46 | 6 | Thomas Southworth, the Clerk of Forestry most instrumental in establishing forest reserves, argued in vain (Ontario Woods and Forests *Report Book II*, 1877-1901) that unless logging was controlled, little could be gained by the reserves apart from denying land to settlers. |
| 49 | 34 | Fernow's Kingston lecture # 10 said in part: "Before an annual sustained yield management will appear profitable in Canada, many changes in economic conditions will have to take place, among which we may single out reduction of danger from fire; opportunity for utilizing inferior material; increase in wood prices by reduction of the natural supplies on which no cost of production need be charged; and the development of desire for permanent investments instead of speculative ones; an extension of government functions leading to the practice of forestry by governments on a large scale." |

Chapter 4   *The Paper Forest*

PAGE   LINE

58	8	*Illustrated Canadian Forestry*, May 1923. Booth died two years later at the age of ninety-two. At one time his timber limits in Central Canada were larger than all of Prince Edward Island.
60	13	Ellwood Wilson was a voluminous writer, and his articles, from which the material here and in following pages is taken, appeared in *The American Journal of Forestry*, *The Canadian Forestry Journal*, *Illustrated Canadian Forest and Outdoors*, and the *Canadian Forestry Magazine*.
61	33	It took about seventy-five mature trees, aged 65 years or more, to make a cord of merchantable pulpwood.
68	9	*Mail and Empire,* March 14, 1921.
68	16	Cited in Lambert with Pross, *Renewing Nature's Wealth*; J.P. Bertrand, "Timber Wolves."
70	18	Quoted in Fensom, *Expanding Forestry Horizons*.
70	29	Address to the Royal Canadian Institute, Toronto, March 28, 1925.
71	8	The Quebec professional organization was established by an act of the provincial legislature in 1922. New Brunswick gave registered rights and responsibilities to foresters in 1935, Ontario in 1945, and British Columbia in 1947.

71   34   Quoted in Fensom, *Expanding Forestry Horizons*. Wilson's view was opposed when, in 1926, he advanced it at the annual meeting of the Canadian Society of Forest Engineers. Professor W.N. Miller of the University of Toronto forestry school said financial profit must be clearly demonstrated before the adoption of silviculture.

73   7   Parsons, interview, Toronto, 1978.

74   3   Quoted by forester J.R. Dickson in Fensom's *Expanding Forestry Horizons*.

Chapter 5   *Cutting Blind*

PAGE   LINE

80   16   The reduction in tree size that goes with the reduction in total volume of timber is shown in the fact that the average board foot content in a 16-foot pine log fell from 175 in 1875 to 70 feet in 1945.

81   21   *Economic Review*, May 1981.

83   25   *Canadian Forests and Outdoors*, November 1930; and paper prepared for the Forest Products Research Society, Chicago, 1947.

85   21   Address to Canadian Society of Forest Engineers, Toronto, January 1943.

85   40   In British Columbia, mechanical logging came much faster than in the east, owing to the size of the timber. In the 1930s the average weight of a Douglas fir log was ten tons, and many weighed more than twenty.

87   17   C.D. Orchard Papers, U.B.C. Special Collection.

87   34   In Fensom's *Expanding Forestry Horizons*.

88   22   By 1934 an estimated 100,00 square miles of timber limits had been granted in Quebec, more than three-quarters of that since Confederation in 1867. Large areas, however, had been abandoned after cutting.

88   21   G.G. Trevor, Inspector General of Forests, India, who had visted Canada, commented in 1933 in a letter to the *Forestry Chronicle*, "Very little progress in the fundamental requirements of forest management seems to have been made [in Canada] since 1923."

89   7   H.R. MacMillan, to the Canadian Society of Forest Engineers, February 1947.

124   38   In Ontario some thirty million trees were planted by the government throughout the province in 1956.

125   27   In an address to the 1948 meeting of the CSFE Godwin said, "Based on accessible mature timber...our known supply of softwoods will last about 53 years. Whether our immature forests will reach merchantability within that time and thus prolong the period, or whether loss by fire in young stands is cancelling increment, is anybody's guess."

            Peppler, addressing the annual meeting at Victoria in 1953, said, "Every once in a while someone makes a calculation of total figures that proves that we are going to run out of wood in 25 to 50 years, and the next fellow makes a calculation and proves that we have two or three times as much as we need. ...My guess is that by the time we have cut over our so-called virgin stands we will be producing three times what we now are per acre from our beat-up woodlots and twice as much from our cut-overs."

126   29   This editorial, widely attributed to Des Crossley, appeared in the June 1967 *Forest Chronicle*.

128   15   Reed, interview, 1983.

Chapter 8   *Des Crossley's Obsession*

130   1   "I Had an Obsession," address at the University of Alberta, Edmonton, 1982.

131   18   Quoted in Huth, *Horses to Helicopters*.

132   11   Huth, *Horses to Helicopters*.

133   4   Crossley, interview, Hinton, Alta., 1983.

135   17   Loomis, interview, Edmonton, 1983.

142   21   In Quebec, a poll of six hundred residents found that eighty per cent preferred plantations that looked like original forest rather than having the trees in orderly rows like a cornfield; cited in "Perceptions of Forest Aesthetics," Thérèse d'Amour, Montreal, 1976.

Chapter 9   *Spreading the Bad News*

PAGE   LINE

145   17   Address to the Wesley United Church, Thunder Bay, 1978.

146   23   Hearnden, interview, Normandale, Ont., 1983.

148 32 Hearnden delivered this speech in January 1959, at Sudbury, Ont. A quarter of a century later George Brown, of Oakville, Ont., a retired forester, raised the same question in a letter in the December 1984 edition of the *Forestry Chronicle*. Pointing out that most foresters work either for government or for industry, both being averse to criticism, he concluded, "This leaves a select few foresters in the academic community and those of us that are retired to enlighten the profession and the public about the plight of our forests."

152 23 Devitt, interview, Victoria, 1984.

153 17 Craig letter to the Director of the Lands, Parks and Forest Branch, Ottawa, March 21, 1940, *Records* of the Canadian Forestry Service.

158 1 Lussier, interview, Quebec City, 1983.

158 6 Plans made before World War I; see page 69.

162 1 Reed, interview, 1983.

168 33 *Forestry Chronicle,* June and August, 1970.

169 16 Correspondence with D.M. Trew, 1983.

170 23 Cary paper to the CIF-OPFA meeting, Thunder Bay, 1976.

171 30 OFIA statement in *The Professional Forester*, May 1977.

171 37 Baskerville, interview, 1983.

172 9 Lussier, interview, 1983.

172 30 Cary, interview, 1984.

173 25 Steenberg, "The Northern Coniferous Forest..."

Chapter 10   *Running Out of Timber*

PAGE   LINE

178 16 Reed, interviews, 1983 and 1984, Montreal, Ottawa, and Vancouver.

183 35 The so-called "fall-down effect" phenomenon was being widely discussed by this time. It occurs when, owing to a large amount of old, over-mature timber, the government-regulated annual allowable cut is permitted to increase, only to diminish again as old growth is harvested. When the old growth is finally gone, the allowable cut may suffer a substantial reduction, or "fall-down effect."

185   23   Jeglum, "The Regeneration Gap." In Norac, *A Report on Northern Planning and Development*, November 1981.

185   26   Haavisto, interview, Sault Ste. Marie, 1983.

188   25   Marek, interview, Beardmore, Ont., 1983.

189   8   Though Ottawa had no direct concern for forest management, except on some federal lands, it had ample reason to support good forestry because of the economic importance of the industry.

194   6   Baskerville, interview, Fredericton, 1983.

195   42   Questions and Answers following delivery of "Forest Management, a Provincial Perspective," Canadian Forest Congress, Toronto, 1980.

199   6   Quoted in *The Times News*, Thunder Bay, Mar.30, 1978.

199   21   By 1984, almost forty per cent of Ontario's licensed area of 243,000 sq km was under Forest Management Agreement.

199   29   In 1979 the provinces were footing 67 per cent of the cost of forest renewal, the federal government 21 per cent, and industry 12 per cent.

Chapter 11   *The Battle for the Trees*

PAGE   LINE

203   27   "Evaluation of the consequences for future tree productivity of the loss of nutrients in whole tree harvesting," in *Forest Ecology and Management*, Amsterdam, 1977.

210   24   In West Germany, one of the areas hardest hit by acid rain, which has badly injured the famous Black Forest, biologists at Göttingen University have suggested the life span of trees is being reduced by one-third or more by the pollution.

210   40   Forestry uses less than one per cent of the herbicides used in agriculture. Though many foresters would like to see this amount increased, they maintain that in no case would there ever be a need to spray more than one per cent of the total forest land.

211   40   Lloyd, interview, Smithers, B.C., 1983.

213   20   Report on an evaluation of the health hazards resulting from the use of phenoxy herbicides in forestry, Dr. Pierre M. Lavigne, Halifax.

Chapter 12   *Pieces of the Puzzle*

PAGE   LINE

215   9   "The Answer to Canada's Looming Wood Shortage," address to the CPPA, January 1984, Montreal.

216   13   Devitt, interview, Victoria, 1984.

223   13   Gordon MacKay, interview, Pictou County, 1978.

223   29   In *Forest Times*, Dept. of Lands and Forests, Truro, N.S.

Chapter 13   *Today's Crisis: Tomorrow's Forests*

226   27   The rate of return on investment in the forest industry in Canada averaged only between 5 per cent and 7 per cent between 1960 and 1975, compared with 15 per cent in the United States.

229   7   In "Recent Reductions in the Canadian Timber Base," an appendix to the *Proceedings* of the Toronto Forest Conference, 1980, Reed said: "The principal finding is that these reductions have reduced the sustainable harvest levels by as much as 22 per cent over the figures confidently predicted back in the mid-1970s."

229   39   One CPPA advertisement released in November 1982 stated that "The most urgent need is reforestation. . . ."

230   1   Address to the annual meeting, CPPA Woodlands, Montreal, 1984.

234   20   Ackerman, quoted in "Forestry for the Nation," by Linda Oglov, issued by CFS, Petawawa, 1984.

234   42   Hearnden, interview.

237   39   A focal point of dispute on land use flared up at Meares Island, B.C., in 1984 when a major company, MacMillan Bloedel, sought to log half the island's 20,000 acres of timberland. The residents, including the Clayoquot Indian Band, opposed the cutting plan, which the company estimated would supply 240 jobs and $25 million worth of timber, and by the end of the year the dispute had developed into a standoff.

238   22   Reed, interview, 1983.

Glossary

Advance growth Trees too young for cutting that have become established naturally in a forest of otherwise mature trees.

Annual allowable cut (AAC) Estimated yearly wood harvest that may be sustained under existing management and utilization. That is, if management standards are stepped up, or uses are found for hitherto unmerchantable wood, the AAC may be raised, or it may be lowered if the reserve is decreased by over-cutting, fire, insects, or other causes.

Artificial regeneration Creating a man-made forest by planting seeds, or more usually seedlings, in the wake of logging or other forest destruction and tending the resulting plantations to exact the best possible growth.

Brush Bushes and short scrubby trees, usually of species called "weed trees" because there is no merchantable use for them.

Cambium The growth layer in the trunk of the tree, between the bark and the sapwood, that produces new fibre.

Canopy The mass of branches and foliage in the crowns of trees forming the more or less continuous upper storey of the forest.

Cleaning The weeding out of undesirable vegetation by hand or by means of chemical herbicides, to give the best saplings a chance to grow.

Clear-cut The removal of all merchantable standing trees from a given area, which may vary in size from a few hectares to several thousand, in one operation.

Climax forest The final stage in the ecological succession of various species in the natural life of a forest. A denuded area may grow back to aspen and progress to more merchantable trees through various species successions over many years.

Conifers Cone-bearing, mainly evergreen softwoods, such as spruce, pine, fir, etc., which constitute eighty per cent of Canada's forests and supply most of the timber for lumber, plywood, veneer, and pulp and paper.

Cord, standard A stack of wood containing 128 cubic feet.

Cunit A hundred cubic feet of solid wood.

Deciduous So called because they shed their broad leaves yearly. They are designated as hardwoods regardless of the density and texture of their fibre, used in furniture, flooring, veneer, and, to a growing extent, pulp and paper.

Diameter limit The smallest size, generally measured about a foot above ground level, of tree that may be cut under government regulations.

Duff The top layer of organic debris, particularly the freshly fallen or only partially decomposed vegetable matter such as leaves and twigs, on the forest floor.

Ecology In forestry, the study of the relationship of trees and other living things to their environment.

Even-aged A stand of timber in which there is a relatively small age difference, twenty years or less, among trees.

Expanded yield A term used to indicate an approach in which intensive forest management enhances the natural productivity of the forest. A step beyond sustained yield.

Forest management The application of science, economics, and social principles to the administration and treatment of forest land for specific objectives.

Herbicides Toxic chemicals, in forestry usually sprayed from airplanes, to kill shrubs and unmerchantable hardwoods that inhibit growth of valuable timber. Those in use in Canada include the phenoxy acids 2,4-D and 2,4,5-T (though the latter has been restricted because of dioxin contamination) and the amino acid whose trade name is Roundup, useful against weeds and grass.

High-grading Cutting the most valuable trees and leaving inferior and unmerchantable ones standing, to the detriment of good forest management and the principles of sustained yield.

Humus Decomposing organic matter, including leaves and twigs, covering or mixed with the mineral soil on the forest floor.

Inventory A survey, carried out from airplanes with spot checks on the ground, to determine the size, age, condition, growth rate, volume, species, and soil productivity of a forest area for various purposes, including timber management and harvesting.

Merchantable timber Trees profitable to harvest because of species, quality, age, size, and economic accessibility given existing market conditions.

Monoculture Timber stands of a single species and approximately the same age.

Multiple use Allocation and management of forest land for harvesting and other uses including recreation, ecological preservation, and industrial purposes, such as oil and mineral extraction.

Natural regeneration The custom of leaving nature to regenerate trees in the wake of forest denudation; a slow, uncertain process resulting often in a new forest that contains fewer trees and less valuable species. There is a growing tendency in Canada to create man-made forests by planting seedlings.

Not satisfactorily restocked (NSR) Potentially productive forest land, including burned and harvested areas, lacking in adequate tree growth, which is regarded as being 1,000 trees or more per hectare.

Over-mature The period in its life when a tree is on the decline in growth and value.

Pesticides Used, generally as an aerial spray, to control outbreaks of such scourges as spruce budworm; they once included DDT but now consist of such toxic chemicals as fenitrothion and Matacil. Some provinces have been making progress with a bacterial insecticide, *Bacillus thuringiensis* (BT), which is regarded as safer for the environment.

Prescribed burning Controlled use of fire to clear out weeds and slash to prepare the land for a new timber crop.

Pulpwood Usually softwood species, such as spruce, balsam fir, western hemlock, and jack pine, harvested specifically for the making of pulp and paper, Canada's largest wood products industry.

Reforestation (or regeneration) The establishment of new timber stands by natural or artificial means.

Regeneration gap The lack of adequate forest renewal in the past, which is expected to lead to a shortfall of mature merchantable timber in future, particularly in the early decades following the year 2000.

Rotation The period required to grow a new timber crop to a state of maturity required for another harvest; a period that varies owing to many factors including species, site and methods (if any) of treatment, and silviculture.

Sapling A young tree, no longer a seedling, that has reached a few feet in height and at least an inch in diameter.

Sapwood The outer layer of wood in a growing tree, containing living cells and reserve food, often lighter in colour than the interior heartwood.

Sawlog A log of a species, size, and quality suitable for producing lumber.

Scarification Ploughing up a site with machines and drag lines after it has been harvested, to expose the mineral soil and prepare it for the regeneration of a new crop.

Selection cutting The cutting of trees, singly or in small groups, in such a way as to assure growth of the remaining trees and therefore a sustained yield in uneven-aged forests.

Shelterwood cutting Harvesting aimed at establishing an even-aged forest within the shelter of the remaining standing trees, which provide a seed source for the new growth.

Silviculture The science and art of growing, tending, and renewing a forest.

Site An area of the forest with its own particular combination of ecological and environmental factors governing the growth rate, species, etc. The practice of forestry is "site specific."

Slash Branches, bark, tree tops, and fallen timber left on the ground after a logging operation.

Stand A community of trees with sufficient uniformity as to species, age, condition, and proximity to form a distinctive entity.

Stocking The number of trees or volume of wood on a given area of land; in silviculture the desirable number of trees for best results; as opposed to over-stocking, which does not permit trees to grow properly, or under-stocking, when too few trees occupy a site.

Stumpage Value of standing timber before it is cut; the royalty charged by government when Crown timber is harvested.

Sustained yield A theory of forest management that implies continuous log production by achieving an approximate balance between growth rate and harvest rate.

Thinning Cutting immature growth to improve the quality of the forest; a "commercial thinning" recovers merchantable timber.

Timber limits (berths or concessions) Specific areas of productive forest land licensed to industry to be logged.

Tolerant species Trees that can grow, however slowly, in the shade of other trees.

Veneer log A log of a size and quality to be made into veneer; also called a peeler.

Volume The amount of wood in the trunk of a tree, or stand of trees; the merchantable wood suitable for harvesting.

Watershed The water catchment area above a certain point in a river or stream.

Water table The upper limit of ground water, below which the soil is saturated.

Selected references

Ainscough, Grant L., "Provincial Forest Policy Changes in Canada, a Review," *Pulp and Paper Canada*, March 1977.

American Forestry Congress Proceedings, Washington, 1883; Report of the Ontario delegates, Fruit Growers' Association of Ontario, 1882.

Armson, Kenneth A., "Forest Management in Ontario," Ministry of Natural Resources, Toronto, 1976.
—"Space, Time and Perspectives in Forestry," Edmonton, 1981.

Banff Centre/Institute for Research on Public Policy, "Canada's Forests: Transition to Management," Calgary, 1983.

Baskerville, Gordon L., "Forest Dynamics and Management Decisions," Fredericton, 1976.
—"Good Forest Management," Fredericton, 1983.

Bédard, Avila, *Forestry in Quebec, Past, Present, Future*, Quebec, 1922.

Bernsohn, Ken, *Cutting up the North*, Vancouver, 1981.

Bertrand, J.P., "Timber Wolves," unpublished MS no. 124, Ontario Archives.

Bonnor, G.M., "Canada's Forest Inventory," Environment Canada, 1981.

Canadian Council of Resource and Development Ministers, Task Force on Forest Policy, "Forest Policies in Canada," Ottawa, 1976.
— "Forestry Imperatives for Canada," 1979.

Canadian Council on Rural Development, "The Relationship of Canada's Forests to Rural Employment and Community Stability," Ottawa, 1978.

Canadian Federation of Professional Foresters Associations, "The Use of Herbicides in Forestry," Ottawa, 1983.

Canadian Forest Congress, "The Forest Imperative," Proceedings, Canadian Pulp and Paper Association, Toronto, 1980.

Canadian Forestry Advisory Committee, "The Forestry Situation in Canada," Ottawa, 1975.

Canadian Forestry Association, Report of the First Annual Meeting, Ottawa, 1900.
— "Tomorrow's Forests: Today's Challenge," National Forest Regeneration Conference, Quebec, 1977.

Canadian Institute of Forestry/Institut Forestier du Canada (prior to 1952, Canadian Society of Forest Engineers), "The Canadian Forestry Situation," Papers at the 36th Annual Meeting, Montreal, 1944.
— "A Case for Improved Forest Management in Canada," presented to the Royal Commission on Development Prospects for Canada, 1983.
— *The Forestry Chronicle*, 1925–.
— Proceedings of the Annual Meeting, Sault Ste. Marie, Ont., 1983.
— "Statement of Forest Policy," Montreal, 1943.

Carson, Rachel, *Silent Spring*, New York, 1962.

Cayford, J.H., and A. Bickerstaff, "Man-made Forests in Canada," Department of Fisheries and Forests, Ottawa, 1967.

Clawson, Marion, (ed.), *Forest Policy for the Future*, Washington, 1974.
— *Forests for Whom and for What?*, Baltimore, 1975.

Crossley, Desmond I., "I Had an Obsession," address at University of Alberta, Edmonton, 1982.

Defebaugh, James E., *History of the Lumber Industry of America*, Chicago, 1907.

Department of Forestry, Ottawa, National Forestry Conference, Montebello, Quebec, 1966.

Deschamps, Roland, "Forestry in Quebec, 1908–1968," *Forestry Chronicle*, October 1969.

Environment Canada, "Federal Policy on the Canadian Forestry Sector," 1979.

—"Forest Insect and Disease Conditions in Canada," Canadian Forestry Service, Ottawa, 1982.

—"A Forest Sector Strategy for Canada," Ottawa, 1981.

—"The Need for Forest Renewal and Management in British Columbia," Ottawa, 1983.

—"Policy Statement, A Framework for Forest Renewal," Ottawa, 1982.

—"Silviculture Statistics for Canada," 1975–80, Ottawa.

Fensom, K.G., *Expanding Forestry Horizons, A History of the Canadian Institute of Forestry/Institut Forestier du Canada 1908–1969*, Ste-Anne-de-Bellevue, 1972.

Fernow, Bernhard Eduard, *A Brief History of Forestry*, Toronto, 1907.

Flowers, J.F., and F.C. Robinson, "Proposed Policy for Controlling the Size of Clearcuts in Northern Forest Regions of Ontario," Ministry of Natural Resources, Toronto, 1976.

Gaudet, J.F., "Forestry Past and Present on Prince Edward Island," Charlottetown, 1979.

Gibson, Gordon, *Bull of the Woods*, Vancouver, 1980.

Gillis, R.P., "The Ottawa Lumber Barons and the Conservation Movement, 1880–1914," *Journal of Canadian Studies*, February 1974.

Gray, J.A., *The Trees Beyond the Shore: The Forest and Forest Industries in Newfoundland and Labrador*, Ottawa, 1981.

Green, G.W., "Registration of Herbicides, Process, Problems and Status," Forest Pest Management Institute, Sault Ste. Marie, 1983.

Hearnden, K.W., "Growing the Second Forest in Ontario," address to members of the Ontario Legislative Assembly, Thunder Bay, 1976.

Hodgins, B., et al., "The Ontario and Quebec Experiments in Forest Reserves, 1883–1930," *Journal of Forest History*, January 1982.

Hopwood, W.A., "Recent Forest Policy Trends in British Columbia," *Forestry Chronicle*, April 1984.

Hughson, John W., and C.J. Bond, *Hurling Down the Pine*, Old Chelsea, Quebec, 1964.

Huth, Robin, *Horses to Helicopters: The Alberta Forest Service*, Edmonton, 1980.

Irving, H.J., and F.E. Webb, "Forest Protection against Spruce Budworm in New Brunswick," *Pulp and Paper Canada*, 1981.

Jeglum, J.K., "The Regeneration Gap," in *Noract, A Report on Northern Planning and Development,* Hearst, Ont., November 1981.

Kimmins, J.P., "The Ecology of Forestry: The Ecological Role of Man, the Forester, in Forest Ecosystems," *Forestry Chronicle*, December 1972.
—"The Evaluation of the Consequences for Future Tree Productivity of the Loss of Nutrients in Whole-tree Harvesting," *Forest Ecology and Management*, Amsterdam, 1977.
—"Forest Ecology—The Biological Basis for the Management of Renewable Forest Resources," *Forestry Chronicle*, February 1973.
—"The Renewability of Natural Resources," *Journal of Forestry*, May 1973.

Koroleff, Alexander, "Pulpwood Cutting," Canadian Pulp and Paper Association, Montreal, 1941.
—"Pulpwood Skidding with Horses," 1943.

Lachance, P.E., "Les Forêts de la Province de Québec," 1958.

Lambert, Richard S., with Paul Pross, *Renewing Nature's Wealth*, Toronto, 1967.

Langton, John, "On the Age of Timber Trees and the Prospects of a Continuous Supply of Timber in Canada," *Literary and Historical Society of Quebec*, vol. 1, 1862.

Little, James, "The Timber Supply Question of Canada and the United States of America," Montreal, 1876.
—"The Lumber Trade of the Ottawa Valley," Ottawa, 1872.

Little, William, "Forest Fires and Making Square Timber in the Woods," Canadian Forestry Association, Ottawa, 1905.

Lortie, Marcel, "Arbres, forêts et perturbations naturelles au Québec," Laval University, 1979.
—"Forest Policy Development in Quebec," *Forestry Chronicle*, April 1984.

Lower, A.R.M., *Great Britain's Woodyard*, Montreal, 1973.
—*The North American Assault on the Canadian Forest*, Toronto, 1938.
—*Settlement and the Forest Frontier in Eastern Canada*, Toronto, 1936.

MacKay, Donald, *The Lumberjacks*, Toronto, 1978.

MacMillan, H.R., "Forests of the Future," Vancouver, 1945.
—Address to the Canadian Society of Forest Engineers, Vancouver, 1947.

Marsh, George Perkins, *Man and Nature*, Cambridge, 1869.

May, Elizabeth, and Kathleen Richards, "Spruce Budworm Spraying and Pesticide Registration," Halifax, 1982.

Mercier, J.C., "Intensive Forest Management in Quebec," Quebec City, 1981.

Montreal Herald, Reports on the American Forestry Congress, Montreal, August 1882.

Nelles, H.V., *The Politics of Development: Forests, Mines and Hydro-Electric Power in Ontario, 1849–1941*, Toronto, 1974.

New Brunswick, Forest Resources Study, Fredericton, 1974.

Nova Scotia Department of Lands and Forests, with Canada Department of Regional Economic Expansion, *The Trees Around Us: A Manual of Good Forest Practice for Nova Scotia,* Halifax, 1980.

Nunn, Mr. Justice D. Merlin, Supreme Court of Nova Scotia. Decision on Use of 2,4-D and 2,4,5-T, September 15, 1983.

Oberle, Frank, "The Green Ghetto: Can We Save Canadian Forestry?" Ottawa, 1983.

Ontario Ministry of Natural Resources, "Design Guidelines for Forest Management," 1973.
—"Evergreen Challenge, The Agreement Forest Story" (undated).
—"The History and Status of Forestry in Ontario," 1943.
—"Private Land Forests, A Public Resource" (undated).
—Proceedings of Ontario Conferences on Forest Regeneration, Thunder Bay, 1978, and Kapuskasing, 1979.

Orchard Forest History Collection (Orchard Papers), University of British Columbia Library Special Collections, Vancouver.

Page, Graham, et al., *Forestry in Newfoundland*, St. John's, 1979.

Place, I.C.M., "The Effect of Logging Operations on Forest Management," Ottawa, 1974.

Québec, Ministère de l'énergie et des ressources, "Le Secteur forestier, Recherche et développement," 1983.
—Ministère des terres et forêts, "Exposé sur l'administration et la gestion des Terres et forêts du Québec," 1965.
—"Exposé sur la politique forestière," 1971.

Reed, F.L.C., "Closing the Gap on Timber Supply," 1982.
—"The Forgotten Forest," 1980.
—"Realizing the Economic Potential of Canada's Forest Resource," 1979.
—"The Role of the Federal Government in Forestry," 1980.
—"Will There Be Enough Trees in Canada?" 1980.

Reed, F.L.C., and Associates, "Forest Management Expenditures in Canada Compared to Taxes Generated by the Forest Sector," 1978.
—"Forest Management in Canada," Ottawa, 1978.
—"Recent Reductions in the Canadian Timber Base," Toronto, 1980.

Reynolds, J. Keith, "Forest Management in Ontario: New Perspectives," Toronto, 1979.

Richmond, Hector Allan, *Forever Green*, Lantzville, B.C., 1983.

Rodgers, A.D., *Bernhard Eduard Fernow: A Story of North American Forestry*, Princeton, 1951.

Rowe, J.S., *Forest Regions in Canada*, Ottawa, 1972.

Royal Commissions:
—Canada, on Pulpwood, Ottawa, 1924.
—British Columbia, on Forest Resources (Sloan), Vancouver, 1945 and 1957.
—British Columbia, Inquiry on Timber and Forestry, Vancouver, 1910.
—Newfoundland, on Forestry, St. John's, 1970.
—Nova Scotia, on Forestry, 1984.
—Ontario, on Forestry (Kennedy), Toronto, 1947.

Science Council of Canada, "Canada's Threatened Forest," Ottawa, 1983.

Sisam, J.W.B., *Forestry and Forestry Education in a Developing Country*, Toronto, 1982.

Southworth, Thomas, "Ontario's Forest Reserves," *The Canada Lumberman*, 1905.

Steenberg, Dr. Borje K., "The Northern Coniferous Forest, A Primary Source of World Resources: Can Canada Meet the Growing Challenge of Expanding World Demands?" Thunder Bay, 1976.

Swift, Jamie, *Cut and Run: The Assault on Canada's Forests*, Toronto, 1983.

Trew, M., "Forestry Management," *B.C. Outdoors*, December–January 1982.

Watson, Robert S., "New Brunswick's Forest Policy—Facing the Future," *Forestry Chronicle*, April 1984.

Zimmerman, Adam, "Investment in Foresters," *Policy Options*, January–February 1982.

Acknowledgements

THE AUTHOR IS GRATEFUL TO THE FOLLOWING for their support for the Forest Awareness Project/Heritage Lost, The Crisis in Canada's Forests.

Governments: Canada, Department of the Environment (Canadian Forestry Service); Alberta, Department of Energy and Natural Resources; British Columbia, Ministry of Forests; New Brunswick, Department of Natural Resources; Newfoundland and Labrador, Department of Forest, Resources and Lands; Nova Scotia, Department of Lands and Forests; Ontario, Ministry of Natural Resources; Prince Edward Island, Department of Agriculture and Forestry; Québec, Ministère de l'énergie et des ressources.

Forest products companies: Acadia Forests Products Ltd., American Can of Canada Inc., Boise Cascade Canada Ltd., CIP Inc., Consolidated-Bathurst Inc., Domtar Forest Products, Donahue Inc., Donahue St. Félicien, Fraser Inc., Great Lakes Forest Products Ltd., Les Industries James Maclaren Inc., J.D. Irving Ltd., Manitoba Forestry Resources Ltd., Normick Perron Inc., Northwood Pulp & Timber Ltd., Nova Scotia Forest Industries Ltd., Pacific Forest Products Ltd., Papeterie Reed Ltée., Prince Albert Pulpwood, Prince George Pulp & Paper Ltd., Saskatchewan Forest Products Corp., Scott Maritimes

Ltd., S.E.R. de la Vallée Inc., Simpson Timber Co., Spruce Falls Power & Paper Co. Ltd., St. Regis (Alberta) Ltd., The Pas Lumber Co. Ltd., Weldwood of Canada Ltd., Weyerhaeuser Canada Ltd.

Others: Canadian Institute of Forestry/Institut Forestier du Canada members and sections, Canadian Paperworkers Union, CN Rail, Les Consultants Plurifor Inc., Finning Tractor & Equipment, Hon. Donald S. Macdonald, Mercantile Bank of Canada, Ness Companies, New Brunswick Forest Products Association, Nova Scotia Tractors & Equipment Co., Ontario Professional Foresters Association, l'Ordre des Ingénieurs forestiers du Québec, Timberjack Inc.

Index